LARRY A. FARMER
124 WEST BOND
SALINA, KANSAS 67401

D1597560

Basic Electronics: Components, Devices, and Circuits

William P. Hand

and

Gerald Williams

GLENCOE PUBLISHING CO., INC.

Encino, California
Collier Macmillan Publishers
London

Glencoe Publishing Co., Inc.
17337 Ventura Boulevard
Encino, California 91316
Collier Macmillan Canada, Ltd.

Library of Congress Catalog Card Number: 79-93245

ISBN 0-02-818260-X

1 2 3 4 5 6 7 8 9   84 83 82 81 80

Table of Contents

CHAPTER

6

CHAPTER

7

CHAPTER

8

CHAPTER

9

CHAPTER

10

CHAPTER

11

CHAPTER

12

CHAPTER

13

CHAPTER

14

CHAPTER

15

Preface

Basic Electronics: Components, Circuits, and Devices provides a comprehensive introduction to electronic technology, with particular emphasis placed on skills that entry-level electronic technicians will need on the job. Recognizing the diverse needs and abilities of today's students, this text presents, in a clear, step-by-step manner, the basic theories and laws relating to electronic components devices and circuits.

OBJECTIVES

The principal objectives of the text are to provide the student with the following:
1. A basic understanding of resistance, capacitance, and inductance.
2. The ability to recognize and determine the value of electronic components.
3. An understanding of how resistances, inductances, and capacitances interact in simple circuits.
4. An understanding of the nature of amplification and of how the important amplifying devices work.
5. A knowledge of how resistors, capacitors, inductors, and amplifying devices operate together to form modern electronic circuits.
6. An introduction to electronics at the systems level.

ORGANIZATION

Chapter 1 introduces simple electrical theory, along with a brief history of electricity and electronics. Magnetic fundamentals are covered in Chapter 2. Direct current, its circuits, symbols and concepts, are presented in Chapter 3. Chapter 4 introduces the student to both analog and digital measuring instruments. Chapters 5 and 6 explain how capacitors and inductors operate in direct current time constant circuits and in alternating current circuits. Vacuum tubes—including magnetrons, klystrons and cathode-ray tubes—are covered briefly in Chapter 7. Semiconductors are extensively treated in Chapter 8. Theory and considerable practical detail is included for bipolar (junction), junction FET, and MOSFET transistors. Chapters 9 and 10 cover power line-operated power supplies, safety in line operated systems, and filtering and regulation techniques for line-operated supplies. Chapter 11 integrates amplifying devices into practical multistage circuits and introduces operational amplifiers and their applications. Chapter 12 looks at oscillators and waveform shaping. Chapter 13 examines the techniques of impressing intelligence on a transmitted radio frequency carrier. Chapter 14 is a very up-to-date treatment of digital circuits. It includes interfacing and microprocessors. Chapter 15 covers communication through radar and navigation aids.

FEATURES

Special effort has been made to make *Basic Electronics: Components, Circuits, and Devices* an effective learning tool. Illustrations provide direct visual correlation to the text material, and the text itself employs a practical, easy-to-follow approach. Topics are developed from the simple to the complex, following techniques that have been tested in both the classroom and the lab.

Particular attention has been given to monitoring the mathematical level of the text. When a mathematical formula is used, an example showing the problem and solution is given to aid the student's understanding. Indeed, the level of difficulty is such that only a simple course in basic algebra should be an adequate prerequisite.

To assist the student with the technical language of the electronics industry, a special technical vocabulary development program is emphasized throughout the text. At the first point of use, the technical term is defined. This term is then reinforced in the summary section and in the "Reviewing Your Electronic Vocabulary" section. Other measures have been taken to develop student understanding of the text materials. Each chapter begins with an introduction, followed by short learning topics, a chapter summary, and a series of end-of-chapter activities that includes a vocabulary review, a chapter review, and problems.

CHAPTER 1
An Introduction to Electricity

INTRODUCTION

In about 600 B.C. the Greeks found that certain substances, when rubbed with fur, caused light pieces of straw and other light materials to be attracted to them. The substances were said by the Greeks to have become "electrified" by this rubbing action. The Egyptians, some three centuries earlier, had noted a blue fire in the dark when a cat was rubbed with certain substances.

Amber, a solidified tree sap, was one of the first materials used in electrical experiments. We know now that amber is a natural relative of many of our manmade plastics. Many modern plastics (polymers) are excellent replacements for the relatively rare amber for present experiments in static electricity.

The word *elektron* in early Greek meant *amber*. The early Greeks, of course, had no knowledge of the existence or properties of our "modern" electron. Amber (*elektron*) is the root word for *electricity* and all of its related words.

In 1733 a Frenchman named Charles F. C. DuFay (1698–1739) made an important discovery while experimenting with two kinds of rods suspended near each other. If both rods were of sealing wax, then when the rods were rubbed with silk, they would *repel* each other. However, when DuFay suspended a glass rod and a sealing-wax rod near each other and rubbed them both with silk, the glass rod would *attract* the sealing-wax rod. A different set of conditions existed if, instead of being rubbed with silk, the glass rod was rubbed with wool. In this case the glass rod repelled the sealing-wax rod. The DuFay experiment indicated that there were two types of (static) electricity and that *like charges repel each other and unlike charges attract each other.*

The terms *positive* (+) and *negative* (−) were introduced by Benjamin Franklin in order to distinguish between the two "different" kinds of static electricity. Franklin defined as *positive* the kind of charge a glass rod has when rubbed with silk. He defined as *negative* the kind of charge a rubber rod has when rubbed with fur.

Franklin's experiments convinced himself, as well as the rest of the scientific community of his time, that there were two kinds of electrical "fluid," one positive and one negative.

Since Franklin's time much has been learned about electrical charges and forces. Conventional current flow states that current flow is from + to -. *Coulomb's law* states that the force of attraction or repulsion between two electrical charges varies *directly* with the product of the quantities of the charges and *inversely* with the square of the distance between them.

1.1 THE STRUCTURE OF MATTER

For many years it was believed that only certain materials, such as amber, glass, wax, silk, and fur, had any "electrical" qualities. It is now known that all materials can be electrified. The class of materials we call *insulators* collect excess electrons (or lose them) in a local area. The result is a concentrated charge that can attract other, oppositely charged objects. In another class of materials, known as *conductors*, charges flow so readily that no significantly heavy concentration of charge can be created. A third class of materials, *semiconductors*, is normally poor at accumulating concentrated charges.

Matter is a more scientific word than materials and may be defined for our purposes as anything that has weight and occupies space. Some examples of matter are air, water, wood, steel, and our own bodies. Matter is always found in one of three states: as either a liquid, a gas, or a solid. An example of one kind of matter found commonly in all three of its states (depending on the temperature and pressure) is water (a liquid), ice (a solid), and steam (a gas).

All matter is made up of one or more of the more than 100 different known *elements*. An element may be defined as "the smallest division of matter that retains all of its chemical properties." Some of these elements became known as a result of nuclear experimentation. The smallest unit of matter that can identify a particular element is called an *atom*. All atoms of a given element are identical in structure and have the same average mass.

The Atom

To study the atom, it helps to have a model in order to form a mental picture of the atom's structure. The structure of the atom is similar to our solar system in that there is a central body (called a *nucleus*) around which a number of particles (called *electrons*) orbit, as seen in Figure 1–1. The elec-

tron is the fundamental negative charge of electricity. The nucleus is made up of a group of particles. The two most important particles are the *protons* and the *neutrons*. The proton is the fundamental positive charge of electricity. The nucleus also contains a great many other entities. Practical electronics does not demand that we understand any more about the nucleus than protons and neutrons.

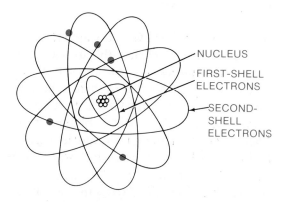

NUCLEUS

FIRST-SHELL ELECTRONS

SECOND-SHELL ELECTRONS

Figure 1-1 A model of the atom.

All atoms have one or more protons and one or more neutrons. Hydrogen, the simplest of the atoms, has a single proton in the nucleus and a lone orbiting electron.

Electron orbits are well defined. The orbits, called *shells* or *energy levels*, are designated K, L, M, N, O, P, and Q, with the K shell nearest the nucleus and Q furthest away. Each shell contains a definite number of electrons, as shown below:

Shell	Number of Electrons
K	2
L	8
M	8 or 18
N	8 or 18 or 32
O	8 or 18
P	8 or 18
Q	8

This is illustrated in Figure 1–2.

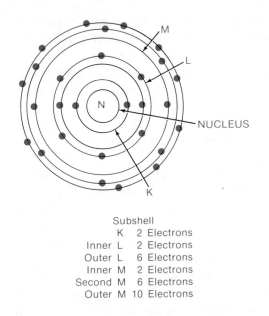

Subshell		
	K	2 Electrons
Inner	L	2 Electrons
Outer	L	6 Electrons
Inner	M	2 Electrons
Second	M	6 Electrons
Outer	M	10 Electrons

Figure 1-2 Location of orbital electrons.

Under normal conditions, the energy shells "fill up" from the innermost shell outward with electrons, and as they fill, the nucleus must also fill, with protons and neutrons, to maintain the atomic and electrical charge balance of the atom. The more electrons, neutrons, and protons in the atom, the greater the weight of the element. Elements such as helium, which has the K energy shell full with two electrons, and neon, with both the K and L energy shells full, have little or no tendency to combine chemically with any other elements since they possess *full* electron energy shells. But hydrogen, with only one electron, tries to combine chemically with most other elements in such a manner that it can either gain or lose an electron in the process, so that the K electron energy shell will be full and stable. Hydrogen normally consists of two hydrogen atoms (H_2), each sharing its one orbital electron with the other atom to give both atoms a full K electron energy shell, thus becoming a stable molecule. This

action of two atoms sharing an electron is called *covalent bonding* and is illustrated in Figure 1-3.

Copper

The properties of copper will be of considerable interest to us in the chapters and sections to come. Here we will examine copper's atomic structure to learn the specific arrangement of this metal's electrons.

Copper atoms have a total of 29 electrons. Energy shell K is full, with 2 electrons; shell L is full, with 8 electrons; and shell M is also full, with 18 electrons, for a total of 28. The twenty-ninth electron is alone in the N shell, which is capable of holding up to 32 electrons. Since this electron is in the N shell alone, it travels a much larger orbit than the other 28 electrons that are held tightly in the first three energy shells. As shown in Figure 1-4, this outer electron in the N shell has such a large orbit that as it passes an adjacent copper atom, it comes close to being in the middle between the two atoms. This position between the atoms results in a situation that is called

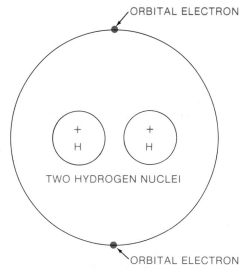

Figure 1-3 Covalent bonding in a hydrogen molecule.

balanced attraction. The electron is thus *free* to move to the N energy shell on the *adjacent* atom. It will in turn be replaced on its original atom by an electron of some other copper atom. All of this movement occurs continuously in a seemingly solid piece of copper where there are millions and millions of *free electrons* drifting from atom to atom. There are approximately 1.4×10^{24} free electrons in one cubic inch of copper.

It is this abundance of free electrons in copper that forms the energy conveying medium in a circuit or wire made of copper.

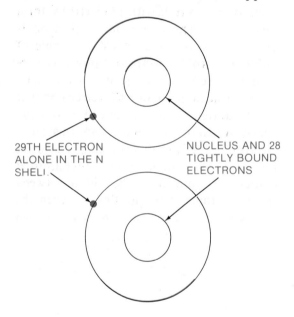

29TH ELECTRON ALONE IN THE N SHELL

NUCLEUS AND 28 TIGHTLY BOUND ELECTRONS

Figure 1-4 Two adjacent copper atoms in a position of balanced attraction.

Energy Shell

Electrons in their energy shells can exist only at certain specific energy levels. If an electron in an energy shell accepts any amount of energy from an outside source, it will accept only enough to allow it to move or jump to the next higher energy shell (an energy shell further from the nucleus). The

kinetic energy (energy of motion) of the electron increased because it travels at a higher velocity in its new energy shell. Its *potential energy* is also increased because of its having been moved against the force of attraction between the electron and the nucleus of the atom. The amount of energy required to move an electron from one energy shell to another, higher energy shell is called a *quantum* of energy. An atom must acquire this energy from some external source, such as heat energy, light energy, or mechanical energy. The mechanical energy may be in the form of a bombardment of the atom by high-velocity electrons from some source. The electrons in the outermost energy shells of an atom acquire this energy to jump shells more easily than those in the inner shells.

If an electron jumps back to a lower energy shell, the atom *must* give up a quantum of energy in order to stay in atomic balance. A good example of this is the action of the fluorescent lamp.

The fluorescent lamp conducts current through a gas. The current, in effect, pumps electrons in the gas atoms up to higher energy levels. Because gas atoms are in fairly violent motion, there are many collisions, and, as a result, electrons drop back spontaneously to lower energy levels. When the electrons drop back to lower levels, they give back acquired energy in the form of ultraviolet "light." Because the human eye cannot see ultraviolet light, the lamp is coated inside with a phosphor that emits energy in the form of visible light when bombarded by (the much higher energy content) ultraviolet. The electrons in the phosphor are raised to higher energy states. When the electrons fall back to the lower level (called the *ground state*) they give up the energy acquired from the ultraviolet bombardment, but in the form of visible light.

1.2 ELECTRIC CHARGE

Charge is a fundamental condition of all matter. All electrons are negatively charged. All protons, which are in the nucleus of the atom, are positively charged. Under normal conditions, equal amounts of positive and negative charges are present. This makes a net charge of zero. It is known as a balanced condition. This balanced condition does not exhibit a charge, and thus it can be said to be electrically *neutral,* or *uncharged.* When this balance between the negative electrons and the positive protons is upset in some way, it causes either an excess or a deficiency of electrons. The atom is then said to be charged. The oldest known method of altering this balance in an atom is by friction.

If a glass rod is rubbed with fur, some of the electrons of the atoms on the outer section of the glass rod are "scraped off" onto the fur. This scraping off of electrons results in a net loss of negative charges; thus, the glass rod will have a net positive charge. There is no *creation* of electrical charge in this process, only a simple transfer of electrons from the glass rod to the fur. It must be noted at this point that *a charge cannot be created or destroyed.* The only thing that can happen is a *transfer* of charges. This is a fundamental law, known as the "Law of Conservation of Charge," that governs all electricity and electronics.

Coulomb's Law

The first quantitative investigation of the effects of force between charged bodies was carried on by Charles A. Coulomb about 1785. Within the limits of sensitivity of the torsion bar balance that he used, he showed that the force (F) of attraction or repulsion between two charged bodies follows an inverse square law, as follows:

$$F \text{ is proportional to } \frac{1}{r^2}$$

where r equals the distance between the two charged bodies. This is known as *Coulomb's law,* and may be expressed as follows:

The force of attraction or repulsion exerted on one charged body by another is proportional to the product of their charges and inversely proportional to the square of their separation.

1.3 CONDUCTORS AND DIELECTRICS

All materials can be classified into one of three categories. The three categories are conductors, semiconductors, and dielectrics or insulators. The atomic structure of a material determines the category into which it fits.

Conductors

A conductor is a material that has a large number of free electrons, (see Section 1.1). All metals are good conductors, although some are better than others. Some of the best conductors are silver, copper, and aluminum.

Dielectrics (insulators)

A dielectric is the opposite of a conductor. It has a very small number of loosely held (free) electrons. The fewer free electrons, the better the insulator. A material with few free electrons will greatly inhibit the movement of an electron charge through or along it. Some common dielectrics are air, rubber, glass, and oil. No known material is a perfect insulator, but all dielectrics are extremely poor conductors.

Semiconductors

In the area between conductors and insulators are materials known as semiconductors. These have very peculiar qualities, as they are neither good conductors nor good insulators. These materials will be covered rather extensively under the discussion of solid state devices. Transistors and solid state diodes are made from semiconductor materials. Silicon and germanium are the most important semiconductors.

1.4 ELECTRIC FIELD

When a body of any type of matter is in a "charged" state, the region around it possesses a unique quality because of the presence of the charge. This special condition existing around the charged body is called an *electric field* (see Figure 1–5).

An electric field can be further defined as that area around a charged body where a force would be exerted upon any other charge that moved into the area.

As an example, let us place a charged body under a sheet of glass. We will now sprinkle some short brush bristles over the top of the glass. The bristles that fall close to the charged body will move from their free fall paths before coming to rest on the glass. From the pattern thus formed by the bristles, we can clearly see that a force was exerted on the bristles by the charged body for a small distance around the charged body. We may say that the charge created a field of force in the space around it. Examination of the bristles on the glass will reveal another fact of considerable interest. That is, the bristles will align themselves in a very definite pattern around the charged body. No matter how many times you do this experiment, you will always get a radial pattern similar to that shown in Figure 1–5. The experimental test for the existence of an electric field at any point is very simple. A charged body, called a test charge, is placed at that point. If some other charge affects the test charge, an electric field is present at that point. The electric field exerts a *mechanical force*.

Whenever we talk about a force we must consider two elements, the force itself and the direction in which the force is applied. Visualize applying force by pushing a large box resting upon a concrete slab. If you apply enough force (i.e., push hard enough), the box will move. Can you imagine the box moving in no direction at all? The direction may not be a special or even desired direction, but it is a direction.

Vectors

Quantities such as force that cannot be adequately described without including the direction are called *vector* quantities. There are ways of indicating vector quantities in equations. A more visual and very popular method is a graph called a *vector diagram*. In vector diagrams a line with an arrowhead is used to describe a vector quantity. The length of the line is proportional to the magnitude of the force involved (a line five inches long might represent five pounds or fifty pounds, and so on). The arrowhead points the direction. Most vector lines have the tail of the arrow at the center of a circle which is divided into 360 degrees. The vector

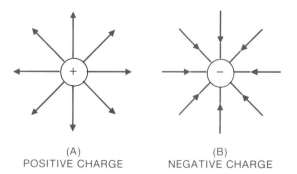

(A)
POSITIVE CHARGE

(B)
NEGATIVE CHARGE

Figure 1–5 Electric field lines of force.

lines are rotated about the center of the circle to indicate direction.

Electric Field Measurement

The force produced by electrostatic charges is very small. It is measured in a unit called a *dyne.* One pound is approximately equal to 450,000 dynes. Stated differently, a dyne is about 1/450,000 of a pound. The unit used to measure electrostatic forces in the metric system is the newton (4.5 newtons is approximately equal to one pound, and 980 dynes is equal to 1 gram).

The unit of charge is the coulomb. One coulomb requires a concentrated collection of 6.28×10^{18} (6,280,000,000,000,000,000) electrons. *Note:* 6.28 is common usage in electronics. 6.25 is also used but with calculators and computers we can be specific to 12 places with the number of electrons (6.283185308). In the foregoing equation, the magnitude *(E)* of the field intensity is expressed in the unit *dynes-per-statcoulomb.* The prefix "stat" means static and tells us that the group of electrons is stationary.

Electrostatic forces operate at a distance but usually only at very small distances. The force exerted on one charge by another decreases as the square of the distance. Doubling the distance between charges reduces the force to one-fourth of its original value. This means electrostatic force decreases much faster than the distance increases.

1.5 POTENTIAL DIFFERENCE

The practical unit of electrical (electromotive) force is the *volt,* named in honor of Alexandro Volta for his pioneering efforts in the development, in about 1800, of the chemical battery.

A difference of 6.28×10^{18} electrons between two posts of a battery means the potential difference is 1 volt.

1.6 ELECTRIC CURRENTS

In an electrostatic situation the main concerns are the forces between charges. However, when the motion of charges is in a conductor of some kind, an electric field is set up and maintained within the conductor. This motion of charges (electrons) in a conductor constitutes what is known as a *current.* (See Figure 1–6).

A conductor, it will be recalled, is any material that has within it electrons that are free to move about when an external force (electromotive) is placed on them. A body may be given a negative charge by piling up excess electrons on it. Excess electrons are those added beyond the number required to balance the positive charges of the protons in the nuclei of the atoms. To give a body a positive charge, electrons must be withdrawn from the body until there are no longer enough to balance the protons' positive charges.

If two identical metallic spheres, one with a positive charge and the other with a negative charge, are suspended and then connected together with a copper wire,

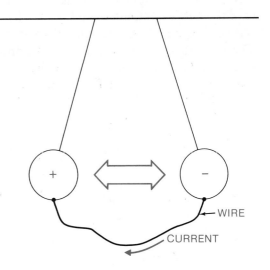

Figure 1-6 Charged spheres.

electrons will flow along the wire until such time as there is no longer a difference of charge between them (see Fig. 1–7). This flow of charge along the wire is known as *current.*

$$I = \frac{Q}{t}$$

where: I = current (amperes)
Q = quantity of charge
t = time

Current is measured in coulombs per second or *amperes,* named for the French physicist, Andre Marie Ampere. *One ampere is the amount of current flowing when one coulomb (6.28×10^{18} electrons) per second passes a particular point on a conductor.*

In the case of the two spheres discussed previously, if we somehow remove 6.28×10^{18} electrons (i.e., 1 coulomb) from sphere A and pile them onto sphere B, there will be a potential difference between the spheres of one volt. If we then connect a wire between the two such that all excess electrons (1 coulomb) on sphere B flow through the wire back to sphere A, and if this happens in a period of one second, then the current flow is 1 coulomb-per-second, or 1 ampere. In this case the entire coulomb of charge will have returned to sphere A at the end of 1 second. The potential difference will have dropped to zero volts. There will be no further electron movement (current flow) between the two spheres.

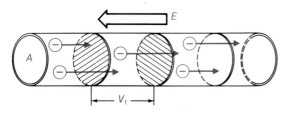

Figure 1-7 Motion of free electrons in a wire.

There are many devices, such as batteries and generators, that maintain a constant potential difference between their two terminals. If we connect a wire between the two terminals of one of these devices, we will get a continuous flow of current.

Electrons flowing through the wire are slowed by collisions with the stationary atoms of the wire, and, after each such collision, they are accelerated again by the potential difference.

Figure 1–7 showed a section of wire where the electric field has been established and the free electrons are flowing to the right. Electrons are assumed to flow at the same average velocity, which will be considered to be a constant velocity *(v).*

Example 1–1:

Problem: What is the effective velocity of the electron flow in a copper conductor with a 0.005 square inch cross section and a current of 5 amperes?

Solution: One coulomb = 6.28×10^{18} electrons. One cubic inch of copper contains 1.4×10^{24} free electrons. Thus 1 coulomb of free electrons will occupy

$$\frac{6.28 \times 10^{18}}{1.4 \times 10^{24}} = 4.49 \times 10^{-6} \text{ cubic inch}$$

The current flow rate is 5 amperes, which is 5 coulombs per second. In copper this is

$$5 \times 4.49 \times 10^{-6} = 2.24 \times 10^{-5}$$

With a cross-sectional area of 0.005 square inches, 2.24×10^{-5} cubic inches will occupy a total length of

$$\frac{2.24 \times 10^{-5}}{0.005} = 4.49 \times 10^{-3} \text{ inches of copper.}$$

Since the 5 coulombs that occupy a length of 4.49×10^{-3} inches in our conductor must pass a given point in 1 second, the average velocity of the electrons along the conductor will be 4.49×10^{-3} inches per second, or $v = 4.49$ thousandths of an inch per second.

Because of the very low velocity of electron movement along a conductor, the effective electron flow in the conductor is often referred to as *electron drift*.

In order to establish a standard for measurements, the coulomb has been defined by international agreement as the amount of electricity that will liberate 0.001118 grams of silver from a solution by electrolysis. From this the ampere can be defined as that rate of flow that will liberate 0.001118 grams of silver per second from a silver solution.

Negatively charged electrons are responsible for the current flow in metallic conductors. In solids the sole current flow is electron flow. In conductive liquids and gases, however, charged atoms called *ions* can also drift through the system under the force of an electric field. An ion is an atom that has either gained or lost a valence electron. An ion with an extra electron has a negative charge and is called a negative ion. A positive ion results when an atom has lost an electron. Electrons and positively charged atoms (positive ions) move in opposite directions. The electrons move toward the most positive part of the system and positive ions move toward the most negative region. Because each proton is approximately 2,000 times as heavy as an electron, the ions move much more slowly than the electrons.

1.7 CONVENTIONAL CURRENT

Most physicists deal with what is known as *conventional current,* where it is assumed that a mythical positive charge takes the place of an electron. The direction of conventional current is opposite that of electron current.

For the bulk of this text, we will deal with electron current. However, in the study of semiconductor devices, we will find that *conventional current* is a convenient fiction that can assist in our understanding.

SUMMARY

1. The word *electron* comes from the Greek word for amber, *elektron.*

2. Early theories of electricity predicted that there were two different kinds of electrical "fluid." We know now that there is only one kind of electricity, composed of electrons.

3. A negatively charged body has an excess of electrons. A positively charged body is deficient in electrons.

4. Like charges repel. Unlike charges attract.

5. The force between two charged bodies decreases proportionate to the square of the distance between them.

6. Matter exists in three states; solid, liquid, and gas.

7. In conductors, some electrons are very loosely bound to the nucleus of the atom; these are called *free electrons.*

8. In insulators, electrons are so tightly attached to the nucleus that they cannot act as carriers of electricity.

9. In semiconductors, the number of *free* electrons depends upon the temperature. Semiconductors are neither good conductors nor good insulators at normal earth temperatures.

10. Electrons are arranged around the nucleus in shells.

11. The specific amount of energy required to move an electron from one energy level to another is called a *quantum* of energy.

12. When an electron drops back to a lower from a higher energy level, the quantum of energy is emitted as electromagnetic radiation, sometimes in the form of visible light.

13. Charge cannot be created or destroyed, but it can be transferred from one place to another.

14. A charged body has an electric *field* around it.

15. An electric field can exert a mechanical force on another charged body.

16. A vector quantity is one in which both amount and direction are described.

17. A difference of 6.28×10^{18} electrons (1 coulomb) between two areas of charge produces a potential difference (voltage) of 1 volt.

REVIEWING YOUR ELECTRONICS VOCABULARY

1. Ampere
2. Atom
3. Charge
4. Conductor
5. Coulomb

6. Current
7. Electron
8. Insulator
9. Potential difference
10. Volt

CHECKING YOUR UNDERSTANDING

1. Do like electrical charges repel or attract each other?
2. In what three states does all matter exist?
3. Does a positively charged body have an excess or deficiency of electrons?
4. State Coulomb's law.
5. Name three good conductors.
6. Name three good insulators.
7. What is the unit of potential difference?
8. What is a quantum of energy?
9. How many electrons must pass a point each second to make one coulomb?
10. What is the relationship between coulombs and amperes?

SOLVING ELECTRONIC PROBLEMS

1. How much current will flow if there are 3 coulombs per second of electrons flowing in a wire?

2. How many newtons are equal to one pound?

3. How many dynes are equal to one pound?

4. How many electrons per second will pass a point in a wire when 3.5 amperes are flowing?

5. What is the approximate number of electrons (free) in 4 cubic inches of copper?

CHAPTER 2
Magnetism

INTRODUCTION

From a study of ancient history, we find that the knowledge of magnetism moved from China to Asia Minor and from there to Europe. Magnetism was known to the early Greeks and Romans in the form of iron oxide called magnetite ($FeO \ Fe_2O_3$). Magnetite becomes a magnet only when acted upon by an external force. In nature, this most often occurs by a stroke of lightning. When magnetite becomes magnetized, it is named lodestone.

Hans Christian Oersted (1771–1855) found that a free magnet suspended in air could be acted upon by a current flowing in a wire placed close to the magnet. In the year 1831 an American named Joseph Henry found that an electric current could be induced or caused to flow in a conductor that was near another conductor whenever the current was either started or stopped. A permanent magnet close to a conductor would also cause or induce a current only when the magnet was in motion.

Michael Faraday, an Englishman, established the same results about eleven months later and since Faraday's results were published first, he is generally given credit for the discovery of electromagnetic induction. The fact that a moving magnetic field can cause current to flow in a wire became the basis of the electric generator, an innovation upon which the power industry is based. The electric motor became possible with the discovery that moving electrons produce a magnetic field. In fact, Faraday actually constructed an electric motor. Faraday's motor was very crude and impractical, but practical motors and generators were built within a very few years.

2.1 NATURE OF MAGNETISM

A magnet is an object that has property of attracting iron and steel. Magnets attract other materials, such as nickel and cobalt, but with less force than they attract iron and steel. Materials able to be attracted by magnets are called *magnetic substances*. There are two kinds of magnets, natural magnets and artificial magnets. Natural magnets are those found in nature, while artificial magnets must be created by magnetizing iron or steel. Artificial magnets can be either permanent or temporary.

Natural Magnets

An iron oxide called *lodestone* or *magnetite*, which exists in nature, exhibits magnetic properties. Historically lodestone has played an important role, because of its use in the Middle Ages to magnetize compass needles. However, lodestone is unstable and has low magnetic strength and today it has very little use as a magnet.

Artificial Magnets

Artificial magnets are made of iron or steel. They are magnetized by stroking the piece of iron or steel with some other artificial magnet or by placing the piece of metal in the field of an electromagnet. A bar of hard steel will hold magnetism for a long period of time, and for this reason it is called a *permanent magnet*. Soft iron can be magnetized easily, but loses its magnetism rapidly and is thus classified as a *temporary magnet*. The property of a substance that causes it to remain magnetized for a long time is called *retentivity,* and the magnetism that remains is called *residual magnetism*. Steel has high retentivity, while that of soft iron is low.

Magnetic Poles

When a bar magnet is dipped into iron filings, a large number of filings will cling to the magnet near its ends, but few will attach themselves to the magnet near its center. This action indicates that the magnetism is concentrated at the two ends. These ends are called the *poles* of the magnet. The magnetic strength of the two poles is equal.

As the result of an experiment by Gauss in 1840, we know that a magnet, left free to rotate, will always turn to a north-south direction. Thus it aligns itself with the earth's magnetic field. The pole of the magnet that always turns toward the north is called the north-seeking pole, or simply the north pole (N); and the pole at the opposite end, the south-seeking pole, or south pole (S).

Force Between Poles

Experiments show that if you bring the S-pole of one bar magnet near the N-pole of another, there will be an attraction between the two poles, and if you bring two N-poles or two S-poles together there will be a repulsion between them. This action is the basic law of magnetism, which states that *unlike poles attract each other and like poles repel each other.*

Earth's Magnetic Field

Magnetic lines of force surround the earth in much the same way that lines of force surround a bar magnet. The earth has two magnetic poles. One is near the geographic north pole and the other near the geographic south pole. Discovery of these facts was responsible for the development of man's most important navigational instrument— the magnetic compass. Dating back to the Middle Ages, the magnetic compass is to this day the most used navigational instrument. Basically, it is an artificial magnet mounted in such a way that it aligns itself with the earth's magnetic lines of force. One end of the magnet always points toward magnetic north.

2.2 CLASSIFICATIONS OF MAGNETS

Materials can be classified magnetically into three basic categories: (1) permanent magnets, (2) temporary magnets, and (3) nonmagnetic materials. Many conductors of electricity, such as copper, aluminum, lead, and silver, are nonmagnetic. There are a very few substances that appear to be antimagnetic, but little is known yet about these materials.

Another, more scientific classification of substances regarding their magnetic qualities is as follows: (a) ferromagnetic substances, (b) paramagnetic substances, and (c) diamagnetic substances.

Ferromagnetic Substances

Ferromagnetic substances from iron ores that become highly magnetized, in the same direction as the magnetizing field.

Steel, with a 0.1 to 2 percent carbon content, like soft iron becomes easily magnetized when it is placed in a magnetic field. But unlike soft iron, steel will retain its magnetism for a long period after it is removed from the original magnetic field. Any magnet that retains its magnetic qualities for a long period of time (has high retentivity) is known as a permanent magnet.

Paramagnetic Substances

Paramagnetic substances are those such as aluminum, chromium, air, and others that, when placed in a magnetic field, will become only very weakly magnetized, and become magnetized in the *same* direction as the magnetizing field. Paramagnetic substances become such weak magnets even when exposed to an intense magnetic field that they are considered nonmagnetic for all practical purposes.

Diamagnetic Substances

Diamagnetic substances are those such as copper, silver, and zinc that, when exposed to an intense magnetic field, become magnetized very weakly in a direction *opposite* to that of the original magnetizing field. Diamagnetic substances, like paramagnetic substances, are, for all practical purposes, considered nonmagnetic.

2.3 MAGNETIC FIELD

The area around a magnet in which its effect can be detected by present instruments is its magnetic field. In theory, the magnetic field extends infinitely in every direction; however, the strength of the field decreases very rapidly as the distance from the magnet is increased.

When we studied electrostatics, we found that a field radiated evenly in all directions; however, in a magnet the effects are not even over its surface. They appear to concentrate at the two points in the magnet called poles. If a line is drawn between the two poles, we have what is known as the *magnetic axis* of the magnetic field. The poles of a magnet are not points, but areas, and are not exactly at the ends of the magnet. However, for most practical magnetic calculations, it is assumed that the poles of a bar magnet are at the ends.

Since the magnetic field is invisible and often difficult to visualize, a convention has been adopted in which the magnetic field is represented by *lines of magnetic force* or *lines of magnetic induction*. These lines are normally drawn so that their direction is that of the magnetic field that they represent.

An excellent demonstration of the lines of magnetic force of a bar magnet may easily be performed by placing the bar magnet under a sheet of paper and sprinkling iron filings over the paper. The filings become magnetized by induction, and, because of their ferromagnetic qualities, arrange themselves in regular lines, as shown in Figure 2–1. (A slight tapping of the paper may be necessary, depending upon the strength of the magnet.) As can be seen from the demonstration, the magnetic lines of force are concentrated at the two poles and make lines around the magnet from one pole to another. Regardless of the longitudinal plane in which the experiment is made, we will get the same results. The demonstration gives us an idea of what a magnetic field might look like if it were visible.

As a convention, and to clarify our understanding of magnetic fields, a magnetic field is said to flow in a direction from the north pole to the south pole of the magnet. These lines of the magnetic field do not begin at the north and end at the south, but are in the form of complete loops. They continue between the south and the north poles inside the magnet, thus forming closed loops.

Let us demonstrate this by taking a bar magnet and cutting it into two parts. When we pull the two parts of the original magnet apart, we can detect the presence of magnetic lines of force between the two halves, as shown in Figure 2–2. The cutting of the

magnet has produced new north and south poles.

When we pulled the two sections of the magnet apart, we noticed a definite force attracting the two sections, trying to keep them together. This shows that magnetic lines of force have strength, and the shorter the lines are, the stronger they are.

Magnetic lines of force always take the shortest and easiest route. Sometimes the easiest is *not* the shortest, as shown in Figure 2–3. This figure shows what occurs when we place a piece of magnetic material into the field, in this case a small piece of soft iron. The field distorts to include the iron bar in its route. This distortion of the magnetic

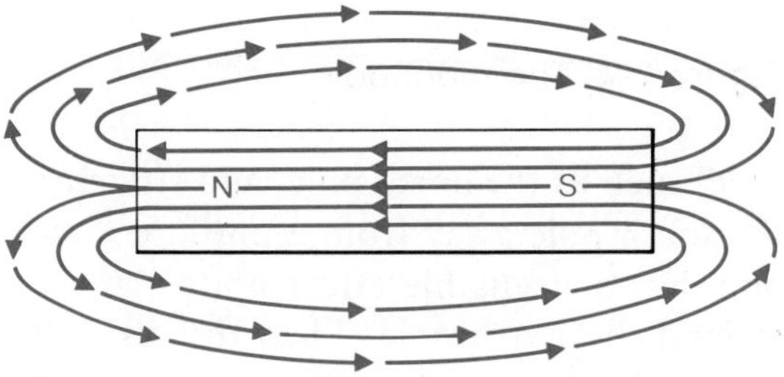

Figure 2-1 The shape of the magnetic field.

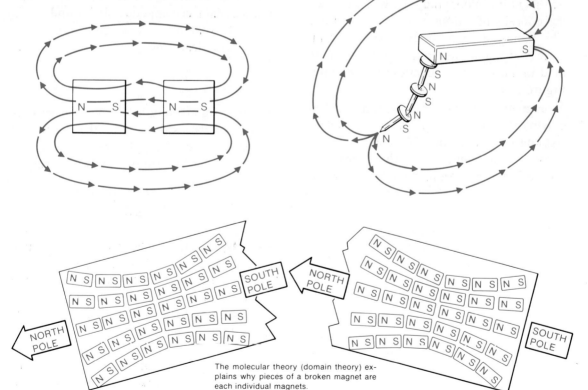

The molecular theory (domain theory) explains why pieces of a broken magnet are each individual magnets.

Figure 2-2 Magnetic lines of force form loops within the magnet.

field is due to the ability of the iron to conduct the magnetic field more easily than the surrounding air. The result of this field distortion by the iron bar is that the field intensity in the bar is greatly increased due to the greater concentration of lines of force. We can draw the following conclusion: *Magnetic fields always tend to arrange themselves in such a way that the maximum number of lines of force per unit area is established.* Another interesting thing occurs in that the piece of iron becomes a (temporary) magnet (with north and south poles) as long as it remains in the original magnetic field. Thus, the piece of iron has become a temporary magnet by *induction.*

Magnetic Monopole

At this point in our study, we will introduce the concept of *monopoles,* or *point poles.* The monopole is a concentration of magnetic charge at a single point with a magnetic field radiating in all directions, as shown in Figure 2–4.

A magnetic monopole can be simulated by moving the poles of a normal magnet very far apart so that the field of each pole becomes very much like that shown in Figure 2–4. This can be done by fixing one

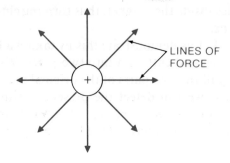

Figure 2-4 The monopole.

pole, such as the north pole, and stretching the south pole away from it until the south pole has a negligible effect upon the area around the north pole. Then the magnetic field pattern of this north pole is a close approximation to the monopole's radial pattern of Figure 2–4. For our study we can assume that the magnetic field around a pole is due to that pole alone, an *isolated pole* for all practical uses.

The Unit Pole

The force of attraction or repulsion between two poles varies directly as the product of the strength of the poles and inversely as the square of the distance between them:

$$F = \frac{M_1 \times M_2}{\mu R^2}$$

Here M_1 and M_2 are the strengths of the two poles, and R is the distance between them. The Greek letter μ (mu) is a constant whose value depends upon the medium in which the poles are located. If the space between the poles is a vacuum of air, μ is one. If the space between the poles contains a magnetic material, μ is some number greater than one.

The unit of pole strength (referred to as a *unit pole*) is derived from the equation for the force between two poles. If M_1 and M_2 are equal, and, at 1 cm apart, they exert a

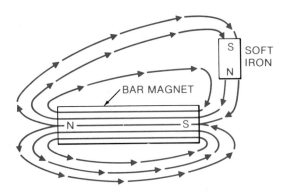

Figure 2-3 Deflection of lines of force by soft iron.

force of 1 dyne, then they are unit poles. Or, a unit magnetic pole has such strength that it will exert a force of 1 dyne upon an equal pole in a vacuum (or air) when placed 1 cm away from it.

UNIT POLE

When two like poles of equal strength are placed in a vacuum 1 centimeter apart, they will repel each other with a force of 1 dyne.

Magnetic Field Strength

The region around a magnet in which its effect can be detected is known as its *magnetic field.* When a magnetic pole is moved about the magnetic field, there will be exerted on the pole forces that vary in both direction and intensity. The direction of a magnetic field at any one place is the direction in which a unit north magnetic pole would have a force applied to it. The intensity or strength (number of lines of force per unit area) at any point is equal to the force that the field exerts on a unit north pole placed at that point. This relation is represented by the equation

$$H = \frac{F}{M}$$

where H is the strength of the field in oersteds, M the strength of the pole brought into the field, and F the force that the field exerts on this pole.

Example 2-1

Problem: Find the strength of a magnetic field at a point where it exerts a force of 60 dynes, acting on a pole to the right. Assume the strength of the pole to be 10 units.

Solution:

$$H = \frac{F}{M}$$

$$H = \frac{60}{10}$$

$$H = 6$$

Therefore, the strength of the field at the point in question is 6 oersteds to the right.

Field Strength and Distance

In the region near a pole, the intensity of the field is not uniform, but diminishes rapidly as the distance from the pole increases. Experiments have shown that the field intensity around a pole varies directly as the pole strength, and inversely as the square of the distance from the pole. This relationship is given mathematically by

$$H = \frac{M}{\mu r^2}$$

or in a vacuum,

$$H = \frac{M}{r^2}$$

where M is the strength of the pole, r is the distance from the pole, and H the force in oersteds. The direction of the magnetic field about a magnet is radially outward from the N-pole and radially inward toward the S-pole. To find the intensity and direction at any point about the magnet, use the equation $H - M/\mu^{r^2}$ with both poles, and add the results vectorially. The resultant vector direction is the direction of the field.

2.4 MOLECULAR THEORY OF MAGNETISM

In experiments consisting of breaking a magnet in two and then breaking each of these parts in two, and so on as far as is physically possible, it is found that each of the parts is also a magnet. It is presumed that if the breaking process were to continue until the parts were the size of molecules, each part would still be a magnet with N and S poles. The concept that a magnet is made up of molecule-size magnets is called the *molecular theory of magnetism.* According to this theory, the molecular magnets in a piece of unmagnetized magnetic material are in the form of small stable groups called *domains,* pointing in various directions. When the unmagnetized material is placed in a magnetic field, the molecular magnets tend to align themselves with the field to a degree depending upon the strength of the magnetic field and the kind of material involved. The molecular magnets in a piece

of steel require a stronger field for alignment than do those in a piece of soft iron. However, upon removal of the magnetic field, the molecules in the piece of steel remain aligned for a longer time than do the molecules in the piece of soft iron.

Another fact which the molecular theory explains is that you can magnetize a piece of steel by holding it parallel with the earth's magnetic field and striking it several times with a hammer. The hammer blows shift the molecular magnets within the piece of steel into a state of alignment, which, according to the molecular theory, is the condition we call magnetism. The theory also offers an explanation for the fact that you can demagnetize a permanent magnet by heat. According to the molecular theory, heating the magnet accelerates the motion

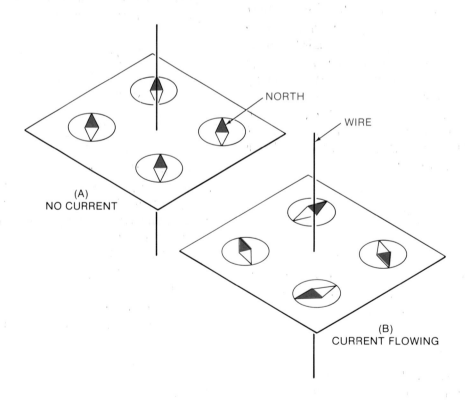

Figure 2-5 Compass deflection by current in a wire.

of the molecules in the magnet and causes them to be thrown into a state of disalignment, a process called *demagnetization.*

2.5 ELECTROMAGNETISM

Up to this point we have only considered permanent magnets. An obvious disadvantage of a permanent magnet is that it cannot be turned off. In 1819, Hans Christian Oersted proved that a magnetic field exists about a conductor through which an electric current flows. From this fact it can be seen that a magnet could be made with the capacity to be turned on or off at will. A very simple experiment can be performed to demonstrate this effect. Place a compass near a conductor without current flowing through it, as shown in part A, of Figure

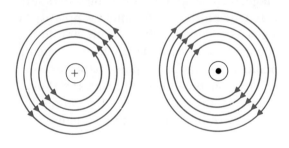

Magnetic fields about conducting wires

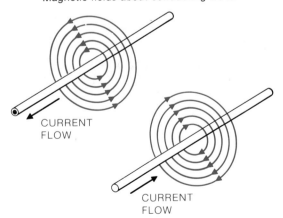

CURRENT FLOW

CURRENT FLOW

Figure 2-6 Magnetic field around a current carrying wire.

2–5. In this situation the compass will act normally; that is, it will align itself in a north-south direction. Now turn on the current as shown in part B of Figure 2–5. When current flows, the compass needle is deflected in the same way as when it is brought close to a permanent magnet.

To find the strength of the field at any point about a long, straight, current-carrying conductor, use the equation $H = 2I/10r$, where H is the strength of the field in oersteds, I is the current in amperes, and r is the distance from the conductor in centimeters.

The magnetic field around a conductor through which current is flowing is in the form of concentric circles of magnetic force, as shown in Figure 2–6.

The direction of the field established around the current-carrying conductor depends upon the direction of the current flow. This is shown in Figure 2–6. The field is concentrated near the conductor and its strength will decrease very rapidly as the distance from the conductor is increased.

A good way to determine the direction of the lines of magnetic flux is to apply the *left hand rule,* as shown in Figure 2-7.

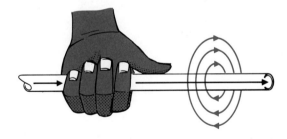

Figure 2-7 The Left-hand rule.

The left-hand rule states that if you grasp a conductor with your left hand in such a manner that your thumb points in the direction of electron flow, your fingers will indicate the direction of the lines of force about any conductor.

If the conductor we have just discussed is formed into a loop, as shown in Figure 2–8, all the lines of force pass through the center of the loop in the *same* direction. Therefore, for a given current, the total number of lines of force has not changed but we have concentrated the lines into a much smaller area, thus strengthening the field in this area. The concentration is due to the fact that all lines of force enter the loop from one side and leave at the other. To find the intensity of the field at the center of the loop, use the equation $H = 2\pi I/10r$, where I is the current in amperes, r is the radius of the loop in centimeters, and H is the field intensity in oersteds.

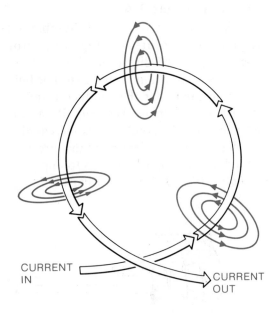

Figure 2-8 The effect of a loop on magnetic fields.

2.6 SOLENOIDS

If a conductor is wound in a loop around a hollow form, as illustrated in Figure 2–9, we have what is known as a *solenoid*. A sole-

noid is a series of loops that will concentrate their magnetic fields into the center, forming an electromagnet. The magnetic fields surrounding each turn will all have the same direction. When the length of the coil is small compared to its radius, you can find the strength of the field at the center by the following equation:

$$H = \frac{2\pi NI}{10r}$$

where N equals the number of turns, r is the radius of the coil in centimeters and I is the current in amperes. When the length of the coil is longer than the radius, the coil is a solenoid.

When current flows through the coiled wire, it is surrounded by a field, as shown in Figure 2–9. One end of the coil is the north magnetic pole, and the other end is the south magnetic pole. To determine the polarity of a given coil, use the left hand rule, as follows: Grasp the coil with the left hand in such a manner that the fingers point in the direction of electron flow. The direction the thumb points is the north pole. To obtain the intensity of the field at the axis and near the

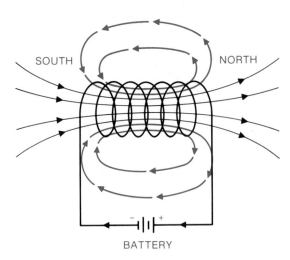

Figure 2-9 The solenoid.

middle of a coil, we can use the equation

$$H = \frac{4\pi NI}{10 \quad 1}$$

where I is the current in amperes, N is the number of turns, 1 is the length of the coil in centimeters, H is the intensity in oersteds, and π is the circle constant 3.14159 (pi).

If we substitute $n = N/1$ (number of turns per unit length), the equation becomes $H = 4\pi nI$. The importance of this substitution is that according to the second equation, the strength of the field about a solenoid depends only upon the magnitude of the current and the number of turns per unit length: Field strength = Amperes × Turns.

2.7 RELUCTANCE AND PERMEABILITY

Both resistance and conductance have their counterparts in magnetic circuits. Resistance to magnetic lines of force is called *reluctance*. Conductance in magnetic terms is called *permeability*. Air (and vacuums) have very high reluctance and low permeability while ferrous materials (such as iron and steel) have very low reluctance and very high permeability.

Magnetic Flux

The total number lines of force in a region of magnetic activity is called the *magnetic flux* and is represented by the Greek letter ϕ (phi). The unit of magnetic flux is one line of magnetic flux and is called the *maxwell*. The number of lines passing (perpendicularly) through a square centimeter is the *flux density* and is represented by the letter B. The unit of flux density is the *gauss*. One gauss is equal to 1 maxwell per square centimeter.

Permeability

The amount by which the flux density (B)

exceeds the field intensity (H) in a coil or solenoid depends upon the type of core. The ratio between these two quantities, which is written B/H, is the permeability of the core. For example, soft iron has a permeability of about 2000. Permeability may be defined as the ease with which a substance conducts magnetic lines of force. Permeability is represented by the Greek letter mu (μ). In any ferromagnetic substance permeability is not a constant quantity, but one that depends upon the intensity of the field. Magnetization curves indicate the relation of flux density B to field intensity H. In the case of steel, the flux density increases practically in a direct proportion to H at low field intensities, but at large field intensities the steel becomes saturated with flux and a large change of H is required to increase B further. This behavior can be seen in the curve in Figure 2–10.

The curve is typical for all ferromagnetic materials, although actual magnitudes vary. Also, the knee of the curve may have either a sharper or shallower bend, depending upon the material.

The permeability can be determined from the curve in Figure 2–10 by solving the equation

$$\mu = \frac{B}{H}$$

Example 2–2

Problem: Find μ when

$$H = 40 \text{ and } B = 1600.$$

Solution:

$$\mu = \frac{B}{H}$$

$$\mu = \frac{1600}{40} = 40$$

At a different point on the curve we can expect a different permeability.

Example 2–3

Problem: Find μ when

$$B = 10000 \text{ and } H = 3$$

Solution:

$$\mu = \frac{10000}{3}$$

$$\mu = 3333$$

Because of iron's high permeability, inserting a soft iron core into a solenoid greatly increases the number of magnetic lines of force. This increase in magnetic lines is not from an increase in the intensity of the field. The field intensity depends only on current and turns per unit length. The increase is the result of additional lines produced by the magnetization of the iron core. According to current magnetic theory, a core of ferrous material adds to the field strength of the aligned magnetic domains.

Domains in unmagnetized iron have their poles pointing in random directions. Random orientation leads to cancellation of fields. This results in no net magnetic direction. When an external field is applied, the domains begin to align themselves in the direction of the applied field. Each domain magnet that becomes aligned adds its field strength to that of the original field. As the external field increases in intensity, additional domains tip into alignment. When the point is reached where all of the domains are aligned by the external field, the condition is called *saturation*. Once saturated, the core behaves as an air or other high reluctance core.

2.8 HYSTERESIS

When a piece of iron is magnetized, considerable energy is expended in lining up the domains in a definite direction. When they

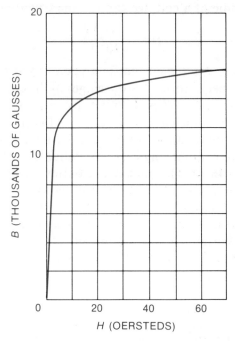

(A.) MAGNETIZATION CURVE OF STEEL

Figure 2-10 Magnetization curve of steel in a solenoid core.

are aligned first in one way and then in the other many times per second, as they are in an alternating current electromagnet, considerable energy is wasted in the form of heat. Such a waste of energy is called *hysteresis loss*. In electromagnets this causes the magnetization of the core not to reverse polarity at the same time that the magnetizing current does.

Hysteresis is when flux density lags behind the magnetic field intensity. The curve describing it is known as a hysteresis loop (see Figure 2–11).

Coercivity is the measure of H in the reverse direction required to reduce B to zero.

Retentivity represents the B, or flux density, retained when the value of H has dropped to zero. In Figure 2–11, retentivity is labeled B_r.

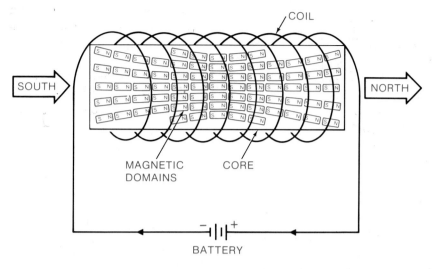

(B.) SOLENOID WITH AN
IRON CORE.

Figure 2-10 (Cont.)

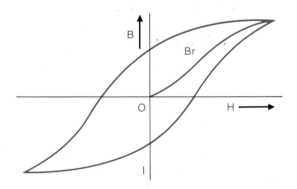

Figure 2-11 Hysteresis loop.

The *work area* is the area inside the closed hysteresis loop. This area is proportional to the energy needed to reverse the direction of a magnetic field in any specific sample of core material. In alternating current circuits where reversals occur all the time, this work area is particularly important. The work done appears in the form of heat.

Energy loss due to hysteresis is proportional to the area bounded by the hysteresis loop. Where alternating current transformers and alternating current electromagnets are used, it is the general practice to choose a kind of core that produces a thin loop.

Other Power Losses

Power loss in cores is also caused by eddy current. Although the losses caused by the work area or hysteresis is the major cause of power loss in cores, eddy current losses can be large. In ac (alternating current) circuits a voltage is induced into the core in the same way as voltage is induced in a transformer. (Transformer theory and the induction process are covered in Chapters 5 and 6.) Induced voltage in the core produces currents, as shown in Figure 2–12. Resistance losses caused by the eddy currents result in heat losses in the core.

There is one other loss in an electromagnetic device, resistance loss in the coil.

All three of these losses described above generate heat. But, a well designed electromagnet has an efficiency of 95% or better.

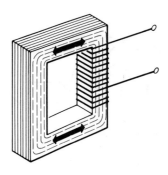

Figure 2-12 Eddy currents.

It will normally feel only slightly warm to the touch when in operation.

Hysteresis loss can be minimized by core material selection. Eddy current losses can be minimized by making the core of a stack of thin sheets (laminations) electrically insulated from one another. The laminations are often made of relatively high-resistance materials, which also helps. Resistive losses in the winding are minimized by using a large diameter wire to keep the resistance low.

2.9 MAGNETIC CIRCUITS

Magnetic flux of lines of force form closed loops. The path that the flux loops follow is called the *magnetic circuit*. Electrical circuits and magnetic circuits have many points in common. The force that produces a flow of electrons in an electrical circuit is called *electromotive force* (emf). In the magnetic circuit the force that produces the flux is called *magnetomotive force* (mmf). Resistance opposes the flow of current in an electrical circuit. Reluctance * opposes the magnetic flux in a magnetic circuit.

Conductance indicates the ease with which electrical current flows. Permeability

---

*No name has been established for the reluctance unit.

indicates the ease with which magnetic lines of force flow in a magnetic circuit.

One unit of reluctance is 1 cm long and 1 sq cm in cross section with unit permeability. Mathematically, the unit of reluctance is expressed by the equation

$$R = \frac{1}{\mu A}$$

where 1 represents length in centimeters, A is the cross-sectional area in sq cm, and μ is the permeability.

The magnetic law is very similar to Ohm's law for electrical circuits (to be discussed further in Chapter 3).

a. Magnetic Ohm's law:

$$\frac{\text{Magnetic flux}}{\text{current}} = \frac{\text{Magnetomotive Force}}{\text{Reluctance}}$$

b. Electrical Ohm's law:

$$\text{Electrical Current} = \frac{\text{Electromotive Force}}{\text{Resistance}}$$

The symbolic representation of the magnetic law is:

$$\phi = \frac{\text{mmf}}{R}$$

where ϕ is flux in maxwells, mmf is the magnetomotive force in gilberts (a *gilbert* is the mmf required to establish a flux of 1 maxwell in a magnetic circuit in which the reluctance is 1 unit), and R is the reluctance.

2.10 APPLICATIONS OF MAGNETIC CIRCUITS

We will present here some practical applications of the magnetic circuit principles we have learned thus far.

Air Core Coils We saw earlier that the magnetic field around a solenoid closely resembles that around a bar magnet. In Figure

2–13 we see an air core coil where the lines of force pass through the center of the coil and complete their closed loop through the surrounding space outside the coil.

About half the lines of force do not travel the complete length of the core. This is because the permeability of the air outside is the same as that of the core, and therefore the magnetic lines of force tend to repel each other and become as short as possible. This requires us to make our calculations in the center of the coil and not elsewhere around the coil.

In Figure 2–14 all the lines of force are crowded into the center cross section of the coil, and they complete their loops through a large area outside the coil. Since the reluctance of a magnetic circuit is inversely proportional to its cross-sectional area, the reluctance of the magnetic path within the coil is higher than that outside it. It is, therefore, a fair assumption that *for long air core coils, the total reluctance is approximately equal to the reluctance of the nonmagnetic core of the coil itself.*

If we insert a core of magnetic material in a coil, the high permeability of the magnetic material will reduce the reluctance of the core compared to that of the outside return path. Thus the total reluctance is reduced.

With a magnetic (low reluctance) core material, the reluctance of the return path in the air outside the coil becomes the major

factor in the total reluctance. This *air return path* reluctance is very difficult to calculate because of its infinite dimensions. Magnetic circuits that offer an *open magnetic path* for the return lines of force are avoided as much as possible in standard practice. One answer to the problem is to wind the coil around a toroid in the manner shown in Figure 2–14.

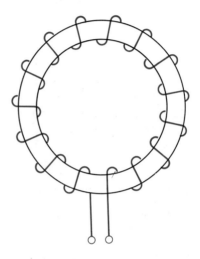

Figure 2-14 Toroid coil.

By winding the coil around a toroid the magnetic field is confined to a path completely within the coil for both magnetic and nonmagnetic cores. Figure 2–15 shows how a coil is wound around a toroid core.

The toroid represents an ideal situation, but toroids are generally expensive. Several closed core configurations that approach toroid characteristics are more common than true toroid shapes. The rectangular and E-shaped cores shown in Figure 2–16 are the most common.

Force on a Conductor in a Magnetic Field. When a current-carrying conductor is located in a magnetic field, the interaction of the field around the conductor and the magnetic field exerts a force upon the con-

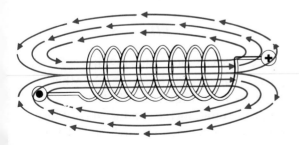

Figure 2-13 Air core coils.

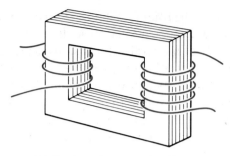

(A) Rectangular approximation.

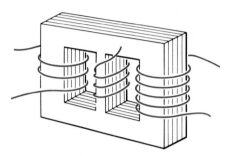

(B) The E core, the approximation of two interacting toroids. A common configuration in transformers.

Figure 2–15 Rectangular approximations of the toroid core.

ductor. This force is proportional to the flux density, the current, and the length of the conductor.

2.11 MOTORS AND GENERATORS

When a current-carrying conductor is placed in the field produced by two magnetic poles, the field about the conductor and the field between the poles react to produce a force that causes the conductor to move either upward or downward. This inter-action between current in a conductor and a magnetic field makes possible the oper-ation of electric motors. For example, examine the illustration in Figure 2–16, which shows the composite of the field poles. Since the electrons in the conductor

flow toward you in accordance with the left hand rule, the field about the conductor is clockwise. The conductor field has the same direction at the top, as the lines of force do between the two magnets. Under this condition, the two fields reinforce each other at the top and oppose each other at the bottom. Where these fields travel in opposite directions, they counteract each other. There is a strong force at the top of the conductor, and a weak force at the bottom. A current-carrying conductor that is located in a magnetic field is always pushed away from the point of stronger force. Therefore, the direction of motion of the conductor illustrated is downward. Had current flowed away from you (Figure 2–16) in the con-ductor, the two fields would have strength-ened each other at the bottom and weakened each other at the top and the conductor would have been pushed upward.

An important factor in connection with a current-carrying conductor in a magnetic field is the relationship between force, flux, and current flow. When the conductor is at right angles to the field, then force, current, and flux are all mutually perpendicular, as shown by the vectors in Figure 2–17. Math-ematically, the relationship is expressed by the equation $F = BIL/10$, which is often referred to as *Ampere's law*. When the con-ductor is not at a right angle, but at some angle ϕ with respect to the field, the vectorial length of the conductor would be effectively $L \sin \phi$ and the equation would be

$$F = BIL \sin \phi$$

Whenever two current-carrying con-ductors are located near each other, as illustrated in Figure 2–18, the magnetic fields surrounding the conductors produce a force that is exerted on each conductor. If the electron flow in the two conductors is in the same direction, the magnetic fields

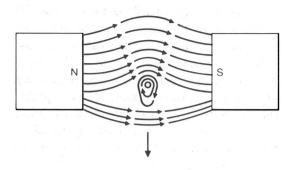

Figure 2-16 Composite magnetic field about conductor located between magnetic poles.

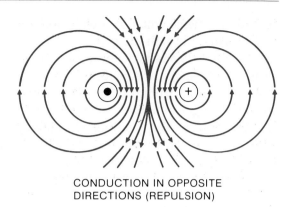

CONDUCTION IN OPPOSITE DIRECTIONS (REPULSION)

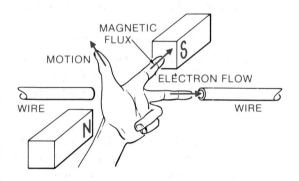

Figure 2-17 Direction of force, flux, and current.

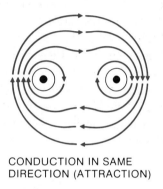

CONDUCTION IN SAME DIRECTION (ATTRACTION)

Figure 2-18 Fields surrounding adjacent conductors.

surrounding each conductor cancel between the conductors and strengthen outside the conductors. This is a force of attraction. When the current flow in the conductors is in the opposite direction, the fields strengthen between the conductors and weaken outside. This force is one of repulsion. (See Figure 2–18.)

It is these attraction-repulsion forces that make electric motors possible.

2.12 INDUCTION

Michael Faraday, in 1831, performed a simple experiment with a coil and a permanent magnet and discovered that a galvanometer connected to a coil would deflect in one or the other direction, depending on whether the magnet was being thrust in or was being pulled out. As the result of this experiment, Faraday concluded that electrons flow through the coil when there is relative motion between the coil and the magnetic field of the magnet, and that an electromotive force (emf is discussed in Chapter 3) was being induced in the coil. Later experiments proved that the magnitude of the induced voltage indicated by the galvanometer depends on the number of turns of the coil and the rate at which the magnetic field moves through the coil. The polarity of the induced emf was found to depend on whether the flux was increasing or decreasing through the coil.

Figure 2–19 shows a coil wound in the form of a solenoid and placed so that its turns are in a horizontal plane. A sensitive voltmeter or galvanometer is connected to the two ends of the winding to indicate either the voltage produced or the current forced through the coil by the induced emf.

When the north end of the magnet is thrust into the center of the coil, a voltage is induced, and the current that arises from this voltage will flow in such a direction as to cause the top end of the coil to appear as a north pole and thereby oppose the downward direction of the magnet.

In Figure 2–19, the north end of the magnet is moving toward the coil and electrons are flowing in the direction indicated by the current arrow. In the external circuit, the polarity of the induced emf is as shown, the top lead being positive and the bottom lead negative.

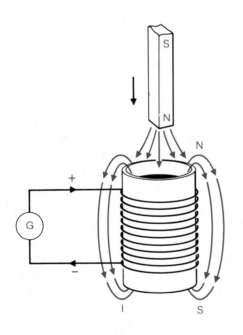

Figure 2-19 Inducing a voltage in a solenoid by moving a magnet.

The induced polarity of the coil *must* be the *same* as that of the moving pole to satisfy the law of energy conservation. If the induced polarity were opposite, it would only be necessary to start the magnet moving and allow the induced magnetism to pull it the rest of the way into the coil. This would be a case of "perpetual motion" which is impossible because it violates the law of the conservation of energy.

Lenz's Law In 1834, a Russian scientist named H. Lenz formulated a law that can be used to determine the direction of induced currents and voltages. The law is as follows:

Whenever an induced current is produced by any motion, current will flow in a direction such that mechanical forces will be produced that oppose the motion.

Figure 2–20 shows a wire moving downward with its length perpendicular to a magnetic field that runs from the left to the right. Think of the lines as being distorted in the manner illustrated. Cutting the lines of flux will induce an emf in the wire, and cause electrical current to flow if the wire forms a complete circuit. The left-hand rule is a simple test to determine the direction of electron flow through the wire. Grasp the wire with the left hand so that the fingers point in the way the distorted lines go around the wire. The thumb, which lies along the wire, will point in the direction of the electron flow.

2.13 MUTUAL INDUCTION

In an electrical circuit, a change of current is always accompanied by a change in the magnetic field surrounding the circuit. If the current is increasing, the field is said to be expanding. If the current is decreasing,

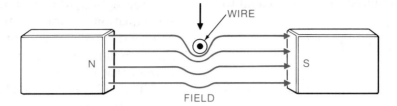

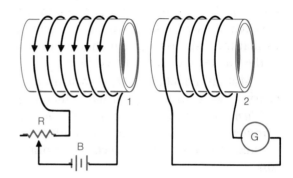

Figure 2-20 Conductor cutting through lines of force.

Figure 2-21 Mutual induction.

the field is said to be collapsing or decreasing in intensity. When a conductor is placed within a magnetic field in which the expanding or collapsing lines of force cut the conductor, a voltage will be induced in it.

Figure 2–21 shows two coils placed close together. Battery B is connected to coil 1. A galvanometer (indicating the amount and direction of current) is connected across the ends of coil 2. The variable resistor, R, in series with Battery B, allows us to vary the current through coil 1. As long as the current flowing through coil 1 does not vary (remains constant), its magnetic field will be steady, neither expanding nor collapsing, and no voltage will be induced into coil 2. The galvanometer will rest at zero. If we change the resistance of R, we will change the current through coil 1. *While the current is changing*, an emf will be induced into coil 2. When we stop changing the setting of R, the induced emf (voltage) drops to zero. In other words, induction occurs *only* while the field in coil 1 is either expanding or collapsing. There is no induced voltage when current (coil 1) and its magnetic field are stationary. On the other hand, if the resistance R is varied, an emf will be induced into coil 2. The induction will take place only while the value of R (and consequently the current in coil 1) is actually changing. Whenever the current in coil 1 stops changing, the induction into coil 2 stops.

When there is zero *change* in coil 1's

current the induced voltage is zero, and the faster the current varies, the greater the induced emf in coil 2. Voltage is induced from one coil into another when the field is in motion (expanding or collapsing). This action is called *mutual induction*.

If the current, Δi, in coil 1 changes rapidly; it causes a change in the flux through coil 2.

When a change in current flow in a coil causes a change in flux in an adjacent coil, the change in flux is proportional to the change in current. Therefore the change in flux, $\Delta \phi$, in coil 2 is proportional to the change in current, Δi, in coil 1. This proportion is expressed as

$$\frac{\Delta \phi}{\Delta t} :: \frac{\Delta i}{\Delta t}$$

The induced voltage is proportional to the rate of change of current in the coil. Thus the voltage induced in coil 2 is equal to

$$e_2 = -M \, \frac{\Delta i}{\Delta t}$$

Note: The symbol Δ means *a change in*
    Example: $\Delta\phi$ is a change in flux and Δi is a change in current.

where M is the amount of mutual inductance. M depends on the magnetic coupling between the two coils. The equation is telling us that the faster the current changes in coil 1, the greater the emf induced into coil 2.

Mutual inductance (M) is measured in henrys. Two coils have a mutual inductance of *1 henry* if *a change in current at the rate of 1 ampere per second* in one coil results in a voltage of *1 volt* being induced in the other coil.

If a soft iron (high permeability) core is inserted in such a way that it is common to both coils, the mutual inductance is greatly increased. However, the mutual inductance can only be increased by an amount dictated by the permeability of the soft iron. And, as we have seen previously, the permeability of the core varies with the current in the coil. As soon as all of the domains in the core are aligned, any further increase in current derives no help from the high permeability core. The core is then said to be saturated.

As we have just seen, a change in current in one coil causes a voltage to be induced in a second coil placed close to the first. At the same time, the flux through the coil in which the change of current took place also changed and a voltage was induced in it as well. When a change in current in a coil results in a voltage being induced in the coil by its own changing magnetic field, it is called *self-induction*. This voltage is also proportional to the rate at which the current is changing and is equal to

$$e_i = -L \, \frac{\Delta i}{\Delta t}$$

L is the self-inductance. The minus sign in the equation indicates that the induced voltage (the counter emf, or back emf) is of such a polarity as to oppose the change of current that caused it.

The unit of self-inductance is also the henry (H). A henry may be defined here as the inductance of a coil in which a voltage of 1 volt is induced by a current change of 1 ampere in 1 second (1 ampere/second).

The inductance of a coil is dependent not only on the change in current (and proportional flux density) but also on the number of turns cut by the lines of flux.

When two coils are placed close together, the relation between the mutual inductance, M, of the two coils and their individual self-inductances, L_1 and L_2, is equal to

$$M = k \, \sqrt{L_1 L_2}$$

where k has a value between zero and one and is called the *coefficient of coupling*.

If all the flux produced by a current in one coil links all the turns of the other, k is equal to 1.

2.14 GENERATORS

Whenever a conductor moves in a magnetic field in such a way as to cut across lines of force, first in one direction and then in the other, an alternating voltage is induced in the conductor. Current arising from this voltage flows first one way and then in the opposite direction. A current that reverses direction periodically is called *alternating current*, abbreviated ac. A current that flows continuously in the *same* direction is called *direct current,* or dc. A generator that produces alternating current (and voltage) is called an *ac generator* (alternator), and one that produces direct current is called a *dc*

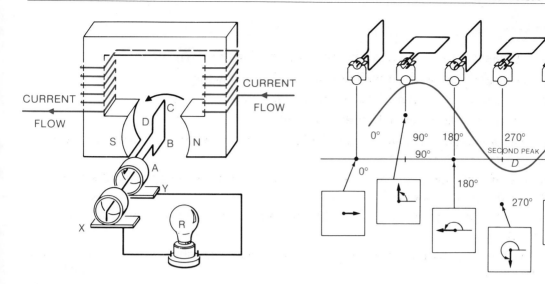

Figure 2-22 Simple generator.

Figure 2-23 Armature rotation and output voltage.

The AC Generator

Figure 2–22 and 2–23 are simple versions of an ac generator. A conductor is formed into a loop (ABCD) and is located in the magnetic field between the poles of an electromagnet (S and N). The two ends of the loop connect to slip rings X and Y, which make electrical contact with two brushes.

When the loop rotates in the plane of the coil and perpendicular to the field, it cuts the flux first in one direction and then in the other. At the instant when the loop is in the position illustrated, the coil sides AB and CD are moving parallel to the field and cut no flux. Therefore there is no voltage induced in the loop at this position. As the coil turns in a counterclockwise direction, AB moves up and CD moves downward through the field and a voltage is induced

generator. The two types are much alike, their principal difference being the method by which the energy generated is taken from the generator.

in A toward B and in C toward D. These two voltages add together in series and make brush X positive and brush Y negative. The voltage that is induced in the loop causes current flow in the lamp from Y to X. This current keeps increasing in magnitude and reaches maximum when the coil is horizontal to the lines of flux, at which time the loop is moving perpendicular to the field and is cutting the greatest number of lines. As the coil turns further, the induced voltage and current decrease until they reach zero where the loop is again in a vertical position. During the other half revolution an equal voltage is produced, except that its polarity is reversed since then both AB and DC cut flux lines in the opposite direction. Due to the reversed polarity of the induced voltage, the current flow through R is from X to Y. This rapidly reversing current is alternating current. If a graph is plotted of the generated output voltage against the angle of rotation of the loop (ABCD), we will have plotted the classical sine wave curve shown in Figure 2–23.

SUMMARY

1. Natural magnets have played an important part in ocean navigation.
2. Natural magnets are an iron oxide mineral called magnetite.
3. Magnetite, when it is magnetized, is called lodestone.
4. Like magnetic poles repel and unlike poles attract.
5. The poles in a magnet are named according to the direction of the earth to which they point when allowed to move freely.
6. The pole of a magnet that rotates toward the earth's north geographic pole is called the north or north-seeking pole.
7. Steel is difficult to magnetize, but holds its magnetism for a long time. Steel has high retentivity.
8. Soft iron is easy to magnetize, but loses its magnetism rapidly. Soft iron has low retentivity.
9. Air, wood, glass, and so on, have a high magnetic resistance called reluctance and a low magnetic conductivity called permeability.
10. Iron and steel have low reluctance and high permeability.
11. The magnetic Ohm's law and the electrical Ohm's law are analogous:

Electrical

| Electromotive Force (emf) | Electrical Current (I) | Electrical Resistance (R) |

Magnetic

| Magnetomotive Force (mmf) | Magnetic Flux (Q) | Reluctance ($\mathcal{R}$) |

12. The area around a magnet that can exert a force on iron or another magnet is called the magnetic field.
13. In the same way that electrical current flows from negative to positive, magnetic current (flux) flows from north to south.
14. If a magnet is broken in two, each half is still a complete magnet.
15. The molecular theory of magnetism is based on the assumption that small groups of atoms align the fields of spinning electrons in the same direction to form miniature molecular magnets. These miniature molecular magnets are called *domains*.
16. When current flows through a wire, a magnetic field is set up around the wire.

17. A wire can be wound into a coil to concentrate the magnetic field into a small package. Such a coil is called a solenoid.

18. The magnetic field strength of a coil depends on the electrical current and the number of turns in the solenoid:

Field strength = amperes × turns

19. The direction of a magnetic field in a solenoid depends on the direction of the current flowing in the coil.

20. The magnetic field strength of a solenoid can be greatly increased by inserting an iron core in its center.

21. The field strength is increased by the iron core because the core domains align with the coil's field, adding their strength to that of the electrically produced field.

22. Hysteresis is a delay in the movement of the magnetic domains. The domains encounter mechanical resistance (friction) as they change positions. As a result, they lag behind the changing electrical field and produce heat loss.

23. As the field expands in a coil, it cuts turns of wire in the coil, producing a voltage that *opposes* the applied coil voltage.

24. The opposing voltage is called counter emf, and the action is called self-inductance, or simply inductance.

25. When a second coil is placed very near the first, the expanding field in the first will cut turns of wire in the second. This will cause an emf to be induced in the second coil (mutual inductance).

REVIEWING YOUR ELECTRONICS VOCABULARY

1. Domain
2. Flux
3. Hysteresis
4. Magnetic pole
5. Mutual inductance
6. Permeability
7. Reluctance
8. Retentivity
9. Self-inductance
10. Solenoid

CHECKING YOUR UNDERSTANDING

1. What was the earliest application of magnetism?
2. Which material, iron or steel, has the higher retentivity?
3. Which material, iron or steel, is easier to magnetize?
4. List five nonmagnetic materials.
5. In which direction does magnetic flux flow?
6. If a magnet is broken in two, what does each half become?

7. On what does the direction of a magnetic field in a solenoid depend?

8. Explain why winding a wire into a coil produces a stronger magnetic field.

9. Explain why placing an iron core in a solenoid makes it a much stronger magnet when current is flowing.

10. Explain how a counter voltage is produced when the current is changing in a solenoid.

SOLVING ELECTRONIC PROBLEMS

1. Find the field strength in a solenoid consisting of ten turns when a current of five amperes is flowing in the solenoid.

2. Which of the following solenoids will produce the greater field strength: (a) a coil having 100 turns with a current of 2 amperes or (b) a coil having 10 turns and a current of 20 amperes?

3. Find the permeability (μ) of a core when B=1,000 and H=25.

4. Write the equation for amperes's law.

5. Express Lenz's law in words.

6. Two mutually coupled coils have a coefficient of coupling of 1. Ten thousand lines of flux cut coil A. How many lines of flux cut through coil B?

7. Write the equation for the mutual coupling of two coils placed close together.

8. An ac generator produces an output voltage of 110 volts at 5,000 rpm. What is the output voltage if the generator speed is increased to 10,000 rpm?

9. If the distance between the poles of two magnets is doubled, by what factor is the attractive (or repulsive) force reduced?

CHAPTER 3
Direct Current Circuits

INTRODUCTION

Before the discovery of the electron and its properties, current was thought to be a flow of positive charges from a point of high potential to a point of lower potential. However, when the electron was discovered and studied, it was found that current flow is a movement of negatively charged electrons.

In Chapter 1 we saw that an electrical current will flow in a wire of conductive material, such as copper, if the wire is connected between two points with a difference in potential. This current flow in the circuit will continue as long as there is a difference of potential between the ends of the wire. If the charges on each end of the wire become equal, the current will cease to flow.

A device illustrated in Figure 3-1 causes the two points in the system to remain at a constant difference of potential. This continuous potential will cause a continuous current to flow in our circuit.

3.1 ELECTROMOTIVE FORCE (emf)

In Figure 3-1 you can see that there is a difference in the number of electrons between the two ends of the continuous potential device. This difference in the quantity of electrons creates a pressure or force that drives the electrons through the

wire, much as water pressure in our water system moves water through the pipes. This is electromotive force (emf) that is measured in volts and is thus commonly known as voltage. Devices that provide a continuous potential always convert some other kind of energy into electrical potential (Fig. 3-2).

- **Batteries**   Convert chemical energy into emf.
- **Solar Cells**   Convert direct sunlight into emf.
- **Generators and Alternators**   Convert mechanical energy into emf.

When there is no voltage applied to a conductor, the free electrons—the current carriers in a conductor—are free to move in a random pattern from one atom to another.

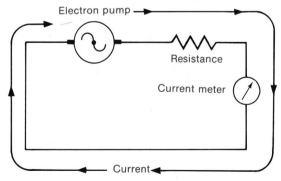

Figure 3-1 An electron pump (battery, generator, solar cell) can keep a continuous current flowing through a circuit.

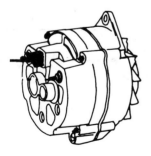

Figure 3-2 Sources of electromotive force.

However, when there is no voltage applied, this electron drift has no *net* drift in either direction. When a voltage is applied to the circuit from some source, the free electrons are attracted by the deficiency of electrons at one end of the conductor and are repelled by the excess at the other end. When this condition is present, the free electrons begin to move, establishing a net drift in one direction along the conductor. Since an electron has a small mass, as it is accelerated along the conductor the potential energy is converted, in part, into kinetic energy (motion), and the electron gathers speed. When a battery is used as a source of free electrons, the energy comes from the chemical energy of the battery. This energy is used to maintain the difference in potential between its terminals and thus within the circuit to which it is connected.

Before the accelerating electron gets very far in the conductor, it collides with an atom of the conductor. This collision will cause a considerable reduction in the electron's velocity. Because of this reduction in velocity, the electron will give up some of its kinetic energy to the atom with which it collided. This energy is in the form of heat. After the collision with the atom and the transfer of heat energy to the atom, the electron will again be accelerated by the applied voltage and acquire more kinetic energy from its acceleration. The electron will again collide with another atom and give up some of its energy in heat to the atom it collided with. Thus the progress of the electrons is a progression of acceleration and deceleration, first gaining energy from the applied voltage and then giving up at least part of the energy to an atom in the form of heat.

This succession of collisions on the part of the free electrons is a simple *opposition to the free flow of the current* and is known as *resistance*. Resistance (R) in an electrical circuit causes energy to be taken from the voltage source and be converted into heat whenever there is any current flow in the conductor. The more current flow in the conductor, the more energy is converted into heat energy.

Since current flow consists of electrons and there are only a given number of them in any given volume of conductor, the current-carrying ability of a conductor will depend upon its cross-sectional area. It is important to remember that electrons are not lost from the system. The energy converted into heat by resistance reduces the voltage.

In Figure 3–3 we see a section of copper bar with width, length, and thickness. For the convenience of our explanation, we have divided the bar in the figure into three thin slices as shown by the dashed lines in the figure.

If the three pieces were *longer*, the current would have to travel further and would have more opportunity for collisions. The increased opposition would thus increase the total resistance of the bar. From this information we can now state a basic fact about resistance: *the resistance of a conductor will increase directly with the length of the conductor.*

Now let us see what happens if we increase the width of the bar so that there are four sections to the bar instead of the original three. When this occurs, the current will have four paths (in parallel) to follow instead of three. The total resistance of the four pieces will be less than that of the original three because of the increase in the number of free electrons available. Increasing the thickness will have the same effect as increasing width. Adding more parallel paths for the current to follow decreases the resistance. We can now state another basic fact about resistance: *the resistance of a conductor will decrease as the width or the thickness is increased.*

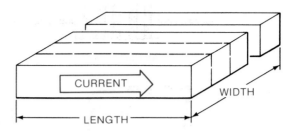

Figure 3–3 Resistance and physical dimension.

There is one last major condition that we must consider in determining the resistance of a given conductor. This is the number of free electrons available in the conductor material. The larger the number of free electrons within a given conductor, the smaller the percentage of the total energy that must be carried by one electron. Therefore, the amount of energy that is converted into heat by collisions is reduced. We can thus state the last major fact of resistance: *the resistance (R) of a conductor will depend upon the material of which the conductor is made.* (See Figure 3–4).

3.2 OHM'S LAW

The German physicist George Simon Ohm conducted extensive experiments into the abilities of various materials to conduct electric energy. He found that materials with the same physical size had different resistances. He was able to establish that, for a fixed voltage, the amount of current flowing through any material depends upon the type and the physical size of the material.

The ratio of voltage and current (resistance) for any given type of conductor is a constant that is dependent upon the material and its dimensions. This ratio can be expressed mathematically as follows:

$$E = IR$$

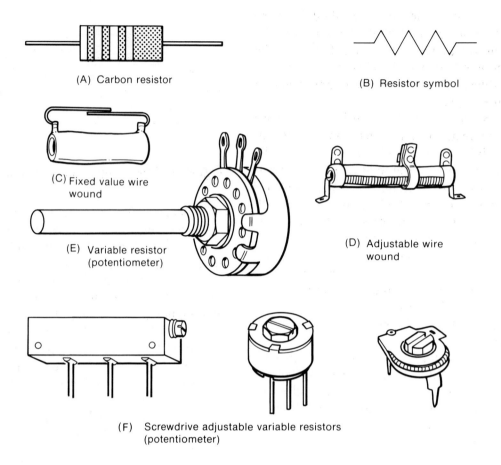

(A) Carbon resistor

(B) Resistor symbol

(C) Fixed value wire wound

(E) Variable resistor (potentiometer)

(D) Adjustable wire wound

(F) Screwdrive adjustable variable resistors (potentiometer)

Figure 3–4 Resistors.

In this equation, E is the applied voltage in volts, I is the current in amperes, and R is the resistance in ohms (the symbol is Ω, the Greek letter omega), the unit of measure for resistance. The equation can be interpreted as: *1 volt* will force *1 ampere* of current through a resistance of *1 ohm*. When it is desired to specify how good a conductor is, rather than how much resistance it offers, the unit is the mho (ohm spelled backward).

Electric conductance/siemens The siemens is the practical unit of conductance. The siemens is the reciprocal of the ohm since the conductance is the reciprocal of the resistance. The relationship between ohms and

$$siemens\ is\ given\ by\ G = \frac{1}{R}\ siemens.$$

A conductance of one siemens will permit a current flow of one ampere (A) under an electrical pressure of one volt (V). The siemens is a new unit honoring a pioneer in electricity. *Formerly, the unit of conductance was called the mho. The symbol for conductance is G, and the abbreviation for siemens is S.*

$$mhos = \frac{1}{ohms}\ and\ ohms = \frac{1}{mhos}$$

The symbol for ohm is the Greek letter Ω (omega).

The symbol for the mho is an upside-down omega, $\mho$.

The three forms of Ohm's law are as follows (Fig. 3–5):

The voltage *(E)** that is required to maintain a certain current in a circuit in which the resistance is known is equal to the product of the current (*I*) and the resistance (*R*).

$$E = IR$$

The current (*I*) in any circuit is equal to the voltage (*E*) applied, divided by the resistance of the circuit.

$$I = \frac{E}{R}$$

The resistance (*R*) needed in a circuit so that a certain current (*I*) will flow when a certain voltage (*E*) is applied is equal to the voltage divided by the current.

$$R = \frac{E}{I}$$

---

* *E* stands for electromotive force. *V* (for voltage) is also commonly used *(V = IR, I = V/R, R = V/I)*.

In order to understand applications of the Ohm's law variations, we will work an example of each type.

The Ohm's law memory aid

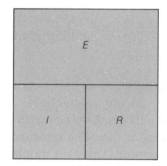

(B) To find *R:*

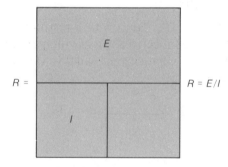

$R = \quad\quad\quad R = E/I$

(A) To find *E:*

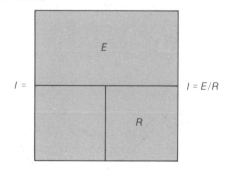

Figure 3–5

Example 3–1

Problem: What voltage must be applied to a circuit containing a resistance of 150 ohms and a required current of 3 amps?

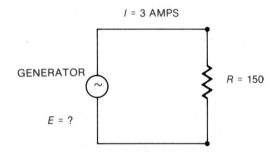

Solution:

$$E = IR = (3)(150) = 450 \text{ volts}$$

Example 3–2

Problem: If a lamp with a resistance of 75 ohms is connected across a voltage source of 117 volts, what current will flow through the lamp?

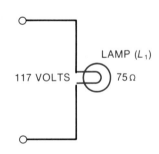

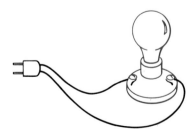

Diagram for example 3-2.

Solution:

$$I = \frac{E}{R} = \frac{117}{75} = 1.56 \text{ amps}$$

Example 3–3

Problem: What resistance will cause a current of 1.2 amps to flow when a voltage of 150 volts is applied?

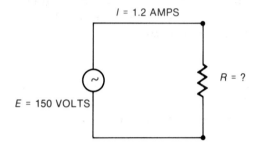

Solution:

$$R = \frac{E}{I} = \frac{150}{1.2} = 125 \text{ ohms}$$

Up to this point we have not considered temperature in our calculations. We have considered only a normal room temperature of 20 degrees celsius. The resistance of any conductor depends upon the number of free electrons in it. Therefore, as the temperature of a conductor is raised, energy is transferred to the atoms because of the temperature increase. This additional energy given to the atoms causes them to move around more than they did, thus causing an increase in the distance between the atoms. The increase in distance will provide more space for the free electrons to move in without colliding with an atom.

When we heat most substances they will enlarge somewhat. As we increase the temperature, it will cause an *increase* in resistance in *most* substances. This is known as a *positive temperature coefficient*. See the graph in Figure 3–6 for copper. Note that it is approximately linear (a straight line graph) over the normal temperature range in which electronic equipment operates.

Scientists have measured the resistance of conductors at varying temperatures and have determined that most metals increase in resistance. The increase is approximately linear over a wide temperature range.

3.3 HEAT AND POWER

Whenever current flows in a circuit there is some power (or I^2R) loss. This loss is in the form of heat.

$$\text{(Power) Watts} = I^2R$$

Commercial resistors have two basic ratings, the resistance in ohms and a power rating expressed in watts. A resistor must be able to dissipate the heat *it* produces. If the internal temperature of a resistor increases to a high level its resistance will change, and often it is a permanent change.

Most common lower wattage resistors, that is, ¼ to 2 watts, have their resistance values specified by a color code printed on

their bodies. The wattage rating is simply a matter of the resistor's physical size, which, with a little practice, can easily be learned. Table 3–1 shows the resistor color code and how it works. Figure 3–7 illustrates the relative sizes of ½, 1, and 2 watt common resistors.

The color code should be memorized, as it will be used in almost all of the electronic equipment you will encounter.

Example 3–4

Problem: Figure the value of a resistor with the following color bands: red, first band; green, second band; orange, third band; silver, fourth band.

Red	2
Green	5
Orange	000 (3 zeros)
Silver	10%

Solution: 25,000 ohms ± 10%

3.4 POWER DISSIPATION IN RESISTORS

The power dissipated by a resistor is the product of the current through it and the voltage across it.

$$P = EI$$

This formula can also be stated in two other forms:

$$P = I^2R$$

$$P = \frac{E^2}{R}$$

Example 3–5

Problem: Find the power dissipation of a resistor with an applied voltage of 10 volts and a current of 0.2 amps (the unit of measure is the watt).

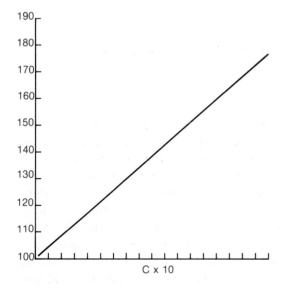

Figure 3-6 Copper temperature coefficient.

Solution:

$$P = 10 \times 0.2 = 2 \text{ watts}$$

The power dissipation can also be calculated when only current and resistance or voltage and resistance are known.

Example 3–6

Problem: Find the power dissipation of a 100 Ω resistor with a current through it of 0.1 amp.

Solution:

$$P = I^2 R$$
$$P = 0.1^2 \times 100$$
$$P = 1 \text{ watt}$$

Example 3–7

Problem: Find the power dissipation of a 100 ohm resistor when there is a voltage of 10 volts across it.

Solution:

$$P = \frac{E^2}{R}$$
$$P = \frac{10^2}{100}$$
$$P = \frac{100}{100} = 1 \text{ watt}$$

3.5 THE SERIES CIRCUIT

In a series circuit *the same current will pass through each element in the circuit before completing its path to the source.*

A simple series circuit is shown in Figure 3–8. This circuit is made up of six lamps in series, like a string of Christmas tree lamps. In order for the current to

complete its path, it must flow through each lamp in turn before flowing back to the battery. If any one of the six lamps burns out, it will open the circuit and the current will cease the flow. This opening of the circuit is like a switch. A switch is a simple device to open a circuit whenever current flow is not wanted.

In part A of the figure, the circuit is redrawn showing resistors in place of the lamps. Many times a circuit such as that shown in part B of the figure can be more easily understood when symbols of an equivalent nature are used.

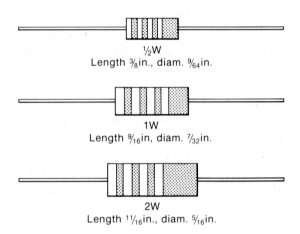

½W
Length ⅜in., diam. ⁹⁄₆₄in.

1W
Length ⁹⁄₁₆in, diam. ⁷⁄₃₂in.

2W
Length ¹¹⁄₁₆in., diam. ⁵⁄₁₆in.

Figure 3-7 Carbon resistor sizes.

3.6 INTERNAL RESISTANCE

Any power source, such as battery or generator, has some internal resistance. Because of this internal resistance there will be some heat produced within the power source whenever a current is flowing in the circuit to which the source is connected. Some energy is converted into heat within the battery itself. If the internal resistance of the battery is R, then the loss of voltage within the battery itself can be found with Ohm's law. This loss is the current times the

Table 3-1   **Standard Color Code**

The resistor color code.

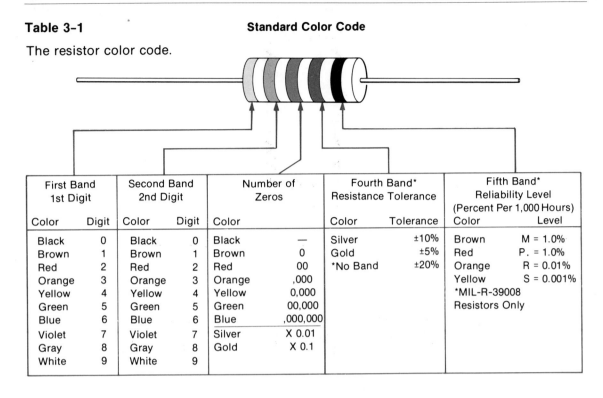

First Band 1st Digit		Second Band 2nd Digit		Number of Zeros	Fourth Band* Resistance Tolerance		Fifth Band* Reliability Level (Percent Per 1,000 Hours)	
Color	Digit	Color	Digit	Color	Color	Tolerance	Color	Level
Black	0	Black	0	Black	—	Silver	±10%	Brown	M = 1.0%
Brown	1	Brown	1	Brown	0	Gold	±5%	Red	P. = 1.0%
Red	2	Red	2	Red	00	*No Band	±20%	Orange	R = 0.01%
Orange	3	Orange	3	Orange	,000			Yellow	S = 0.001%
Yellow	4	Yellow	4	Yellow	0,000			*MIL-R-39008	
Green	5	Green	5	Green	00,000			Resistors Only	
Blue	6	Blue	6	Blue	,000,000				
Violet	7	Violet	7	Silver	X 0.01				
Gray	8	Gray	8	Gold	X 0.1				
White	9	White	9						

resistance; or

$$E = IR$$

V_t is the voltage between the battery terminals, such that

$$V_t = E - IR$$

The battery terminal voltage is equal to *E only* when there is *no* current being drawn from the battery. Any current would cause an *IR* (voltage) drop that must be subtracted from the battery voltage. For most practical purposes this internal resistance may be ignored, but there are times when it must be considered. It can be a considerable source of trouble; for example, in older automobile batteries.

Figure 3–9 is a simple series circuit with one resistor and a battery power source. The voltmeter V_1 will measure the battery voltage with switch S_1 open. However, voltmeter

V_2 will measure zero volts with the switch open. Upon the closing of switch S_1 the conditions in the circuit will follow those rules we established in section 3–2. The current through R_1 and R_2 will depend upon the applied voltage and the resistances.

3.7 VOLTAGE DROPS IN SERIES CIRCUITS

In any series circuit, if the voltage is measured across each resistance and the values are added, the sum will equal the supply voltage. Figure 3–10 illustrates the point $E_1 + E_2 + E_3 = E_s$.

The voltage across each resistor is known as a *voltage drop*. Because $E = IR$, a voltage drop is often known as an *IR* drop.

In Figure 3–10 there are three resistors in series. The electrons flowing in this circuit have only one path to follow in flowing around the circuit, and the current must

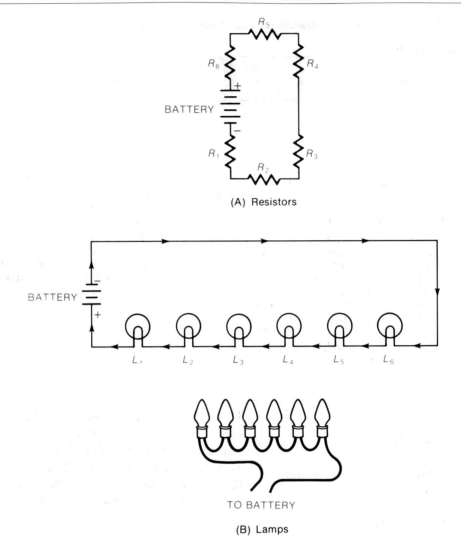

(A) Resistors

(B) Lamps

Figure 3-8 Series circuits.

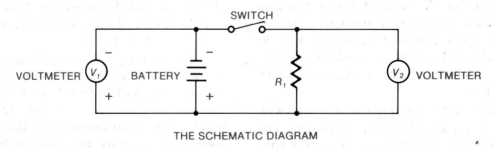

THE SCHEMATIC DIAGRAM

Figure 3-9 The simplest series circuit.

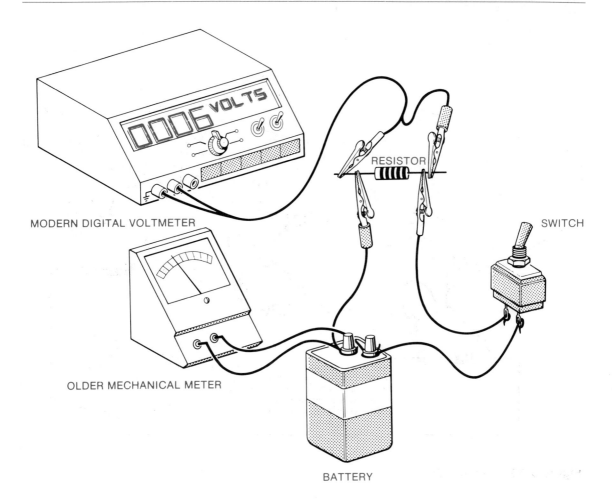

MODERN DIGITAL VOLTMETER

RESISTOR

SWITCH

OLDER MECHANICAL METER

BATTERY

Figure 3-9 (Continued)

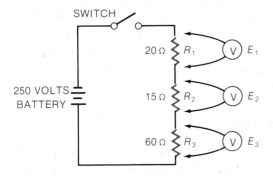

Figure 3-10 Series circuit.

flow through each resistor in turn. Because of this, the total voltage will be the sum of all the individual voltage drops across each resistor. The equivalent resistance in a series circuit is equal to the sum of the resistances of the individual resistors. This relationship can be shown by

$$R_t = R_1 + R_2 + R_3$$

This equation will have as many R numbers as there are resistors in the circuit. Once we have R_t, or the total resistance, we can use

(B) Pictorial diagram

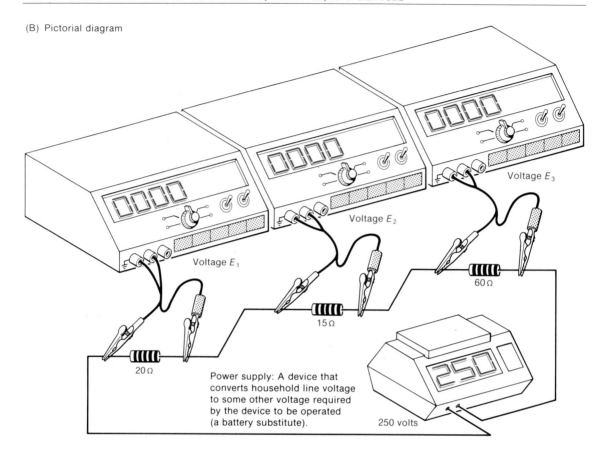

Voltage E_3

Voltage E_2

Voltage E_1

60 Ω

15 Ω

20 Ω

Power supply: A device that converts household line voltage to some other voltage required by the device to be operated (a battery substitute).

250 volts

Figure 3-10 (Continued)

Ohm's law to solve for all the various circuit unknowns. Let us look at an example where the resistance equation and Ohm's law are used:

Example 3-8

Problem: What current will flow in a circuit consisting of a 20 ohm, a 15 ohm, and a 60 ohm resistor in series with a voltage source of 250 volts?

Solution:

$$R_t = R_1 + R_2 + R_3 \text{ (see Figure 3-10)}$$
$$= 20 + 15 + 60$$
$$= 95 \text{ ohms}$$

$$I = \frac{E}{R} + \frac{250}{95} = 2.63 \text{ amps}$$

In example 3-8, as far as the battery is concerned, there is only a single 95 ohm resistor connected in the circuit. This *single equivalent* resistor is far easier to work with in calculations than three separate resistors.

Example 3-9

Problem: In a series circuit consisting of three lamps, one requires 25 volts at 100 milliamps (0.1 amp), and two require 35 volts at 100 milliamps. The voltage source is 110 volts. What additional resistance, if any, is needed to maintain the correct voltage across each lamp?

25 + 35 + 35 = 95 volts is dropped by the lamps.

For a 110 volt source, an additional resistor is needed to give us the additional voltage drop of 15 volts.

Solution:

$$R = \frac{E}{I} = \frac{15\ V}{0.10\ A} = 150\ ohms$$

Remember: 100 mA (milliamps) are equal to 0.1 ampere.

Let us return to the resistance equation. By performing some algebraic manipulations on it, we can arrive at the following:

$$I(R_t) = I(R_1 + R_2 + R_3)$$
$$IR_t = IR_1 + IR_2 + IR_3$$

Since we know that

$$I = \frac{E}{R}$$

then $IR_t = E$ (the applied voltage).

Kirchoff's Second Law

This equation demonstrates that the sum of all the voltage drops across each individual resistor *must* equal the applied voltage. This is known as Kirchoff's second law. It is also a special statement of the law of the conservation of energy. Gustav Kirchhoff discovered in his experiments that this law applies to *any* complete circuit. A formal definition of the law is as follows:

In any complete electric circuit, the sum of the individual voltage drops around a complete series circuit is equal to the applied voltage. For in-

stance, if a battery has 30 volts this means it has a + or

$$+30\ V = -15V\ -5V\ -10V$$
$$+30V = -30V$$
$$+30V\ -30V = 0$$

$$+E_T = -E_{R1}\ -E_{R2}\ -E_{R3}$$

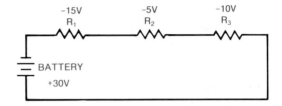

Each voltage drop means a − or drop in potential available to the other resistors.

Let us use Kirchhoff's law to solve a problem. One extra step is required to solve the problem using this method, as can be seen in the following example.

Example 3–10

Problem: What current will flow in a circuit consisting of a 20 ohm, a 15 ohm, and a 60 ohm resistor in series with an applied voltage of 250 volts?

Solution:

$$E = IR_1 + IR_2 + IR_3$$
$$250 = 120 + 115 + 160$$
$$E = IR$$
$$250 = I\ (95\ \Omega)$$

Therefore,

$$I = \frac{250}{95}$$
$$= 2.63\ amps$$

In a series circuit, the ratio between any two voltage drops is the same as the ratio of the two resistances across which these two voltage drops occur. We can show this mathematically using Ohm's law. Since the current in a series circuit is the same through any point in it, it follows that

$$I = \frac{E_1}{R_1} = \frac{E_2}{R_2} = \frac{E_3}{R_3} = \frac{E_s}{R_t}$$

Using the rules of algebra we have

$$\frac{E_1}{R_1} = \frac{E_2}{R_2}$$

and therefore,

$$\frac{E_1}{E_s} = \frac{R_1}{R_t} \text{ and } E_1 = E_s \frac{R_1}{R_t}$$

This equation can be very useful when some of the information about the circuit under study is not known. We can find a voltage drop across a resistor without knowing the current through it. Suppose we look at an example:

Example 3–11

Problem: If a 25,000 (R_1) ohm resistor and a 35,000 (R_2) ohm resistor are connected in series across a 325 volt source, what is the voltage drop across the 25,000 ohm resistor?

Solution:

$$E_1 = 325 \frac{25,000}{60,000}$$

$$E_1 = 325 \times 0.41666$$

$$E_1 = 135.41 \text{ volts}$$

This can be verified by the long method.

$$R_t = R_1 + R_2 = 60,000$$

$$I = \frac{325}{60,000} = 0.0054166$$

$$V_1 = (0.0054166)(25,000)$$

$$V_1 = 135.42$$

3.8 PARALLEL CIRCUITS IN DC OPERATION

In Figure 3–11 we can see the differences in the series and parallel circuits. In part A of the figure there is only *one* path for the current to follow. This single path through the two resistors and back to the battery makes it a series circuit. In part B of the figure, we have a much different situation. There are *two* different paths that the current can, and does, follow. Currents I_1 and I_2 both flow from the battery to the junction of the two resistors. At that point the current splits; current I_1 will flow through R_1 and current I_2 will flow through R_2. The two currents then recombine after flowing through the resistors and flow back to the battery, thus completing the circuit.

A very important distinction should be noted here about circuits. It is not totally correct to state that two components connected across each other make a parallel circuit. As you can see in Figure 3–11, both series and parallel circuits are connected *across* the power source, in this case, the battery. In part A, the series circuit, as we already know, the same current is flowing through both resistors and the battery.

In part B of the figure, R_1 and R_2 are connected across each other and the *combination* of the two resistors is connected across the battery. The two resistors R_1 and R_2 cannot be in series because *different* currents flow through each resistor.

It can be seen that the way in which the current flows in a circuit determines whether it is a series or a parallel circuit; and that the total current or combined current, is the sum of the currents flowing through each branch, as shown by

$$I_t = I_1 + I_2 + I_3 - - - - -$$

In parallel circuits the total current flowing through any parallel combination

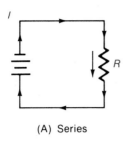

(A) Series

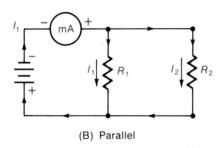

(B) Parallel

Figure 3–11 Series and parallel circuits.

can always be found by applying Ohm's law to each branch in turn and then adding the resulting currents.

Example 3–12

Problem: What is the total current flowing, when a 200 ohm, a 150 ohm, and a 300 ohm resistor are connected in parallel across a 100 volt source?

Solution:

$$I_1 = \frac{100}{200} = 0.5$$

$$I_2 = \frac{100}{150} = 0.66$$

$$I_3 = \frac{100}{300} = 0.33$$

$$I_t = 0.5 + 0.66 + 0.33 = 1.49 \text{ amps}$$

From this example it can be seen that the total current is much greater than the

current through any one of the individual parallel branches.

We now have enough data to state Kirchhoff's *first* law:

At any junction point in an electric circuit, the algebraic sum of the currents entering the point must be equal to the algebraic sum of the currents leaving the point.

Let us look at an example of this law.

Example 3–13

Problem: What is the current through the resistor R_2 in the circuit?

Parallel circuit.

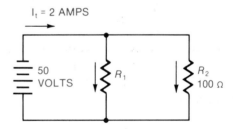

Diagram for example 3-13.

$$I_2 = \frac{E}{R_2} = \frac{50}{100} = 0.5 \text{ amps}$$

Solution:

$$I_2 = \frac{E}{R_2} = \frac{50}{100} = 0.5 \text{ amps}$$

Therefore, from Kirchhoff's Law

$$I_t = I_1 + I_2$$

$$I_2 = I_t - I_1$$

$$= 2 - 0.5$$

$$= 1.5 \text{ amps}$$

In the examples it was shown that the

total current in a parallel circuit can be found by adding the current in each branch. Because the currents are additive in a parallel circuit, the total equivalent resistance of the circuit is less than that of any one of its individual branches. If we add more resistors in parallel to the network, the total equivalent resistance will decrease.

3.9 CONDUCTANCE

Let us now look at the total resistance from another point of view; that is, of the ability of a circuit to *pass* current, and not oppose it as resistance does. This is called *conductance* and it is the reciprocal of resistance. Conductance is defined by the following equation:

$$G = \frac{1}{R}$$

In this equation G is conductance in siemens (mhos), and R is the circuit resistance in ohms. Resistance is also the reciprocal or conductance;

$$R = \frac{1}{G}$$

also

$$G_t = G_1 + G_2$$

The total conductance is equal to the sum of the conductances of each of the individual branches.

In the following example we see how conductance can be useful.

Example 3–14

Problem: If we have a 45 ohm and a 65 ohm resistor in parallel, what single resistor will draw the same current from the source?

Solution:

$$G_t = G_1 + G_2$$

$$= \frac{1}{45} + \frac{1}{65}$$

$$= 0.02222 + 0.015$$

$$= 0.0376 \text{ mho}$$

$$R_{eq} = \frac{1}{G}$$

Therefore,

$$R_{eq} = \frac{1}{0.0376} = 26.59 \text{ ohms}$$

When we have only two resistors in the parallel network, we can reduce this equation to a form that can be used directly to convert their values into the equivalent resistance. The equation is as follows:

$$R_{eq} = \frac{R_1 R_2}{R_1 + R_2}$$

This equation for finding the equivalent resistance by their product over their sum is *only* valid for two resistors in parallel and no more. As a practical example, we will solve the problem in example 3–14 using this equation.

Example 3–15

Problem: What is the equivalent resistance of a 45 ohm resistor and a 65 ohm resistor in parallel?

Solution:

$$R_{eq} = \frac{R_1 R_2}{R_1 + R_2}$$

$$= \frac{(45)(65)}{45 + 65} = 26.59 \text{ ohms}$$

You can see from example 3–15 that the use of this equation makes the work much shorter, and there is less chance for mathematical error because of the fewer steps involved.

In a *parallel circuit*, the ratio between any two branch circuits is the *same* as the ratio of their conductances or the *inverse* of their resistance ratio.

Let us use this ratio to solve a problem.

Example 3–16

Problem: If the total current of a parallel network composed of a 22,000 ohm and a 28,000 ohm resistor is 0.45 amperes, what is the current through the 28,000 ohm resistor?

Solution:

$$\frac{I_1}{I_2} = \frac{R_2}{R_1} = \frac{28,000}{22,000} = \frac{28}{22} = 1.27$$

$$I_1 = 1.27 \, I_2$$

Substituting, we have:

$$1.27I_2 + I_2 = 0.45$$

$$1.27I_2 = 0.45$$

$$I_2 = 0.354 \text{ amp}$$

Up to now we have shown only two resistors in our parallel circuits. However, there are often more than two resistors in any parallel network. Therefore, we must consider how to approach a three or more resistors parallel network.

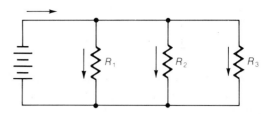

Figure 3–12 Multiple resistor circuit.

Figure 3–12 is a simple three resistor parallel network; there can be any number of resistors in the network. In all parallel networks all the previous equations are usable except the equation $(R_1R_2)/(R_1 + R_2)$, which is a unique situation covering *only* two resistors in parallel. If we have three resistors in a parallel circuit such as that shown in Figure 3–12, we can say that

$$G_t = \frac{1}{R_1} + \frac{1}{R_2} + \frac{1}{R_3}$$

and

$$G_1 = \frac{1}{R_1} \; , \; G_2 = \frac{1}{R_2} \text{ and } G_3 = \frac{1}{R_3}$$

Therefore:

$$G_t = G_1 + G_2 + G_3$$

To demonstrate that this works, we will use an example.

Example 3–17

Problem: Find the equivalent total resistance of a parallel network consisting of a 4 ohm, a 3 ohm, and a 6 ohm resistor.

Solution:

$$G_t = G_1 + G_2 + G_3 = \frac{1}{4} + \frac{1}{3} + \frac{1}{6}$$

$$= 0.75 \text{ mho}$$

$$R_{eq} = \frac{1}{G_t} = \frac{1}{0.75} = 1.33 \text{ ohms}$$

Now to check, we can use the equation $(R_1 R_2)/(R_1 + R_2)$ twice, as follows. First R_1 and R_2.

$$R_{eq} + \frac{(4)(3)}{4+3} = \frac{12}{7} = 1.71 \text{ ohms}$$

Now using this 1.71 ohms as an equivalent resistance in parallel with R_3, we get

$$R_{eq} = \frac{(1.71)(6)}{1.71+6} = \frac{10.26}{7.71} = 1.33 \text{ ohms}$$

A second method to solve this problem is

$$R_{eq} = \frac{1}{\dfrac{1}{R_1} + \dfrac{1}{R_2} + \dfrac{1}{R_3}}$$

$$= \frac{1}{\dfrac{1}{4} + \dfrac{1}{3} + \dfrac{1}{6}} = \frac{1}{.25 + .333 + .666}$$

$$= \frac{1}{0.75} = 1.33 \text{ ohms}$$

As you can see in the last section of example 3–17, we used the reciprocal of the conductances and were able to go directly to R_t from the individual resistor values given. We therefore can state that in multiple parallel resistor networks

$$R_{eq} = \frac{1}{\dfrac{1}{R_1} + \dfrac{1}{R_2} + \dfrac{1}{R_3}}$$

This equation is valid for *all* parallel resistor networks with two or more resistors in the circuit.

However, with today's calculators it is much easier to state the formula as:

$$\frac{1}{R_T} = \frac{1}{R_1} + \frac{1}{R_2} + \frac{1}{R_3}$$

Example 3–18

Problem: What is the equivalent resistance of a parallel resistor network with resistors of 20 ohms, 10 ohms, 40 ohms, and 200 ohms in parallel?

Solution:

$$R_t = \frac{1}{\dfrac{1}{20} + \dfrac{1}{10} + \dfrac{1}{40} + \dfrac{1}{200}}$$

$$= \frac{1}{0.05 + 0.1 + 0.025 + 0.005}$$

$$= \frac{1}{0.180} = 5.555 \text{ ohms}$$

One final fact should be remembered about a parallel resistor network. In such a network if the resistance of one of the branches is changed, it will have *no* effect on the voltage across the other parallel branches; except in the case where the voltage source is not able to supply the required current because of internal resistance in the source. This exception occurs where, for example, one of the branches is reduced to zero ohms, in which case we would have

$$I = \frac{E}{R} = \frac{E}{0}$$

As you know, the rules of math prohibit division by zero. If the resistance became infinitely small, the current would have to become infinitely large. We would have a short circuit on our hands.

A very good example of a change in one branch not having any effect on the other branches is the lighting circuit in a house. Each light in the house is connected in parallel with all the others to the 117 volt source, and switching one of the lights on or off has no effect on the others in the house.

3.10 VOLTAGE DIVIDERS

The basic voltage divider normally consists of a series of resistors having two input terminals, across which the input voltage from the power source is applied. The out-puts are across the various resistors depending upon what part of the input voltage is desired. The simple voltage divider is a special series circuit.

Shown in Figure 3–13 is an example of a voltage divider.

Example 3–19

Problem: Figure 3–13 shows a simple voltage divider. Find the voltage between each terminal and ground.

Solution:

a. Calculate total current

$I_t = E/(R_1 + R_2 + R_3)$ (Ohm's law)

$I_t = 100/1000 = 0.1$ amp

b. Using the resistance between terminal A and ground and the total current, calculate the voltage

$E = IR$

$E = 0.1 \times 100$

$E = 10$ volts

c. Using the total resistance between terminal B and ground and the total current, calculate the voltage

$E = IR$

$E = 0.1 \times 300 + 100$

$E = 0.1 \times 400$

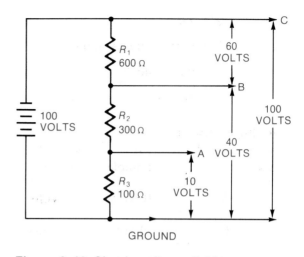

Figure 3-13 Simple voltage divider.

$E = 40$ volts

There is no need to calculate the voltage between terminal C and ground because it is directly across the battery.

Suppose we increase the value of resistors R_1, R_2, and R_3 to $6k$, $3k$, and $1k$, respectively, and solve the problem again.

a. Calculate the total current
Keep in mind that k means 1,000.

$I_t = E/(R_1 + R_2 + R_3)$

$I_t = \dfrac{E}{6k + 3k + 1k}$

$I_t = \dfrac{100}{10k} = 0.01$ amp

b. Using the resistance between terminal A and ground and the total current, calculate the voltage.

$E = IR$

$E = 0.01 \times 1000$

$E = 10$ volts

c. Using the total resistance between terminal B and ground and the total current, calculate the voltage.

$$E = IR$$

$$E = 0.01 \times 3000 + 1000$$

$$E = 0.01 \times 4000$$

$$E = 40 \text{ volts}$$

Voltage between terminal and ground	first example	second example
A	10 volts	10 volts
B	40 volts	40 volts
C	100 volts	100 volts

The two examples make the important point that the terminal voltages in a voltage divider depend only upon the resistance ratios and not on the absolute values of the resistors.

3.11 SERIES-PARALLEL CIRCUITS IN DC OPERATION

As the name implies, the series-parallel circuit is a combination of series and parallel circuits. Figure 3–14 shows the two basic types of series-parallel circuits and their simplified equivalent circuits. As can be seen from Figure 3–14, a series-parallel circuit can be defined as one that has the combined characteristics of both series circuits and parallel circuits in the total network. If there are two or more components in a parallel branch in a complex network, all of the characteristics of a parallel network apply to this part of the complex network. If there are two or more components in series in the complex network, all of the characteristics of a series network apply to this part of the circuit.

The best way to solve a series-parallel network problem is to break it down into separate parallel and series networks. When

this separation is done, each of the sections can be simplified in turn.

In example 3–20 we will show a simple series-parallel network problem along with each step of the simplification process.

Example 3–20

Problem: A 12-ohm resistor is placed in series with a parallel network of 10 ohms and 40 ohms. A 100 volt supply is connected to this series-parallel combination. What is the current through each resistor? What is the total current?

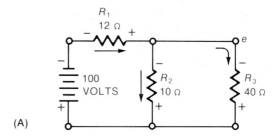

(A)

Circuit for example 3–20A

Solution:

Step 1   Isolate R_2 and R_3. Find the equivalent resistance:

$$R_{eq} = \frac{(10)\,(40)}{10 + 40} = \frac{400}{50} = 8 \text{ ohms}$$

Now the circuit is reduced to

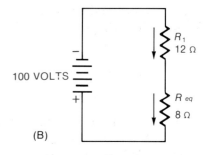

(B)

Circuit equivalent for example 3–20B

Step 2   Find the series equivalent resistance.

$$R_t = 12 + 8 = 20 \text{ ohms}$$

Circuits

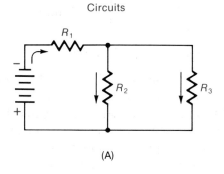

(A)

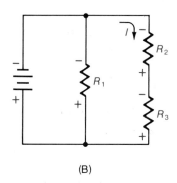

(B)

Figure 3-14 Series-parallel circuits and simplified equivalent circuits.

Equivalents

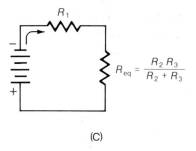

(C)

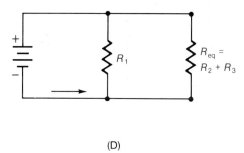

(D)

Step 3   From Ohm's law we have

$$I_t = \frac{100}{20} = 5 \text{ amps}$$

Step 4   Also from Ohm's law we have

$$E_1 = I_1 R_1 = (5)(12) = 60 \text{ volts}$$

Step 5   From Kirchoff's law we have

$$E_5 = E - E_1 = 100 - 60 = 40 \text{ volts}$$

We thus have 40 volts applied across the parallel section of the original network. Therefore E_2 and E_3 are both 40 volts.

Step 6   From Ohm's law we have

$$I_2 = \frac{40}{10} = 4 \text{ amps}$$

$$I_3 = \frac{40}{40} = 1 \text{ amp}$$

To check this, we see if we get the same answer as we did in step 3.

$$I_t = I_2 + I_3$$
$$= 4 + 1$$
$$= 5 \text{ amps}$$

It can be seen that there are several steps in solving a series-parallel network problem. So many steps gives rise to the possibility of error, which we must try to avoid. However, Kirchhoff's laws provide us with a method of solving series-parallel circuit problems without having to reduce the network down to a simple equivalent series or parallel circuit. Using Kirchhoff's laws leaves the complex network in its original form, and thus the possibility of calculation error can sometimes be reduced. The method can also save time.

Example 3–21

Problem: What is the total current and each branch current in a circuit of a 12 ohm resistor in series with a 10 ohm and a 40 ohm resistor in parallel with 100 volts applied?

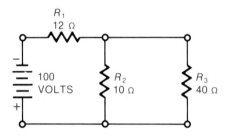

Diagram for example 3–21

Solution:

$$I_1 = I_2 + I_3$$

$$I_1 = \frac{E_1}{R_1}, I_2 = \frac{E_2}{R_2}, I_3 = \frac{E_3}{R_3}$$

therefore,

$$\frac{E_1}{R_1} = \frac{E_2}{R_2} + \frac{E_3}{R_3}$$

$$\frac{E_1}{12} = \frac{E_2}{10} + \frac{E_3}{40}$$

Since R_2 and R_3 are in parallel,

$$E_2 = E_3$$

$$I_2 = \frac{40}{10} = 4 \text{ amps}$$

$$I_3 = \frac{40}{10} = 1 \text{ amp}$$

Therefore, $I_{total} = 5$ amps

In example 3–21 we had a choice of methods of solving the problem. At times the data given or otherwise known does not lend itself to a particular method; therefore, part of the problem-solving process involves the selection of the method, or methods, most appropriate to the problem at hand. In example 3–22 we will be unable to determine the equivalent resistance of the series circuit; thus, out of necessity we will use Kirchhoff's laws to obtain the needed solution to the problem.

Example 3–22

Problem: In the series-parallel network shown, what is the current through R^3?

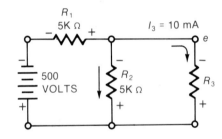

Diagram for example 3–22.

Solution:

$$E_t = E_1 + E_2$$

$$E_t = I_1 R_1 + I_2 R_2$$

$$I_2 = I_1 - 0.01$$

Therefore,

$$E_t = R_1 I_1 + R_2 (I_1 - .01)$$

Thus,

$$I_1 = 45 \text{ mA}$$

$$I_2 = 0.045 - .01$$

$$= 0.035 \text{ amps}$$

Now since R_2 and R_3 are in parallel, $E_2 = E_3$, and thus

$$E_2 = I_2 R_2$$

$$= (0.035)(5,000)$$

$$= 175 \text{ volts}$$

Thus, from Ohm's law we have,

$$R_3 = \frac{175}{0.01} = 17,500 \text{ ohms}$$

3.12 THE LOADED VOLTAGE DIVIDER

An important case of series-parallel circuits is the loaded voltage divider. Figure 3–15 shows the basic circuit with values for the following example. The loaded voltage divider is a special case of a series-parallel circuit. It means there is a load connected across the voltage dividing resistors. This makes a series-parallel circuit out of the normal series circuit of a voltage divider.

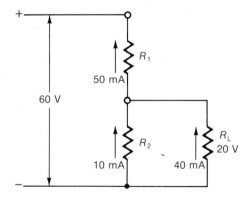

Figure 3-15 Loaded voltage divider.

Example 3–23

Problem: A 60 volt power supply is available. The device we wish to operate requires 20 volts at 40 mA (0.04 amp). Design a voltage divider to provide the proper voltage at the required current. Assume that the unloaded divider will draw a current of 10 mA. This is called the *bleeder current*.

Important facts about the circuit.

1. The path of the current in R_L (R_L means *load resistor*), is from ground through R_1 and back to the supply. It does not pass through R_2. Thus R_2 carries only the 10 mA bleeder current.
2. The current in the load on the 60 V terminal does not pass through any of the divider resistance, and so it does not enter into its calculation.

Therefore, one mA flows through R_2 and 50 mA flow through R_1.

Solution:

$$R_1 = \frac{E_{R_1}}{I_{R_1}} = \frac{60 - 20}{0.05} = \frac{40}{0.05} = 800$$

$$R_2 = \frac{E_{R_2}}{I_{R_2}} = \frac{20}{0.01} = 2,000$$

Now suppose we calculate the power dissipation in each resistor.

$$P_1 = I^2 R_1$$

$$R_1 = (0.05)^2 \times 800$$

$$P_1 = .0025 \times 800 - 2.0 \text{ watts}$$

$$P_2 = I^2 R_2$$

$$R_2 = (0.01)^2 \times 2,000$$

$$P_2 = .0001 \times 2,000 = 0.2 \text{ watts}$$

3.13 THE WHEATSTONE BRIDGE

The Wheatstone bridge is an important series-parallel circuit in electronic measuring instruments, servomechanisms, and other electronic devices. There are many variations of the bridge circuit, but the Wheatstone is the most common.

The Wheatstone bridge, shown in Figure 3–16, operates on the voltage divider principle. The circuit is made up of four resistors, R_1, R_2, R_3, and R_4. You will note that

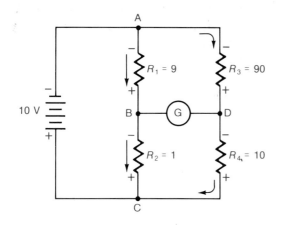

(A) Drawn as a series-parallel circuit

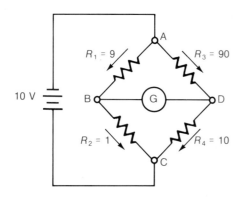

(B) The bridge circuit as it is conventionally drawn

Figure 3–16 The Wheatstone bridge.

R_1 and R_2 are in series and R_3 and R_4 are in series. The two series resistor pairs are in parallel with each other. Remember that the sum of the branch currents is equal to the total circuit current.

The two circuits, R_1R_2 and R_3R_4, are parallel and the current through each is independent of the other and dependent *only* upon its own resistance. The resistance of R_1R_2 has no effect upon the current in the R_3R_4 branch, and vice versa. This is because in a parallel circuit, the sum of the voltage drops in *each* branch *must* be equal to the applied voltage; in Figure 3–16 this is 10 volts.

The equivalent resistance in the figure is

$$R_{eq} = R_1 + R_2 = 9 + 1 = 10 \text{ ohms}$$

Using Ohm's law, the current is

$$I = \frac{E}{R} = \frac{10}{10} = 1 \text{ amp}$$

Looking at the other parallel branch, we have

$$R_{eq} = R_3 + R_4 = 90 + 10 = 100 \text{ ohms}$$

and from Ohm's law we have

$$I = \frac{E}{R} = \frac{10}{100} = 0.1 \text{ amp}$$

Under the conditions stated, the voltage drop between point A and point B across R_1 is equal to

$$E_1 = IR_1 = (1)(9) = 9 \text{ volts}$$

The voltage drop across R_2, between point B and point C, is

$$E_2 = IR_2 = (1)(1) = 1 \text{ volt}$$

The sum of E_1 and E_2 is equal to

$$E_1 + E_2 = 9 + 1 = 10 \text{ volts}$$

This is the applied battery voltage.

Now looking at the other branch, that is, R_3, the voltage drop between point A and point D is

$$E_3 = IR_3 = (0.1)(90) = 9 \text{ volts}$$

The voltage drop across R_4 from point D to point C is

$$E_4 = IR_4 = (0.1)(10) = 1 \text{ volt}$$

The sum of E_3 and E_4 equals

$$E_3 + E_4 = 9 + 1 = 10 \text{ volts}$$

This is the applied battery voltage.

Let us now look at each of the points in the circuit with respect to each other. From the foregoing, we can see that point B is nine volts negative with respect to point A, but point B is one volt positive with respect to point C. Now, note that point D is also nine volts negative with respect to point A and one volt positive with respect to point C.

Since points B and D are both nine volts negative with respect to point A and one volt positive with respect to point C, there is *no* voltage difference between points B and D. In this *balanced* condition, a very sensitive galvanometer, which is an ammeter that measures very small amounts of current, can be placed between points B and D without measuring *any* current flow. Note that this condition exists *not* because of the resistances $R_1 = R_3$ and $R_2 = R_4$, but because the *voltage drops* equal each other.

In order for there to be no current flow through the meter, it is only necessary for *the ratio of R_1 to R_2 to be equal to the ratio of R_3 to R_4.*

Where the ratios of the branches of the bridge legs are the same and *no voltage differences* exist, *no* current will flow through the galvanometer, thus the ratio of the resistances are equal. If the ratio of one leg is 20:1, then the other is also 20:1. The bridge is balanced. There is no current flow. This can be stated as follows:

$$R_1 : R_2 :: R_3 : R_4$$

or another way,

$$\frac{R_1}{R_2} = \frac{R_3}{R_4}$$

This equation provides us with a method of determining a value of an unknown resistance. It can be modified to

$$R_1 R_4 = R_2 R_3$$

From the above equation, if three of the four resistor values are known, the fourth can be found. For example if R_1, R_2, and R_3 are known, then

$$R_4 = \frac{R_2 R_3}{R_1}$$

Example 3–24

Problem: In the circuit below, what is the unknown resistance R_4 if the bridge is balanced?

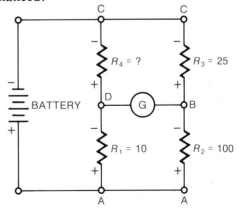

(A) The bridge circuit drawn as a series/parallel circuit.

Circuit for example 3–25.

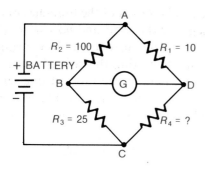

A

$R_2 = 100$ $R_1 = 10$

+ BATTERY

B —— G —— D

$R_3 = 25$ $R_4 = ?$

C

(B) The bridge circuit as it is
usually drawn.

THE BALL STAYS PUT. THERE IS NO
POTENTIAL HILL TO ROLL DOWN.

20 Ω

30 Ω

200 Ω

300 Ω

Balanced bridge.

Circuit for example 3–24 (Continued)

Solution:

$$R_4 = \frac{(100)\,(25)}{10} = \frac{2500}{10} = 250 \text{ ohms}$$

SUMMARY

1. Potential difference or voltage is the result of a larger concentration of electrons at one point in a circuit than in another.

2. If a conductive path is available, electrons will flow from the area of higher electron concentration to the area of lower concentration.

3. The electrons in motion (called *current*) can do work as they move from one place to another. Current is measured in amperes.

4. 6.28×10^{18} electrons is 1 coulomb of charge.

5. One coulomb per second equals 1 ampere.

6. Ohm's law states that 1 volt will force 1 ampere (or 1 coulomb per second) through 1 ohm of resistance.

7. Batteries and generators are devices that can produce a constant voltage that can cause a continuous current to flow.

8. Resistance is the opposition to current flow. The unit is the ohm. One ohm will limit the current flow to one ampere with an electromotive force (voltage) of 1 volt.

9. The resistance of a material depends on the kind of material involved.

10. Resistance increases with the length of the path the electrons must follow.

11. Resistance decreases when the cross-sectional area is increased. That is, the larger the diameter of a wire, the less its resistance.

12. There are three ways of writing Ohm's law:

(1) $E = IR$ (2) $I = \dfrac{E}{R}$ (3) $R = \dfrac{E}{I}$

13. The sum of the voltage drop across all of the resistors in a series circuit equals the supply voltage.

14. The same current flows through all of the resistances in a series circuit. The voltage across each resistor is dependent on the resistor value in ohms. The higher the resistance, the greater the voltage drop across it.

15. In a parallel circuit, the voltage across all resistances is the same. The current through each branch depends on the resistance. The lower the resistance, the greater the current.

16. A series-parallel circuit is a compound circuit composed of both series and parallel branches.

17. The simple voltage divider is a special series circuit. The various output voltages depend on the supply voltage and the proportion that each resistance is of the total resistance. The output voltages are independent of the absolute resistance values.

18. The loaded voltage divider is a special series-parallel circuit.

19. Kirchhoff's first law:
    At any junction point in a circuit, the total current entering the point is equal to the current leaving the point.

20. Kirchhoff's second law:
    The sum of the voltage drops around a circuit total up to the applied voltage from battery or generator.

21. Power is measured in watts. The power formula can be written in three forms:

    1. Power = volts $\times$ amps or $P = E \times I$

    2. Power = amps^2 $\times$ volts or $P = I^2R$

    3. Power = volts^2 $\div$ resistance (ohms) or $P = \dfrac{E^2}{R}$

REVIEWING YOUR ELECTRONICS VOCABULARY

1. Ampere
2. Circuit
3. Current
4. Ohm
5. Potential difference

6. Power
7. Resistance
8. Volt
9. Voltage
10. Watt

CHECKING YOUR UNDERSTANDING

1. What type of energy is converted into voltage by a battery?
2. What type of energy is converted into voltage by generators and alternators?
3. From what terminal to what terminal does current flow in a battery?
4. State the three forms of Ohm's law.
5. Describe a series and a parallel circuit. Point out some important differences between the two.
6. What is a series-parallel circuit?
7. What is a simple voltage divider?
8. State Kirchhoff's first law.
9. State Kirchhoff's second law.
10. Write three forms of the power formula.

SOLVING ELECTRONIC PROBLEMS

1. What current must be flowing through a 450 ohm resistor in order to produce a voltage drop of 45 volts in a resistor in series with it that has a conductance of 0.004 mho?
2. What is the voltage drop across a 450 ohm resistor that is in series with a 650 ohm resistor with 450 volts applied to the network?
3. What is the current through a 45,000 ohm resistor with 350 volts applied to it?
4. What is the current flowing through R_2 in the circuit shown?

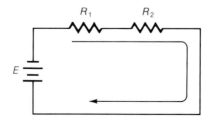

5. If the resistance of a given circuit is 2,500 ohms, what resistance is needed in parallel with it in order to make the equivalent resistance 2,100 ohms?

6. A load that draws 50 mA is connected to terminals A and B of the following diagram. What is the voltage across A and B?

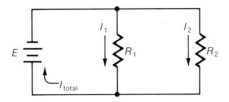

7. In the following circuit, determine the currents in the branches by means of Kirchhoff's voltage law.

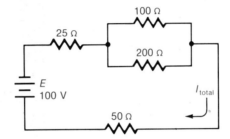

8. Using Kirchhoff's law, solve the following series circuit. Three resistors, a 2 ohm, a 3 ohm, and a 5 ohm resistor are connected across a 20 volt source. What is the total current flowing in the circuit?

9. If 650 volts is applied to a 17,500 ohm circuit, what is the current through the circuit?

10. The current through a 420 ohm circuit is 68 milliamperes. What is the voltage across the circuit?

CHAPTER 4
Measuring Instruments

INTRODUCTION

Modern test instruments allow us to measure the electron actions in an electronic system or circuit. Instruments are available to measure current, resistance, voltage, and other electrical quantities. An instrument called an oscilloscope displays a graph (wave form) of voltages that vary with time. Instruments are electronic diagnostic tools. Measuring instruments come in two basic types, analog and digital.

4.1 ANALOG INSTRUMENTS

In most analog instruments the reading is taken from numbers on a scale where a pointer indicates which numbers to read on the scale. Figure 4–1 is a typical analog meter.

The instrument in Figure 4–1 is a multipurpose, multirange instrument. Ranges and functions are selected by the operator using front panel switches. The instrument measures dc volts, dc amperes, resistance, and ac volts. The instrument is fundamentally a direct current device, and alternating current must be converted to dc by a built-in device called a *rectifier*. Alternating current ranges are usually calibrated at 60 hertz, and other frequencies can be read only with considerable error. Some more specialized instruments of the general type shown in Figure 4–1 are usable over a wide range of

TRIPLETT CORP.

Figure 4-1 Typical analog meter.

alternating frequencies. These instruments require considerable electronic circuitry to convert the incoming ac into equivalent dc without high frequency errors. Such instruments are much more expensive than the more general purpose ones.

4.2 DIGITAL INSTRUMENTS

Digital instruments read out directly on a numerical display device. In many digital instruments, range selection and decimal point placing are accomplished automatically. As digital instruments become cheaper, they are gradually displacing analog devices in most applications. There are, however, a few applications where digital instruments prove much less satisfactory than analog devices. It is unlikely that analog instruments will be entirely displaced in the foreseeable future.

Digital instruments are available to measure voltage, current, resistance, and frequency.

This special class of instruments produces test signals that can be injected into equipment to measure circuit characteristics and to locate troubles.

Signal generators are available over frequency ranges of one cycle per day to many gigahertz (GHz). One gigahertz equals 1,000,000,000 Hz. They produce output waveforms that can be sine waves, square waves, sawtooth waves, pulses, and many other specialized waveshapes.

Oscilloscopes

The oscilloscope is an essential tool for observing waveforms. The "scope" displays a graph of the current or voltage variations in a circuit on the same kind of tube used in TV. Scopes are available that do little more than display waveforms, but more expensive ones can also measure the frequency (or period) and the voltage peaks. In some scopes frequency and amplitudes (voltages) are measured by counting squares engraved into the screen faceplate. Others digitally display the information with no effort on the part of the operator.

Figure 4–2 shows a typical laboratory test setup containing a variety of instruments.

4.3 ELECTROMECHANICAL METERS

Figure 4–3 shows an expanded view of an analog meter movement. This type of meter is an electromechanical device that measures

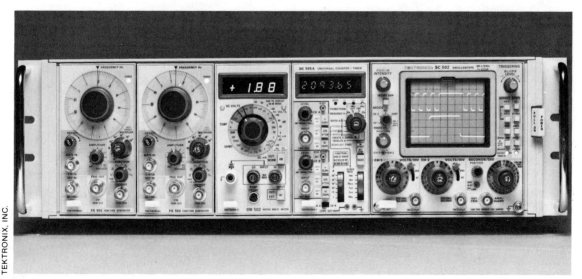

Figure 4–2 Typical laboratory instrument station.

current flow by taking advantage of magnetic action. Figure 4–3 shows the component parts of a d'Arsonval type of movement. Dr. Jacques Arsene d'Arsonval, a French physicist, developed this moving coil for the measurement of direct current.

Figure 4–4 illustrates the operating principles of the d'Arsonval meter. Current in the moving coil develops a magnetic field around the coil. This field will react with the permanent magnet to produce a torque (rotary force). The magnitude of the developed torque is directly proportional to the current in the coil, and the direction of rotation is determined by the polarity of the current flowing in the coil. The deflection of the coil, and thus the pointer movement, is directly proportional to the current through the coil. The pointer scale can be calibrated in terms of current through the coil.

Because of the inertia in the moving coil and pointer, all types of meters will tend to overshoot the correct value on their scale. They will oscillate around it before settling down to a steady reading. In most meter movements special damping devices are incorporated to prevent this oscillation.

The permanent-magnet moving-coil d'Arsonval meter has built-in electrical

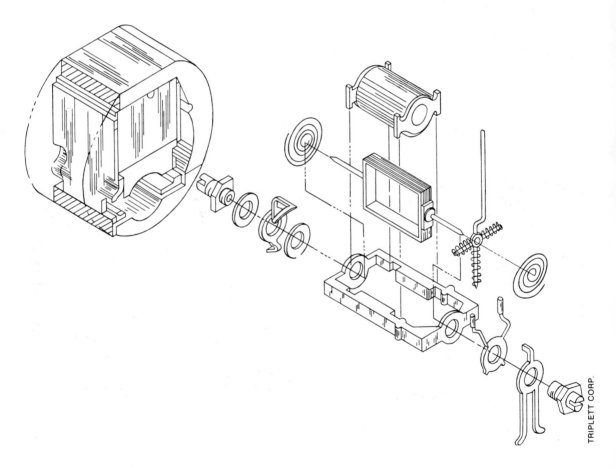

TRIPLETT CORP.

Figure 4-3 Expanded view of the d'Arsonval meter movement.

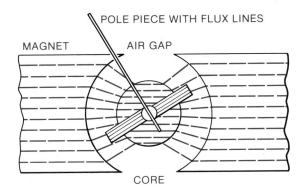

POLE PIECE WITH FLUX LINES

MAGNET   AIR GAP

CORE

Magnetic flux of instrument with no current in coil, thus no torque. Dashed lines and arrows indicate the direction of flux in pole pieces, air gap, and core.

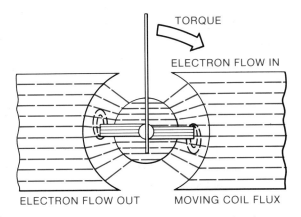

TORQUE

ELECTRON FLOW IN

ELECTRON FLOW OUT   MOVING COIL FLUX

Magnetic flux of instrument with direct current flowing through moving coil. Coil flux, interacting with magnet flux, exerts forces on both sides of the coil, thus developing a clockwise torque about the axis of the coil.

Figure 4-4 Operating principles of d'Arsonval meter.

damping. A counter electromotive force is induced in the coil as it cuts lines of force (or flux) and this counter electromotive force (generator action) causes a reverse current that will oppose the operating current. This reverse current is proportional to the speed at which the coil is cutting the lines of magnetic flux, so this damping effect tends to prevent the pointer from oscillating before it comes to rest at the correct point. Minimum external circuit resistance provides maximum damping effect. If the coil

is self-supporting, the counter electromotive force is the only damping present in the meter.

Coil forms, if used, are usually made of lightweight aluminum to increase the damping and to provide mechanical support for the coil. The aluminum coil form will act like a single, shortcircuited turn in which the current induced by cutting the flux lines is of a polarity that causes the resulting magnetic field to oppose the rotation of the coil. The external circuit resistance does not affect the damping effect of the aluminum coil form.

Taut-Band Movement

Another type of meter, known as taut-band suspension, was developed to eliminate the pivots, jewels, and control springs. Figure 4-5 shows how this movement is constructed. This movement design is less sensitive to shock and can stand somewhat more over-current than the inherently fragile jewel and pivot suspension.
considerable decrease in friction, taut-band meters can be made much more sensitive than most other kinds of movements.

In most meters the pointer indicates the amount of current on a graduated scale. See Figure 4-6. The design of the scales and pointers depend upon many factors. These factors are accuracy of the meter, size of the scale, and sensitivity of the meter. Where a high degree of accuracy in reading is needed, visual reading (parallax) errors are prevented by placing a mirror near the scale, and under the knife-edge pointer.

Current Measurement

The deflection of the meter depends on the amount of the current through the coil and the number of turns in the coil. A micro-ammeter has a coil wound of many turns of very fine wire, while the coil of a milli-ammeter has fewer turns of larger wire. The

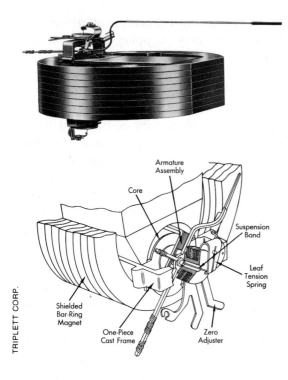

TRIPLETT CORP.

Figure 4-5 The taut-band movement.

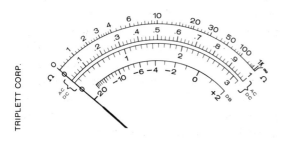

TRIPLETT CORP.

Figure 4-6 Multimeter.

coils of most commercial meters are designed to carry from 0.1 to 20 milliamperes. There are microammeters with full-scale deflection of 2 microamperes or less available, but they are expensive and not very common. *Note:* A micro-ampere is *one millionth* of an ampere. A milliampere is *one thousandth* of an ampere.

In order for a meter that can only carry 20 milliamperes to measure higher current without damage to the coil, a resistance called a *shunt* is connected in parallel with the meter. Figure 4-7 is the schematic diagram of a meter with a shunt across it. The shunt is connected so that the meter will carry only part of the current. The current in Figure 4-7 divides, with part of it flowing through the meter coil and part flowing through the shunt. By selecting the proper shunt, the meter can be calibrated to read any desired current. High range milliammeters and low range ammeters utilize shunt resistors mounted inside the meter case (internal). For high currents (50 amps and up) external shunts are almost always used.

Converting a Current Meter into a Voltmeter

Because $I = E/R$, the current through a meter movement can be controlled by adding an external resistor. The meter scales can be labeled in volts, and the meter becomes a voltmeter. Figure 4-8 shows how this works.

The resistor in series with the coil is known as a *multiplier*. Its value is calculated so that it will limit the meter current to the full-scale deflection value at the highest voltage that the meter is designed to measure. We can now mark the scale in volts. The multiplier resistor is calculated by using the following equation:

$$R = \frac{E}{I} - R_m$$

where R is the multiplying resistor, I is the full-scale current rating of the meter, E is the needed full-scale voltage, and R_m is the internal resistance of the meter.

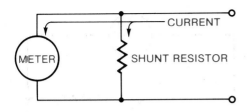

Figure 4-7 Current meter showing current shunt.

Voltmeter sensitivity is normally defined as *ohms per volt*. The ohms per volt rating is the simple ratio of the total resistance to full-scale deflection voltage.

Example 4–1

Problem: If a voltmeter has a total resistance of 250,000 ohms and a full scale of 250 volts, what is the sensitivity of the meter?

Solution:

$$\frac{250,000}{250} = 1,000 \text{ ohms per volt}$$

Example 4–2

Problem: What is the full-scale current through the meter described in Example 4–1?

Solution:

$$\frac{1 \text{ (volt)}}{1,000 \text{ (ohms)}} = 1 \text{ milliampere}$$

The higher the sensitivity, the less current is needed to give a full-scale reading. A higher sensitivity results in less loading of the circuit being measured.

Example 4–3

Problem: What is the sensitivity of a 350 volt full-scale meter that takes only 50 microamperes for full-scale deflection?

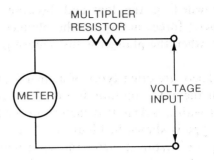

Figure 4-8 Meter and multiplier resistor.

Solution:

$$\frac{1}{0.00005} = 20,000 \text{ ohms per volt}$$

Alternating Current Meters

Alternating current meters must either use rectifiers to convert ac to dc or they must be constructed differently than the meters described earlier. An example of a meter designed for the measuring of alternating current is shown in Figure 4–9. This is known as an attraction-type meter. It is based on the electromagnetic effect and works much like a solenoid.

The plunger in the coil will move to a position that results in maximum flux in the coil irrespective of the direction of current in the coil. The scale of this type of meter

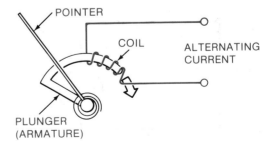

Figure 4-9 Attraction-type ac meter.

is crowded at the low end because the magnetic forces acting on the plunger are lower when the plunger is just entering the coil.

There are other types of ac meters, but by far the most common is a rectifier combined with a d'Arsonval meter movement. This type is shown in Figure 4–10. By utilizing a d'Arsonval meter the sensitivity is high and a uniform scale is possible.

A series rectifier is placed between the series, limiting resistor and the meter in a dc voltmeter circuit. The rectifier converts alternating current (ac) into direct current (dc).

Resistance Measurement

By using the Ohm's law relationship, we can use a meter (called an ohmmeter) to measure an unknown resistance and mark the meter scale to read directly in ohms.

Figure 4–11 is a diagram of a simple ohmmeter. For example, with the switch in the X_1 position and the plus and minus terminals shorted, the meter will read full scale and indicate 0 ohms. With a resistor placed between plus and minus, the current through it, and thus through the meter, will be determined by the resistance being measured.

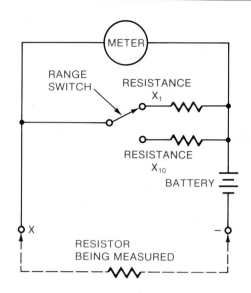

Figure 4–11 Basic ohmmeter circuit.

Volt-Ohm-Milliammeter

A volt-ohm-milliammeter, better known as a *VOM* (or *multimeter*) is a multirange meter. The instrument has a switch to change shunts and/or multiplier resistors to enable the user to measure many different ranges of voltage, current, and resistance with the same meter.

Figure 4–12 is a typical VOM that can be used to measure voltage, current and resistance.

Electronic Voltmeters

A vacuum-tube voltmeter, commonly known as a *VTVM*, is a voltmeter that uses a vacuum tube circuit to increase its sensitivity. In modern meters the circuit uses transistors. Figure 4–13 is a typical solid state electronic multimeter.

4.4 THE OSCILLOSCOPE

An oscilloscope is a device that will trace a "picture" of the current or voltage variations

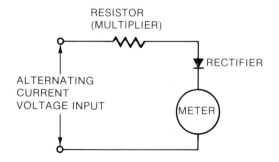

Figure 4–10 Rectifier type ac meter.

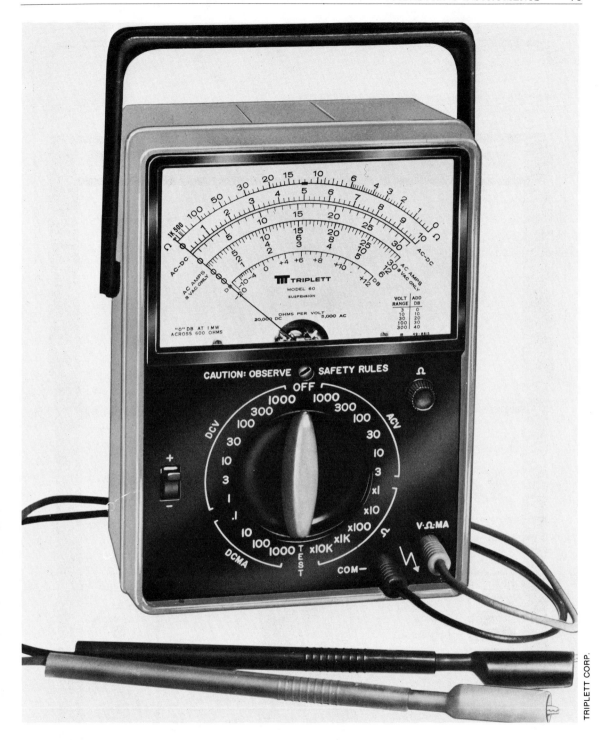

Figure 4-12 Typical Volt-ohm-milliammeter (VOM).

Figure 4-13 Typical solid state volt-ohmmeter.

in an operating circuit.

The oscilloscope illustrated in Figure 4–14, with the proper modules, will make most measurements that will ever be needed in electronic maintenance.

How It Works

A block diagram of the simplest form of oscilloscope is shown in Figure 4–15.

The signal to be observed is applied to

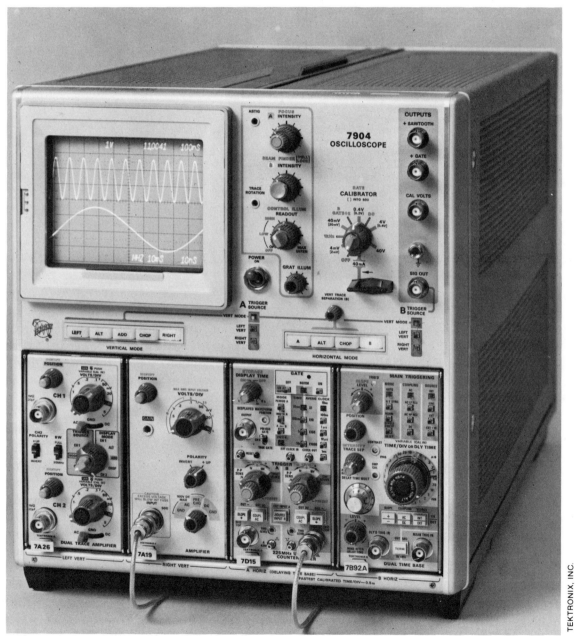

Figure 4-14 Tektronix Model 7904 oscilloscope.

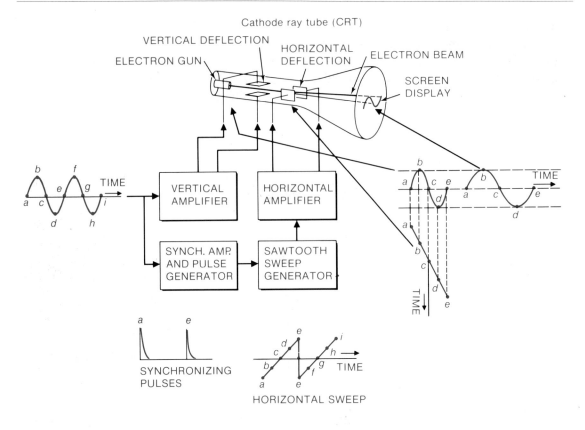

Figure 4-15 Oscilloscope block diagram.

the input of the vertical amplifier where it is amplified and applied to the cathode ray tube's vertical deflection plates. A stream of electrons, produced by the electron gun, is deflected vertically in proportion to the voltage between the deflection plates.

The vertical signal is also applied to the synchronizing amplifier and pulse generator. The vertical signal is shaped into synchronizing pulses to control the timing of the sawtooth sweep generator.

The sawtooth generator begins its voltage rise at point *a* in the horizontal sweep waveform. The output voltage of the sweep generator drives the horizontal deflection plates, which moves the electron beam across the screen. The inside glass face of the cathode ray tube (CRT) is coated with a

phosphor that gives off a spot of light wherever it is struck by the electron beam.

The combination of the up-and-down beam movement and the movement of the beam across the screen traces out the waveform.

At point *e* in the waveforms, the synchronizing amplifier and pulse generator produces a short pulse. This synchronizing pulse causes the sweep generator to rapidly reset, returning the beam back to the left side of the screen. The sweep generator immediately begins ramping upward in its output voltage, moving the beam steadily toward the right-hand side of the screen. This happens at time *e* and the up-down movement of the beam traces out the next waveform (from *e* to *i* in the input waveform). At time *i* the pulse generator produces another pulse, the beam is returned to the left of the screen, and the scope begins to draw the next waveform.

4.5 SIGNAL GENERATORS

A signal generator produces signals with the proper waveform and frequency for the testing of electronic equipment.

The signal generator often provides a signal that substitutes for the normal equipment signal. For example, in audio amplifier testing a microphone would be inconvenient because of varying noise inputs. It would also be difficult to make tests or adjust tuned circuits in a normally operating television set because of constant scene changes and changing picture information. Thus a special signal to be used for testing purposes is more convenient in both cases.

Most signal generators are variable in frequency and amplitude. Some have the ability to impress one signal on another (see Modulation in Chapter 13) or modify its output waveshape as needed.

4.6 FREQUENCY MEASUREMENT

Frequency measurement is a very critical measurement in electronic maintenance. If a transmitter is not on the correct frequency, not only will the receiver have trouble receiving transmissions, but also there may be violation of strict Federal Communications Commission (FCC) regulations specifying the frequency accuracy for all transmitting systems and the frequency measurement equipment to be used with them.

Figure 4–16 is an excellent frequency measuring system using a frequency counter as its major component.

Whenever frequency measuring is accomplished, it is compared to some type of standard. In the system of Figure 4–16, the standard frequency is in the 5245L counter. However, at times the internal oscillator is not accurate enough. When extreme accuracy is needed, an external standard frequency, such as that of Figure 4–17, is used.

The unit in Figure 4–17 is called a *cesium frequency standard* and is the kind of system used by the National Bureau of Standards for the nation's master timekeeping clock.

4.7 DIGITAL VOLTMETERS

The digital voltmeter (DVM) converts a dc voltage into a direct reading display in ordinary digits. Nearly all digital voltmeters contain a decimal counting unit and numerical readouts to display the count. In the simplest system, the dc input voltage is converted into a string of pulses whose frequency is proportional to the dc voltage being measured. The counter is allowed to count for a predetermined period (one second, for example) and the count is held and displayed at the end of the count period.

Figure 4–18 is a block diagram of this kind of digital voltmeter.

The voltage controlled oscillator produces an output frequency proportional to the dc voltage being measured. Assume that the oscillator produces 1,000 pulses per second with 1 volt input. If the counter is allowed to count for exactly 1 second and stopped, the digital display will show 1000. Proper placing of the decimal point would yield 1.000 volts. With an input voltage of 2 volts the counter would register 2000 on the display. With the decimal in the right place, the reading would be 2.000 volts. See Figure 4–18 for the display.

Other digital voltmeters use a fixed-frequency pulse generator to drive the counter, and use the voltage to be measured to control the length of time the counter is allowed to count.

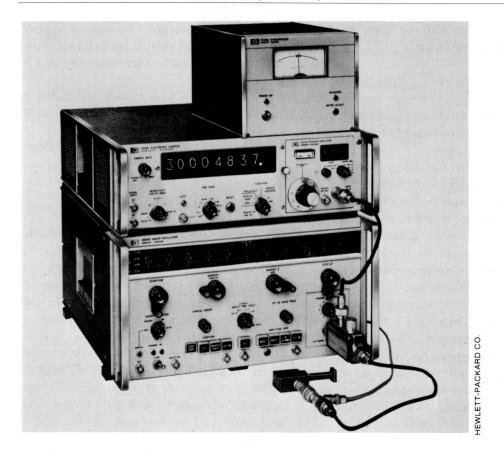

Figure 4-16 Hewlett-Packard Model E40-5245L dc-to-40-GHz Digital Frequency Measuring System.

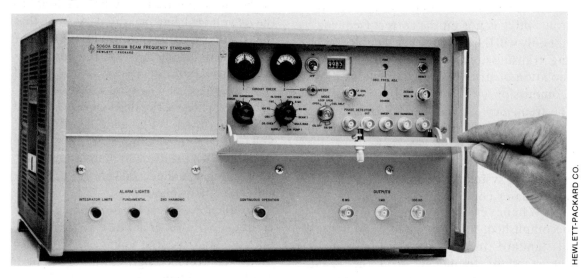

Figure 4-17 Cesium beam frequency standard.

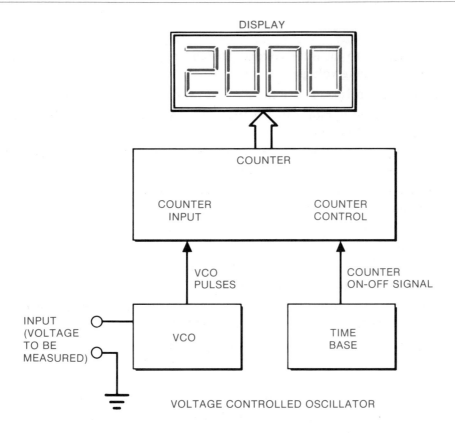

Figure 4-18 Digital Voltmeter using a voltage controlled oscillator.

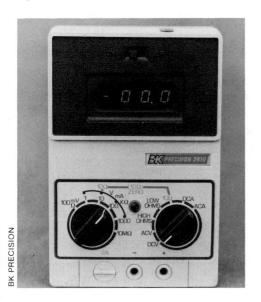

Figure 4-19 Digital multimeter.

Ac voltages are rectified to dc by a precision rectifier using an operational amplifier (see Chapter 14).

The ohmmeter circuit for DVMs is also constructed around an operational amplifier. Figure 4-19 shows a typical digital voltmeter.

SUMMARY

1. Instruments are needed to measure voltage, current, resistance, and frequency and to observe graphs of changing voltages.

2. Most modern analog type meters use the d'Arsonval or taut-band meter movement.

3. The taut-band movement is more rugged than the d'Arsonval type, but because of its relatively high cost it is less common.

4. Analog meters indicate the voltage, current, or other measured activity on a numbered scale. A pointer tells which numbers to read.

5. Multirange meters use a switch to select multiplier resistors for different voltage ranges and the proper shunt resistor for different current ranges.

6. Electronic multimeters use tubes or transistors to improve meter sensitivity and reduce loading on circuits under test.

7. Alternating current meters generally use a d'Arsonval or taut-band movement with a rectifier to convert alternating into direct current.

8. Special meters designed to measure alternating current without a rectifier are available. They are not very sensitive and the scale is crowded at the low end.

9. The oscilloscope is used to electronically draw a graph of changing voltages in a circuit. The graph is displayed on the face of a cathode ray tube (CRT) similar to a television picture tube.

10. Signal generators generate varying voltage signals. The signal may be anything from a simple sine wave to a complex television signal that will produce a test pattern on a TV screen.

11. Digital instruments convert voltages or cycles into digital information that can be displayed and read in ordinary numbers.

REVIEWING YOUR ELECTRONICS VOCABULARY

1. Analog
2. D'Arsonval movement
3. Digital
4. Digital counter
5. Meter rectifier
6. Multiplier resistor
7. Oscilloscope
8. Shunt resistor
9. Signal generator
10. Taut-band movement

CHECKING YOUR UNDERSTANDING

1. Why do we need instruments in electronics?

2. List some of the most frequently used electronic measuring devices.

3. Why is the taut-band meter movement superior to the d'Arsonval movement? Why is it used less frequently?

4. What is the purpose of a multiplier resistor when used with a d'Arsonval or taut-band meter?

5. What is the purpose of a shunt when used with a meter movement?

6. What is the difference between analog and digital instruments?

7. Why are d'Arsonval meters and rectifiers preferable to special solenoid-type alternating current meters?

8. For what is the oscilloscope used?

9. What is the purpose of signal generators? Give some examples.

10. What is the function of digital counters? What are they used to measure?

SOLVING ELECTRONIC PROBLEMS

1. If a voltmeter has a resistance of 50 k ohms and a full scale of 10 volts, what is its sensitivity?

2. What would be the full-scale current through a voltmeter with 5,000 ohms/volt sensitivity?

3. If you have a milliampere meter with a full scale of 1 mA and a voltage of 250 volts must be measured with it, what is the value of the multiplier resistor needed?

4. If you have a 100 mA meter but must measure a current of 250 mA how can this be accomplished? The internal resistance of the meter is 1 ohm.

5. What is the sensitivity of a 300 volt full-scale meter that takes 25 microamperes for full-scale deflection?

CHAPTER 5
Capacitance, Inductance, and Transformers

INTRODUCTION

In this chapter we will examine two energy storage devices, the capacitor and the inductor. The capacitor stores energy in an electrostatic field, and the inductor stores energy in an electromagnetic field. We will also look at the transformer in which one inductor transfers energy to an adjacent inductor by way of a common magnetic field. Capacitors and inductors are electrical opposites of each other, a topic that will be more fully discussed in a later chapter.

5.1 THE CAPACITOR

The capacitor is an energy storage device consisting of two metal plates, which are separated by an insulator called the *dielectric.* The amount of energy a given capacitor can store increases with the area of the plates and decreases as the thickness of the insulating material increases. The storage capacity of a capacitor can be greatly increased by using high quality dielectric material. The standard of comparison for measuring the quality of dielectric materials is the quality of a vacuum as a dielectric. The vacuum (a poor quality dielectric medium) is assigned a value of 1, and all other dielectric materials are rated in comparison to it. Figure 5–1 illustrates a simple capacitor, and Table 5–1 lists the dielectric constants of some common dielectric materials.

The figure of merit for dielectric materials is called the *dielectric constant (K).* Air is nearly as poor a dielectric as a vacuum is and has a constant of approximately 1. A material with a *K* of 10 would be ten times as effective a dielectric as a vacuum (or air). Capacitors are classified according to the type of dielectric material used. Mylar capacitors are rolled into cylinders in order to get a large amount of plate area into a compact unit. The mylar capacitor is illustrated in Figure 5–2.

Figure 5–3 shows outline drawings for some of the more common commercial capacitor styles. Each type comes in many electrical and physical sizes.

The unit of capacitance is the *farad* (F). One farad can store one coulomb (6.28×10^{18}

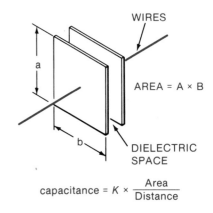

capacitance $= K \times \dfrac{\text{Area}}{\text{Distance}}$

Figure 5-1 The capacitor.

Table 5-1 Dielectric constants.

Material	Dielectric Constant *(K)*
Vacuum	1
Air	1
Paper	2–5
Oil	2–5
Mica	3–8
Glass	6–9
Mylar	5–8
Ceramics	80–1200

Figure 5-2 Mylar capacitor construction.

electrons) with a charging potential of one volt. The microfarad (1 μF = 1 × 10^{-6}F), and the picofarad (1 pF = 10^{-12}F) are more practical units.

5.2 HOW CAPACITORS WORK

When the switch in Figure 5–4A is closed, the battery forces electrons onto the upper capacitor plate and draws them off the lower plate. Electrons flow until the capacitor is charged to the same voltage as the battery. At that time the voltage across the battery and the capacitor charge voltage are equal and opposing. No further current flows. If the switch is then opened, the capacitor will hold the charge for a considerable period of time. There is always a minute leakage

through the dielectric, however, and the capacitor charge will gradually bleed off. This may take anywhere from seconds up to several weeks. Charged capacitors in an otherwise *dead* piece of equipment can represent a safety hazard. All capacitors with a value of 1 μF or larger should be discharged by shorting across the terminals with a tool with an insulated handle before any work is done on the equipment.

Figure 5–4B shows the capacitor holding a charge. Plate B is the negative plate because it carries an excess of electrons. Plate A is the positive plate because it is deficient in electrons. If we were to measure the voltage across the capacitor with a voltmeter, we would find the voltage to be equal to that of the battery.

Unless the capacitor is a very large one, we would have to take the measurement with a high input resistance electronic voltmeter. Ordinary multimeters would tend to discharge the capacitor before we could get a reading.

In Figure 5–4C the capacitor is shown discharging through a resistor. The resistor slows down the discharge rate. The discharge time depends upon the size of the resistor and capacitor. A large capacitor takes longer than a smaller one to discharge through a given resistance. Also, the larger the resistance, the slower the capacitor will discharge.

Figure 5–4D shows the capacitor discharge behavior. The particular curve is the result of the decreasing voltage across the capacitor as it discharges. At the start of the discharge cycle the voltage across the capacitor is at its highest, and it can drive the highest current through the resistor. As the capacitor discharges, its voltage decreases and the discharge rate slows down as well.

Figure 5–4E shows the capacitor charging through a resistor and Figure 5–4F

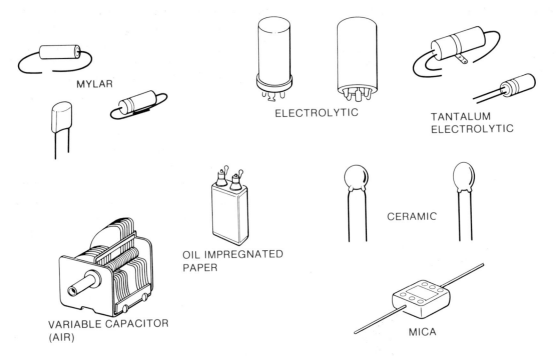

MYLAR

ELECTROLYTIC

TANTALUM
ELECTROLYTIC

OIL IMPREGNATED
PAPER

CERAMIC

VARIABLE CAPACITOR
(AIR)

MICA

Figure 5-3 Commercial capacitor outline drawings.

shows the charging curve. Notice that the charge and discharge curve *shapes* are identical; only the direction is different.

The Dielectric

Adding a quality dielectric to a capacitor has much the same effect as adding an iron core to a coil. The orbiting (and spinning) electrons in the dielectric tend to align themselves with the electrostatic field in the same way that magnetic domains align themselves with the magnetic field. The aligned electrons add their fields to the field produced by the displaced electrons on the capacitor plates.

The dielectric constant (K) is a measure of how easily the atoms in the dielectric can alter their orbits under the influence of an external electric field.

Although all dielectrics are insulators, it is not always true that the best insulators are also the best dielectrics.

Capacitors in Series and Parallel

Placing capacitors in parallel increases the total effective plate area, increasing the capacitance. Capacitors in series behave like resistors in parallel. Figure 5–5 summarizes the equivalent values of capacitors in series and parallel.

5.3 TIME CONSTANTS

Most electronic timing devices use a charging capacitor to measure the time. Such devices as photographic timers, time delay circuits for alarm systems and garage lights, and so on, are common examples. A resistor capacitor (RC) time constant is determined by the simple product of the two values. The formula is

Time Constant = Resistance × Capacitance

$$T = RC$$

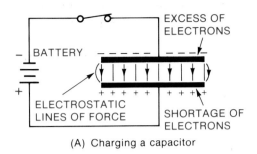

(A) Charging a capacitor

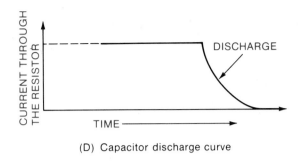

(D) Capacitor discharge curve

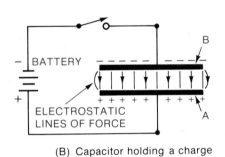

(B) Capacitor holding a charge

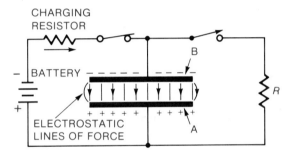

(E) The capacitor charging through a resistor

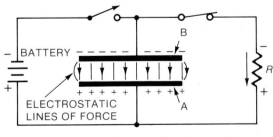

(C) Capacitor discharging through a resistor

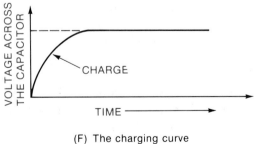

(F) The charging curve

Figure 5-4 Capacitor action.

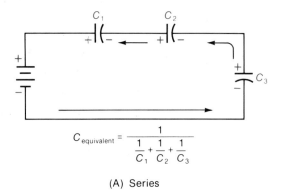

$$C_{equivalent} = \frac{1}{\dfrac{1}{C_1} + \dfrac{1}{C_2} + \dfrac{1}{C_3}}$$

(A) Series

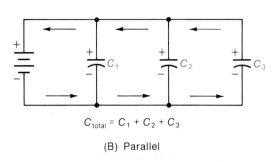

$C_{total} = C_1 + C_2 + C_3$

(B) Parallel

Figure 5-5 Capacitors in series and parallel.

If we set up the circuit in Figure 5–6, we can measure the voltage (charge) across the capacitor at the end of each time constant. In this case we would take a measurement at the end of each second.

At time zero (T_0) the switch is closed. By the time one second has elapsed, the capacitor has charged to 63 volts. The blocks above the digital voltmeter show the voltage across the capacitor at each successive one-second interval. Table 5–2 summarizes the amount of charge during each one-second interval.

As the capacitor charges, the charge voltage opposes the applied (battery) voltage. This reduces the current and causes the capacitor to charge more slowly as time goes on. The amount of charge taken on after five time constants is very small. For

Table 5-2   Amount of charge taken on during each successive one-second interval.

From	To	Voltage Increase
T_0	T_1	63 volts
T_1	T_2	23.31 volts
T_2	T_3	8.62 volts
T_3	T_4	3.19 volts
T_4	T_5	1.18 volts

practical purposes the capacitor is considered to be fully charged after five time constants.

The universal time constant chart shown in Figure 5–7 can be used for any values of resistance and capacitance, any time period, and any voltage. If the capacitor is being discharged, the universal chart can be used to find the voltage left in the discharging capacitor by simply changing the label *charging current* in Figure 5–7A to *capacitor voltage, discharging*. The time constant chart (graph) can be plotted by using the setup in Figure 5–6 if time intervals are measured close enough together.

5.4 THE CAPACITOR IN ALTERNATING CURRENT CIRCUITS

Notice that the maximum current in Figure 5–7 occurs at the beginning of the charge cycle, while the maximum voltage occurs at the end of the charge cycle.

In a charging capacitor, the maximum current flows when the capacitor voltage is near zero. The *current* maximum occurs first, and the current is said to *lead* the voltage in time.

The capacitor *voltage* is minimum when the charging current is maximum, and capacitor charge voltage is maximum when charging current is minimum.

Figure 5–8A shows part of the uni-

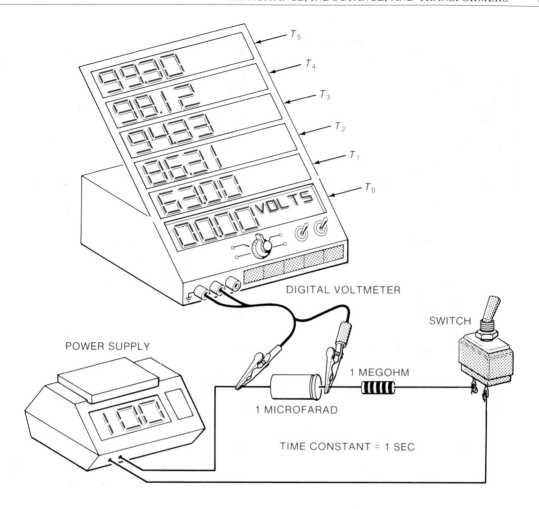

Figure 5-6 Measuring the voltage across a charging capacitor.

versal time constant chart for direct current capacitive circuits. Figure 5–8B shows the slightly modified universal time constant curve that results when alternating current is applied to a capacitive circuit.

The shape of the curve is slightly different because of the varying voltage in an alternating current as opposed to unchanging direct current. The important point is that the current reaches its maximum sooner than the voltage in an ac circuit. This time displacement results in a shift in time between the current and the voltage.

In an alternating current capacitive circuit: the current leads the voltage in time.

We will examine alternating current and capacitors in greater detail in the next chapter.

5.5 INDUCTORS

The inductor is the reverse counterpart of the capacitor. It stores energy in its magnetic

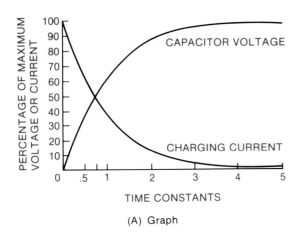

(A) Graph

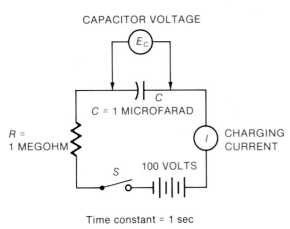

Time constant = 1 sec

Figure 5-7 The universal capacitor time constant chart.

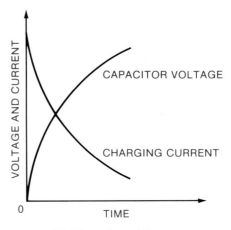

(A) The universal time constant curve with direct current in a capacitive circuit

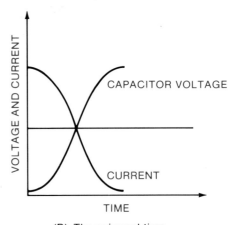

(B) The universal time constant curve with alternating current in a capacitive circuit

Figure 5-8 Voltage-current time displacement in a capacitive circuit.

field instead of an electric field. The inductor "charging" behavior follows the universal time constant curve, but with the current lagging behind the voltage instead of leading it in time. In an ac circuit, the inductor produces a time shift, but in a direction opposite that of the capacitor.

Inductive action occurs only while the magnetic *field* is in motion, either expanding or collapsing; when voltage and current are changing. With the field fully expanded, the inductor stores energy in its magnetic field. The amount of energy an inductor

can store is increased by placing an efficient (iron) core in the magnetic field.

The strength of an inductor's magnetic field depends upon the *current* through it.

Inductance resists any *changes* in current. The concept of change is crucial. An inductor stores energy in its magnetic field and possesses a property called *reac-*

tance. The inductor neither absorbs nor gives up energy when the current is constant. If we try to increase or decrease the current, we will encounter a resistance (reactance) to that change. Energy stored in the field will cause the inductor to generate an electromotive force voltage that opposes any attempt to change the current. The stored energy produces this counter voltage. In the next chapter we will see that an electric generator produces an output voltage only when the armature coil is moving with respect to a magnetic field. (Or if the field is moving with respect to the coil.) In an inductor the field expands and contracts as the current through the coil changes. This expansion or contraction of the field represents a movement of the field with respect to the coil. As the lines of force cut turns in the coil an emf is produced. The inductor *generates* a voltage output which always opposes the applied voltage. This phenomenon is called self-inductance or, simply, inductance.

5.6 THE INDUCTIVE TIME CONSTANT

In an inductor the voltage leads the current in time; just the opposite of the behavior of a capacitor.

In the inductor when current starts to flow, the lines of force in the field start near the core and expand outward. When the current first starts to flow, the field tries to expand rapidly, but in doing so, it generates a large counter voltage that pushes back against the applied voltage, restricting the current flow. The counter voltage is greatest when the field begins to move outward from the center of the coil and least when the field is nearly fully formed. Consequently, the current is minimum at the beginning of the field's expansion and maximum when the field is fully expanded.

In an inductor the only limit to steady state current flow is circuit resistance. The current would be infinite if zero resistance were possible and the field were not moving. If the field is not in motion, no counter voltage is generated and the coil resistance is the only thing that limits the current.

Figure 5–9 compares the time constant curves for capacitance and inductance.

Notice that we have identified the upward-traveling curve as either inductor current *or* capacitor voltage, and the downward curve as either inductor voltage *or* capacitor current. The graph tells us a number of things. First, both devices displace current and voltage in time. In an inductor the voltage leads, while in a capacitor the current leads. The two are exact opposites, and as we will see, inductance and capacitance tend to cancel each other. The symbol for inductance is *L*.

One (1) inductive time constant = L/R, where L is the inductance in henrys and R is the resistance in ohms.

$$T = \frac{L}{R}$$

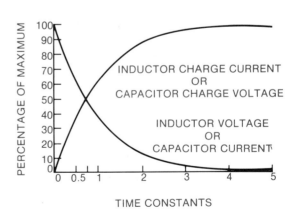

TIME CONSTANTS

Figure 5-9 Universal time constant chart for inductance and capacitance.

The Henry Defined

The unit of inductance is the henry. A 1 henry inductor will produce a 1 volt counter emf when the current through it is *changing* at the rate of 1 ampere per second. Figure 5–10 shows some typical commercial inductor styles.

5.7 INDUCTANCES IN SERIES AND IN PARALLEL

When inductances are in series, the values are added. When inductances are in parallel, they are treated like resistors in parallel.

(A) High frequency air core inductor

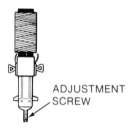

ADJUSTMENT SCREW

(B) Medium frequency adjustable powdered iron core inductor

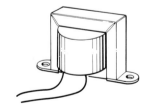

(C) Low frequency laminated iron core inductor

Figure 5–10 Typical commercial inductors.

$$L_{eq} = \cfrac{1}{\cfrac{1}{L_1} + \cfrac{1}{L_2} + \cfrac{1}{L_3}} \cdots$$

L = Inductance in henrys

5.8 TRANSFORMERS

What does a transformer do?

• Steps voltage *up*.

• Steps current *up*.

• Steps voltage *down*.

• Steps current *down*.

• Transforms impedances (alternating current opposition).

Transformers are highly efficient devices (80 to 95% efficient) that can be used to increase an alternating current voltage at the expense of current, or to decrease a voltage with an increase in available current. The transformer consists of two or more coils wound on a common core. The coils are mutually coupled, an idea we will discuss more thoroughly in the next chapter.

In a transformer the input power (voltage current product) must equal the output power minus some small losses. This is demanded by the law of energy conservation.

The typical line voltage is about 120 volts, but a TV picture tube requires about 20,000 volts for proper operation. We need a voltage set-up transformer.

Many transistor devices require a maximum of 20 volts. A step-down transformer can be used to reduce the 120 volt power line voltage to the proper value.

Arc welding, for example, requires very high currents but small voltages. A voltage step-down transformer steps the voltage down while increasing the available current.

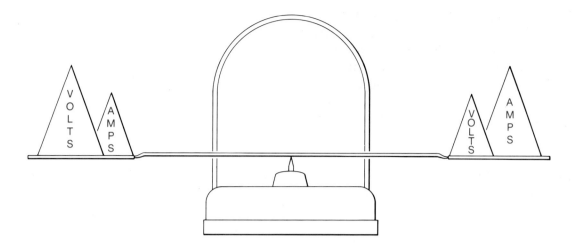

Figure 5-11 The volt-amp product (power) input must equal the volt-amp product out of the transformer.

Transformer voltage step-up and step-down is determined by the ratio of the number of turns in the *primary* and *secondary*. The input side is called the primary and the output side is called the secondary. The actual number of turns in each case is not important to the voltages. Only the ratio counts.

For example, a 1 volt input to the transformer in Figure 5–12 will produce an output voltage of 2 volts. Eight volts input will produce 16 volts out and so on. The ratio is 1 to 2 voltage step-up. Primary and secondary windings can be reversed to get a 2 to 1 voltage step-down transformer. In this case (with primary and secondary exchanged), the output voltage will be one-half the input voltage.

Transformers and Direct Current

Transformers can be used with direct current only if the current is interrupted frequently. The automobile ignition system is a common example of a transformer used with interrupted direct current.

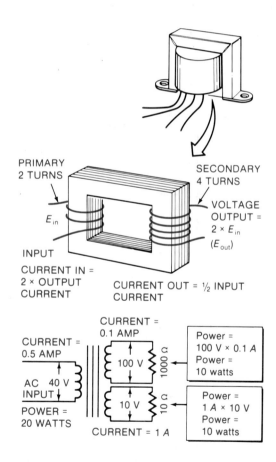

Figure 5-12 Voltage and turns ratios in a transformer.

The ignition coil is a transformer that steps the 12 volt car battery voltage up to the 20,000 or so volts needed to jump the gap in the spark plug. The breaker points interrupt the current as they are opened and closed by a cam driven by the engine crankshaft. The system is shown in Figure 5–13.

Multiple Winding Transformers

Multiple windings can be placed on a single core to provide the several different voltages required by a particular system. The core, frame, and other metal parts generally make up most of a transformer's cost, so a multiple winding transformer is much cheaper than several individual transformers. A multiple winding transformer schematic is shown in Figure 5–14.

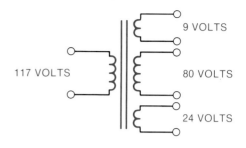

Figure 5-14 Multiple winding transformer.

5.9 REFLECTED LOAD IN A TRANSFORMER

In high fidelity amplifiers and other systems transformers are used to match impedances, or to make some resistance look larger or smaller than it actually is. The reflected load

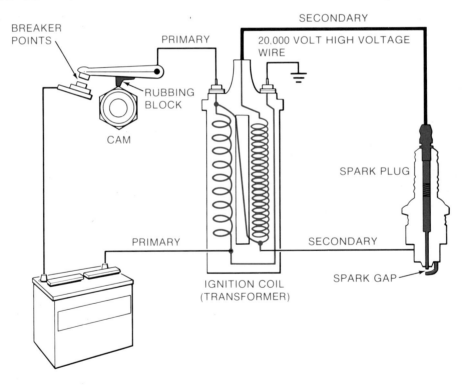

Figure 5-13 Transformer used with direct current in automobile ignition system.

behavior of transformers is taken advantage of in these cases.

The reflected load formula is

Reflected Load Resistance =

$$\frac{N^2_p}{N^2_s} \times \text{Load Resistance}$$

Where N_p is the number of turns in the primary and N_s is the number of turns in the secondary. In the Example 5–1 a 500 ohm resistor appears in the primary reflected as 20 ohms.

Example 5–1

Problem:

Primary turns = 100
Secondary turns = 500
The load = 500 ohms

Solution:

$$\text{Reflected load} = \frac{500^2}{100^2} \times 500$$

$$\text{Reflected load} = \frac{250,000}{10,000} \times 500$$

Reflected load = .04 × 500

Reflected load = 20 ohms

Problem: If we reverse the transformer by exchanging primary and secondary connections, we can transform the 500 ohm load to a higher value.

Solution:

$$\text{Reflected load} = \frac{100^2}{500^2} \times 500$$

$$\text{Reflected load} = \frac{10,000}{250,000} \times 500$$

Reflected load = 25 × 500

Reflected load = 125,000 ohms

Isolation Transformers

All transformers except autotransformers isolate the secondary from the primary. The only connection is through the magnetic field; there is no direct connection.

There is a special transformer, the *isolation transformer,* that does not step voltage up or down. The ratio from primary to secondary is 1 to 1. The transformer's sole purpose is isolation for the safety of people and line-operated equipment. The commercial uses include a "hot" and a ground line for its 120-volt ac service. If you touch the hot side and any grounded pipe or metal you can get shocked. (See Figure 5–15).

Autotransformer

The autotransformer does not provide isolation because one wire of the primary is connected to one wire of the secondary. This does not interfere with transformer action, but it does destroy the isolation between primary and secondary. In practice the autotransformer is often wound as a single tapped winding.

It is important to remember that most of the variable transformers called *variacs®*

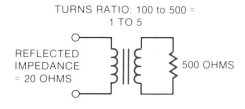

TURNS RATIO: 100 to 500 =
1 TO 5

REFLECTED
IMPEDANCE
= 20 OHMS

500 OHMS

Figure 5-15 Reflected load.

or *power-stats* are autotransformers and are not isolated. A separate isolation transformer is often used with variable transformers to ensure the safety of both the people working and the equipment.

SUMMARY

1. Air is a poor dielectric. Some plastics, glass, and ceramic materials are better.
2. Capacitors are classified according to the dielectric material; mylar, paper, ceramic, and so forth.
3. The unit of capacitance is the farad.
4. A 1 farad capacitor can store enough electrons to deliver 1 ampere for 1 second when charged to 1 volt.
5. A 1 ampere-second is 1 coulomb, about enough energy to light a 100 watt household lamp for 1 second.
6. The farad is too large a unit for most electronics applications. The microfarad (μF), $1/1,000,000$ (10^{-6}) of a farad, is more often used.
7. Capacitors in parallel increase the effective plate area. Therefore, a 1 μF capacitor in parallel with a 2 μF capacitor yields an effective total of 3 μF.
8. Capacitors in series must be treated like resistors in parallel to find equivalent values.
9. A capacitor charged from a direct current source builds an increasing counter force as it charges.
10. All charging and discharging capacitors follow a special curve known as the universal time constant curve.
11. Energy Storage:
    a. An inductor stores energy in its magnetic field.
    b. A capacitor stores energy in its electric field.

Inductors (coils)

1. The value of an inductor can be raised by adding an iron core.
2. Inductive action occurs only while the magnetic field is expanding or contracting.
3. The unit of inductance is the henry.
4. A 1 henry inductor produces a 1 volt counter voltage when the current through it is changing at the rate of 1 ampere per second.
5. The time constant of a resistance-inductance circuit is $T = L/R$.

REVIEWING YOUR ELECTRONICS VOCABULARY

1. Capacitance
2. Dielectric constant
3. Farad
4. Henry
5. Inductance

6. Reflected load
7. Time constant
8. Transformer
9. Universal time constant
10. Voltage ratio

CHECKING YOUR UNDERSTANDING

1. What dielectric material has the lowest dielectric constant?
2. To what percentage of the applied voltage will a capacitor be charged at the end of 1 time constant?
3. What is the formula for the capacitor time constant?
4. What is the effect on the inductance of a coil when an iron core is added?
5. Write the inductive time constant formula.
6. An inductor or capacitor is considered fully charged at the end of how many time constants?
7. For what is the universal time constant chart used?
8. If the resistance in an *RC* time constant circuit is increased in value, is the charging time increased or decreased?
9. List three things for which transformers can be used.
10. What is an isolation transformer? What is its purpose?

SOLVING ELECTRONIC PROBLEMS

1. If a 0.005 microfarad capacitor is charged to 300 volts and is then allowed to discharge through a 2 megohm resistor, what time is required to discharge the capacitor to 50 volts?
2. There are three capacitors connected in parallel. They are 4 μF, 6 μF, and 10 μF. What is the total effective capacitance?
3. In the following circuit, find the resistor voltage 200 microseconds after the switch is closed.

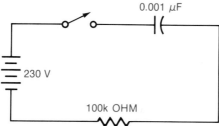

4. In the following circuit, find the initial rate of charge for the capacitor.

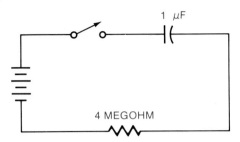

5. What is the effective capacitance of the following circuit?

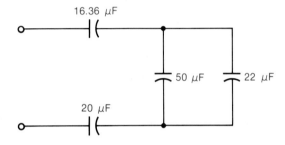

6. What is the equivalent inductance of a 3 millihenry and a 6 millihenry inductance connected in parallel?

7. Two inductors of 4 henrys each are connected in parallel. What is the equivalent inductance?

8. What is the energy stored in the magnetic field of an inductor of 4 henrys with a resistance of 2 ohms and is connected to a 20 volt source?

9. Two inductors of 5 henrys and 3 henrys are connected in series. What is the total inductance. There is no coupling between them.

10. A 2 henry inductor has 1,200 turns of wire. How many turns must be added to increase the inductance to 3 henrys?

CHAPTER 6
Alternating Current

INTRODUCTION

Alternating current (ac) is probably the most common, and most important, available form of electricity. Alternating current is a current that begins at zero, rises to some set value, and then falls to zero again. It then reverses its direction of current flow and rises to the same set value in the reverse direction, and then falls to zero again. This reversal of current flow direction is in contrast to direct current (dc), which always maintains the same direction of flow. Standard alternating current can be plotted on a graph as shown in Figure 6–1. The graph shows how the waveform is produced by an alternating current generator as the armature (rotating part) rotates through 360 circular degrees for each cycle.

6.1 ALTERNATING CURRENT

As the generator armature moves through one 360° rotation (full circle), the generator voltage goes through one complete cycle, as shown in Figure 6–1. The curve displayed in 6–1 can also be described by the mathematical equation

$$e = E_m \sin \omega t \qquad (\omega = 2\pi f)$$

where e equals the voltage, E_m the maximum value of generated voltage, and ωt the angular velocity multiplied by the time.

When a generator produces an ac volt-age, the current arising from it varies in step with the voltage. Like the voltage, the current can be represented graphically by a sine wave and by the following equation:

$$i = I_m \sin \omega t$$

where i equals the current, I_m the maximum value of generated current, and ωt the angular velocity multiplied by the time.

Frequency and Cycle

While the coil in a generator rotates 360° (one complete revolution), the output voltage goes through one complete cycle. During one cycle, the voltage increases from zero to positive E_m in one direction, decreases to zero, increases in the opposite direction to negative E_m, and then decreases again to zero. The first 180° (one-half of the voltage cycle) is called the *positive alternation* and the last 180°, from 180° to 360°, is called the *negative alternation*. The value of the E_m voltage at 90° is called the *amplitude* or *peak voltage*. The time required for a positive and a negative alternation is called the *period*. The number of complete cycles per second is the frequency of the sine wave. When the angular velocity, ω, at which the coil rotates is expressed in radians per second, the mathematical relation between ω and f is given by the equation

$$\omega = 2\pi f$$

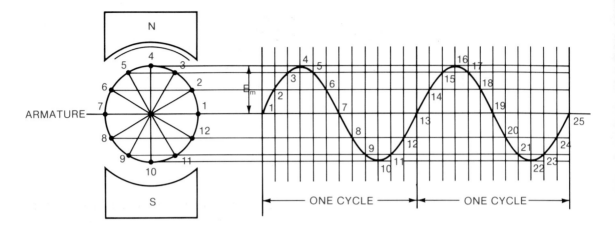

Figure 6-1 A sine wave voltage.

The Effective Value

Since a sine wave of ac current (or voltage) varies continually between zero and maximum (or peak) values, first in one direction and then in the other, there are many numerical values that could be used to describe voltage.

The value of ac most commonly used is *effective value*, or *rms* (root-mean-square) value. The effective value of alternating current is the amount of alternating current that produces the same heating effect as an equal amount of direct current. By definition, one ampere (effective value) of ac will produce the same amount of heat in a given conductor (in a given time) as one ampere of dc. The heating effect of a quantity of current is proportional to the square of the current. The effective value of alternating current can be found by: squaring the sine value for each angle in the cycle, adding all the squares, taking the mean average of these squares, and then extracting the square root. The effective value is then the square root of the mean square of the instantaneous currents. This value is 45°, or 70.7% of the peak value.

To further understand the meaning of effective current, study the diagram in Figure 6–2. The instantaneous values of i are plotted in the upper curve and the corresponding values of i^2 are plotted in the lower curve. The i^2 curve is also a sine curve. It has twice the frequency of the i curve and varies about a new axis.

The vertical axis is the average of the i^2 values, and the square root of the vertical axis values indicates the rms, or effective value of current. Because the i^2 curve varies uniformly from zero to I_m, its average value is $1/2 \ I_m^2$. Thus, the rms value is

$$I_m^2/2 \quad or \quad \frac{I_m^2}{2}$$

which simplified is equal to 0.707 I_m. The rms, or effective value, is commonly represented by I. Hence, the mathematical relation between effective and maximum (or peak) values of current can be expressed as $I = 0.707 \ I_m$.

The relation between maximum (or peak) values of voltage and effective (rms) is the same as the relation between peak and effective current. *Therefore,*

$$E = 0.707 \ E_m$$

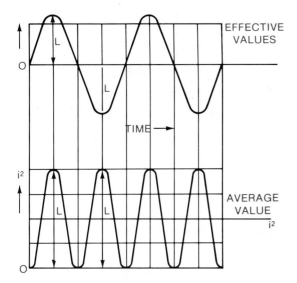

Figure 6-2 Determining the effective value of alternating current.

The reciprocal of 0.707 is 1.414, and therefore,

$$E_m = 1.414\ E$$

and

$$I_m = 1.414\ I$$

The Average Value

Another sine wave value sometimes used is the average value of the voltage during the positive alternation. *Average value* is not as widely used as the rms value, but in some instances it is a more descriptive value of current or voltage. However, it can always be assumed that when an ac voltage is described by a value not otherwise designated (for example, as peak or average value), the rms value is intended. For example, the 120 volt alternating current that is used for lighting and other purposes in your home is 120 volts rms. The mathematical relation between I_{av}, I_m, I_v, and I is given by the formula,

$$I_{av} = 0.636\ I_m = 0.9I$$

Similarly, the relation between E_{av}, E_m, E_v, and E is given by the formula,

$$E_{av} = 0.636\ E_m = 0.9E$$

Period and Frequency

The length of time required for one cycle is called a *period*. This period normally has the symbol t, for time. The number of cycles that occur in one second is known as the *frequency* of the sine wave. The symbol for frequency is f and its unit is the Hertz (cycles per second).

Since the period is the length of time for one cycle and the frequency is the number of cycles in one second, it can be shown that the frequency and the period are reciprocals of each other, as shown by the following equation:

$$f = \frac{1}{t}\ \text{and}\ t = \frac{1}{f}$$

Phase

Whenever there are inductors or capacitors in a circuit, these devices cause the voltage and current to pass through their zero values at different times. This phenomenon is called *phase-shift*.

If an ac voltage and an ac current of the same frequency pass through their corresponding zero values at the same time, they are said to be *in phase*. If the current passes through its zero value before the corresponding zero value of the voltage, the current and voltage are *out of phase* and the current is said to lead the voltage. The voltage is also said to *lag* the current in this latter case.

Figure 6–3 is a diagram of the sine wave for a current of i amperes lagging a voltage of *e* volts by a *phase angle of θ*.

If we take the voltage as the reference, we can find the current by

$$i = I_m \sin (\omega t - \theta)$$

The effective value of an alternating current can be found experimentally by finding what direct current produces the same amount of heat in a given time *(t)* as a source of alternating current. It is assumed that the resistance is the same in both cases.

We can find the instantaneous power in our ac circuit by using Ohm's law for ac circuits. Power is the product of the instantaneous voltage and current as shown in the equation

$$P = ie = i^2 R = \frac{e}{i}$$

6.2 RESISTANCE IN AC CIRCUITS

Resistance, as you will recall from the previous discussion of dc, is the property by which a conductor opposes the flow of current. The resistance of a conductor opposes alternating current in the same way that it opposes direct current.

6.3 INDUCTANCE IN AN AC CIRCUIT

In the discussion of induction you learned that a coil opposes a change in the current through it by building up a counter voltage. This counter voltage is an induced voltage that is equal to

$$e_i = L \frac{\Delta i}{\Delta t}$$

where e_i is the counter voltage, *L* the inductance in henrys, Δi the change in current, and Δt the change in time. The term $\Delta i / \Delta t$ is the rate of change in current with respect to time (how fast the current changes).

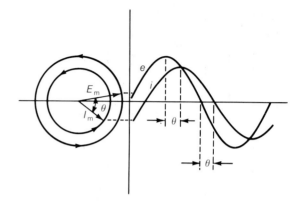

Figure 6-3 Phase shift.

In alternating current, the instantaneous value of *i* is

$$e_i = LI_m \cos \omega t$$

This is the equation for the instantaneous value of the alternating voltage. It is also the equation of a cosine curve, a curve that has the same shape as a sine wave curve but differs in phase from it by $90°(1/4$ cycle). This phase difference exists because the counter voltage reaches its maximum not at the time of maximum current, but at the time the current is *changing* most rapidly; that is, at the time when *i* is zero. The counter voltage is in such a direction as to oppose the change in current. Hence, if *i* is increasing, the counter voltage will be in the opposite direction to the current. Figure 6-4 illustrates this condition. When *i* is decreasing, the direction of the voltage is the same as that of the current. The counter voltage *(e_c) lags* the current *(i)* by 90 degrees.

An Analogy In Figure 6-5 what is in the black box? By Ohm's law 10 volts will drive 1/2 amp of current through 20 ohms of resistance:

$$R = \frac{E}{I} \quad (R = 10/0.5 = 20 \text{ ohms})$$

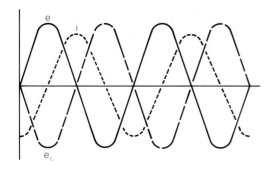

Figure 6-4 Voltage and current relationships in an inductor.

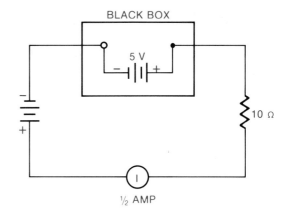

Figure 6-6 The secret of the black box.

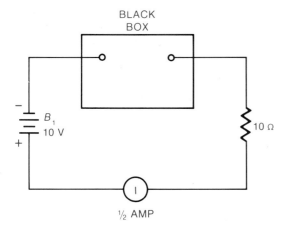

Figure 6-5 Black box example.

Because there are 10 ohms of resistance visible in the drawing, we must assume that the black box contains a 10 ohm resistor.

There is another alternative, however. A 5 volt battery connected in opposition to the battery B_1 makes the total potential applied across the 10 ohm resistor only 5 volts (see Figure 6-6). Again by Ohm's law,

$$I = \frac{E}{R} \left(I = \frac{5V}{10} = 1/2 \text{ amp} \right)$$

6.4 INDUCTIVE REACTANCE

The counter voltage produced in a coil with an alternating current passing through it opposes the applied voltage. As in the pre-vious analogy, the opposing voltage reduces the current. This apparent opposition to current flow in an inductor is called *inductive reactance*. The unit of measurement is the ohm. The higher the inductance value of the coil, the greater will be the counter voltage, and larger counter voltages mean higher reactances. The counter voltage is also dependent upon how fast the field is changing. The rate of change for alternating current is determined by the frequency (frequency implies a cyclical change). Inductive reactance is found by using the formula,

$$X_L = 2\pi f L$$

where X_L = the inductive reactance in ohms, 2π = 6.28, L = the inductance in henrys, and f = the frequency in hertz.

Example 6-1

Problem: Find the inductive reactance of a 10 henry inductor at a frequency of 60 hertz (Hz):

Solution:

$$X_L = 2\pi f L$$

$$X_L = 6.28 \times 60 \times 10$$

$$X_L = 3768$$

Example 6–2

Problem: Find the current in the circuit in Figure 6–7.

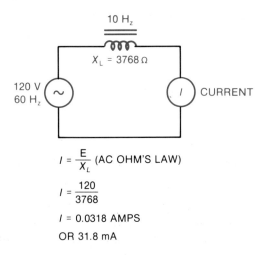

$$I = \frac{E}{X_L} \quad \text{(AC OHM'S LAW)}$$

$$I = \frac{120}{3768}$$

$$I = 0.0318 \text{ AMPS}$$

OR 31.8 mA

Figure 6-7 Inductive current example.

Solution:

$$I = \frac{E}{X_L}$$

$$I = \frac{120}{3768}$$

$$I = 0.0318$$

or

$$31.8 \text{ mA}$$

6.5 RESISTANCE AND INDUCTANCE

When there are both resistance and inductance in the same circuit, the situation gets more complicated. Part of the opposition to the current is resistive and does not involve getting voltage and current out of time; that is, it introduces no phase shift. The inductor opposes current by inducing a counter voltage that opposes the driving (generator) voltage.

The counter voltage is 90° out of phase with the generator voltage. Thus, its opposition to current is also out of phase by 90°. To deal with this situation we need some new tools.

Vectors

A convenient way to describe phase angles, voltages, and reactances in ac circuits is to use *vectors*. In vectors, numerical values of numerical values of voltage and reactance are shown by the length of a line. Phase angles are shown by rotating the line about an axis. Since a resistor produces no phase shift between current and voltage, resistance is represented by a horizontal line of appropriate length, as shown in Figure 6–8A. The inductive reactance is represented by the vertical line (rotated counterclockwise by 90°).

The vector diagram can also be used to solve alternating current (ac) Ohm's law problems. The most general form of Ohm's law is

ac Ohm's law	dc Ohm's law
a. $E = IZ$	a. $E = IR$
b. $Z = \dfrac{E}{I}$	b. $R = \dfrac{E}{I}$
c. $I = \dfrac{E}{Z}$	c. $I = \dfrac{E}{R}$

Where: E = voltage (volts)
   I = current (amperes)
   Z = impedance (ohms)
   R = resistance (ohms)

Impedance

Impedance is called a *vector quantity*, the vector sum of resistance and inductance

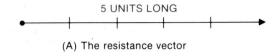

(A) The resistance vector

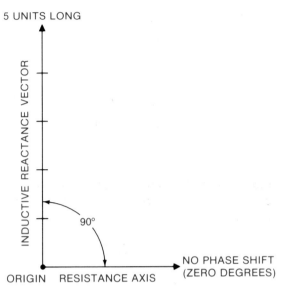

5 UNITS LONG

90°

NO PHASE SHIFT
(ZERO DEGREES)

ORIGIN   RESISTANCE AXIS

NOTE: Vector lines can be scaled to let one division
equal 5, 50, 500, 5000, and so on, ohms.

(B) The inductive reactance vector

Figure 6-8 Vectors.

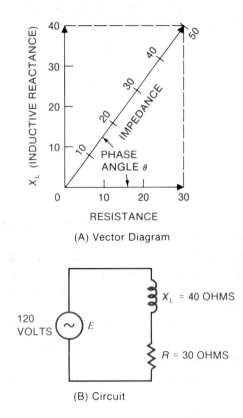

(A) Vector Diagram

(B) Circuit

Figure 6-9 Impedance

(and capacitance if there is some in the circuit). Impedance can be found easily using a vector diagram.

Example 6–3

Problem: Find the impedance (the total opposition to current flow) in the circuit in Figure 6–9.

Solution: To find the impedance, simply,

a. Plot the resistance as shown in Figure 6–9A. The scale is one division = 10 ohms.

b. Plot the inductive reactance as shown in Figure 6–9A. The scale must be the same; one division = 10 ohms.
Note: $1/4'' = 1$ division in the diagram.

c. Complete the parallelogram as shown in dotted lines.

d. Draw the impedance vector as the diagonal of the parallelogram (as shown in Figure 6–9).

e. Measure the length (with a ruler) of the impedance vector. In this case it is 5 units. Since each unit is $10\ \Omega\ (5 \times 10 = 50)$, $Z = 50\ \Omega$.

Example 6–4

Problem: Now let us find the current in the circuit in Figure 6–9B.

Solution: Using the appropriate Ohm's law formula, we get

$$I = \frac{E}{Z}$$

$$I = \frac{120}{50}$$

$$I = 2.4 \text{ amps}$$

6.6 THE PYTHAGOREAN METHOD

The graphical (vector) method is perhaps the easiest way to solve this kind of problem, but it is slow and inaccurate. There are other methods that yield better accuracy, and, with a pocket calculator, are just as simple.

The impedance vector could also be drawn as shown in Figure 6–10 because both diagonals are equal.

The Pythagorean theorem gives the following relationship among the sides of a triangle with one right angle:

$$C = \sqrt{a^2 + b^2}$$

For our purposes, we will use different symbols;

$$Z = \sqrt{R^2 + X_L^2}$$

Example 6–5

Problem: Find the inductive reactance in the previous example (Fig. 6–9) using the formula

$$Z = \sqrt{R^2 + X_L^2}$$

Solution:

$$Z = \sqrt{30^2 + 40^2}$$

$$Z = \sqrt{900 + 1600}$$

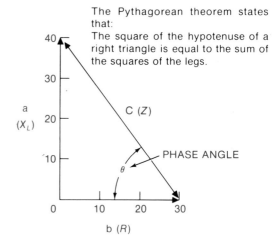

The Pythagorean theorem states that:
The square of the hypotenuse of a right triangle is equal to the sum of the squares of the legs.

Figure 6-10 The impedance vector shown as the other diagonal (the Pythagoran method).

$$Z = \sqrt{2500}$$

$$Z = 50 \text{ ohms}$$

The angle θ in Figure 6–10 is the phase angle measured counterclockwise from the resistance axis. If you measure the angle θ with a protractor, it will prove to be 36.8°.

6.7 POWER

In a dc circuit, power is equal to $E \times I$ (voltage times current). In an ac circuit, the actual power is less than the voltage-current product, whenever there is any phase shift in the circuit. This is true because maximum voltage and maximum current do not occur at the same time. The maximum voltage-current product is never realized and thus the maximum power is not produced.

The voltage-current product *(E × I)* is called *apparent* power. The *true* power depends upon the phase angle and is expressed by the formula:

true power = apparent power × cosine of the phase angle,

or true power = $E \times I$ cosine θ

The cosine is simply the ratio of resistance to impedance.

The cosine is a trigonometric relationship defined as

$$\text{cosine } \theta = \frac{R}{Z}$$

Problem: In the previous examples, the applied voltage was 120 V and the current was found to be 2.4 amps. The resistance was 30 ohms and we calculated the impedance as 50 ohms. To find the *true* power:

$$P = EI \ (R/Z); \text{ or, } P = EI \cos \theta$$

Find the value of the cosine of θ.

Solution:

$$\cos \theta = \frac{R}{Z} = \frac{30}{50} = 0.6$$

$$P = EI \cos \theta$$
$$P = 120 \times 2.4 \times 0.6$$
$$P = 172.8 \text{ watts}$$

Power Factor

The cosine of θ is also known as the *power factor*. It is often multiplied by 100 so that it can be expressed as a percentage. In the case of the previous example the cosine of θ was found to be 0.6. Multiplying by 100, the power factor is 60%. This is interpreted to mean that the *true* power is equal to 60% of the *apparent* power.

More Cos θ

The cosine of θ can also be expressed as

$$\cos \theta = \frac{E_R}{E_Z} \qquad \textit{series circuits only}$$

or

$$\cos \theta = \frac{I_R}{I_Z} \qquad \textit{parallel circuits only}$$

where E_R is the voltage across the resistor, I_R is the current through it, E_Z is the voltage across the total impedance, and I_Z is the circuit current. These quantities can also be plotted on a vector diagram.

If cosine values are plotted against time, the result will be a curve identical in shape to the sine curve, but displaced in time by 90°.

6.8 INDUCTIVE REACTANCES IN SERIES AND PARALLEL

When inductances are connected in series and are not close enough to be in the magnetic field of each other, the inductances and their inductive reactances add like resistances connected in series. Thus, in a series circuit the sum of the inductive reactances can be expressed by the equation,

$$X_{Lt} = X_{L1} + X_{L2} + X_{L3} + ---$$

and the sum of the inductances by the equation,

$$L_t = L_1 + L_2 + L_3 + ----$$

When inductances are connected in parallel, their inductances and the inductive reactances add by the sum of the reciprocals method, like resistances connected in parallel. In a parallel circuit, the sum of the inductive reactances is expressed by the equation,

$$X_{Lt} = \frac{1}{\dfrac{1}{X_{L1}} + \dfrac{1}{X_{L2}} + \dfrac{1}{X_{L3}} + ----}$$

and the sum of the inductances, by the equation,

$$L_t = \cfrac{1}{\cfrac{1}{L_1} + \cfrac{1}{L_2} + \cfrac{1}{L_3} + - - - -}$$

When mutual coupling exists between two inductances, the equations become somewhat more involved. For example, in the case of two inductances, L_1 and L_2 with a mutual inductance of M, the total reactance is equal to

$$X_{Lt} = X_{L1} + X_{L2} \pm X_{2m}$$

The plus or minus sign preceding X_{2m} (mutual coupling) is a necessary part of the equation since the two coils may be located in such a way that the fields either aid or oppose each other. When the fields are aiding, X_{2m} is preceded by the plus sign; when they are opposing, it is preceded by the negative sign.

6.9 CAPACITIVE REACTANCE

A capacitor also exhibits an opposition to current in an ac circuit. The mechanism is similar to that of inductive reactance in the sense that the opposition is due to an opposing voltage instead of heat-producing resistance.

Capacitive reactance (X_c) also produces a 90° phase shift, but in the opposite direction from the phase shift in an inductor. In a capacitor, the current leads the voltage by 90° where current lags by 90° in an inductor. Figure 6–11 shows a vector diagram of resistance, capacitive reactance, and inductive reactance.

The reactance of a capacitor is also dependent upon the frequency of the ac sine wave current. However, capacitive reactance *decreases* as the frequency increases as opposed to inductive reactance which *increases* as the frequency increases.

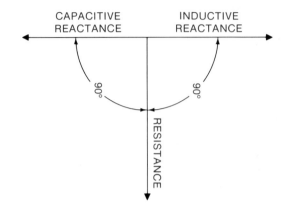

Figure 6-11 Resistance, capacitive reactance, and inductive reactance.

The formula for capacitive reactance is

$$X_C = \frac{1}{2\pi f C}$$

Where X_C = capacitive reactance

2π = 6.28

f = the frequency in hertz (cycles per second)

C = capacitance in farads

Example 6–7

Problem: Find the capacitive reactance of a 1 μF capacitor at 60 Hz.

Solution:

$$X_C = \frac{1}{2\pi f C}$$

$$X_C = \frac{1}{6.28 \times 60 \times 0.000001}$$

$$X_C = \frac{1}{0.000377}$$

$$X_C = 2650 \text{ ohms}$$

If there is only capacitance in the circuit, the special forms of ac Ohm's law apply.

$$I = \frac{E}{X_C}, \; E = IX_C, \; X_C = \frac{E}{I}$$

where I = current, E = voltage, and X_C = capacitive reactance.

6.10 CAPACITANCE AND RESISTANCE

When capacitance and resistance are combined in a circuit, we must again look to the vector diagram to find impedance so we can use ac Ohm's law.

Example 6–8

Problem: Given the circuit in Figure 6–12, find the impedance using a vector diagram.

Solution: If we complete the parallelogram (dotted lines) and draw the diagonal, we get the impedance vector. If we measure its length with a ruler, we get an impedance value of approximately 28 ohms. The phase angle θ is measured with a protractor and will be found to be 45°.

The Pythagorean Method

If we redraw the vector diagram as a triangle, as shown in Figure 6–13, we can use the Pythagorean method to obtain better accuracy with less effort.

Example 6–9

Problem: Using the circuit from the previous

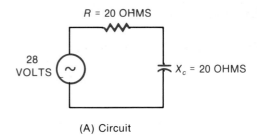

(A) Circuit

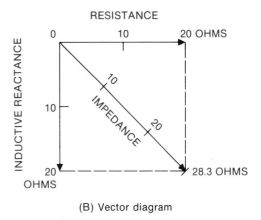

(B) Vector diagram

Figure 6-12 Example of impedance in a capacitive-resistive circuit.

example, find the circuit impedance.

Solution:

$$Z = \sqrt{R^2 + X_C^2}$$

$$Z = \sqrt{20^2 + 20^2}$$

$$Z = \sqrt{400 + 400}$$

$$Z = \sqrt{800}$$

$$Z = 28.28 \text{ ohms}$$

The current in the circuit can be found by using ac Ohm's law, as follows:

$$I = \frac{E}{Z}$$

$$I = \frac{28 \text{ volts}}{28 \text{ ohms}}$$

$$I = 1 \text{ amp}$$

Example 6–10

Problem: Find the *true* power and the power factor for the circuit in Figure 6–13.

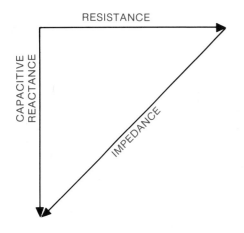

Figure 6-13 The vector diagram redrawn.

Solution:

a. $\cos \theta = R/Z = 20/28 = 0.714$
    Power factor is 71.4%
b. True power $= EI \cos \theta$
    True power $= 28 \times 1 \times 0.714$
    True power $= 19.99$ or approximately 20 watts

6.11 CIRCUITS WITH INDUCTANCE, CAPACITANCE, AND RESISTANCE

Many circuits contain all three components —inductance, resistance, and capacitance. The vector diagram (B) in Figure 6–14 is the diagram of a circuit with $X_C = 200\ \Omega$, $R = 100\ \Omega$, and $X_1 = 100\ \Omega$.

When you examine the figure, you will see that the X_C and X_L vectors point in opposite directions. If we find the difference between X_C and X_L, we get the effective reactance. In this case we have

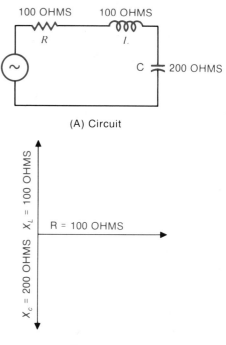

(A) Circuit

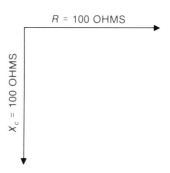

(B) Vector diagram

(C) The equivalent vector diagram

Figure 6-14 Inductance, capacitance, and resistance.

$$X_C = 200\ \Omega \text{ and } X_L = 100\ \Omega$$

$$X_C - X_L = 100\ \Omega \text{ } capacitive$$

We can now draw an *equivalent* vector diagram as shown in Figure 6–14c. You will notice that the inductive reactance has simply vanished, leaving us with a resistor-capacitor circuit. In finding Z, we can now treat this circuit as a capacitor-resistor circuit.

As far as the circuit impedance is concerned, with one exception the circuit will always turn out to be an inductor-resistor or a capacitor-resistor circuit. If the numerical value of X_C is larger than X_L the circuit will be capacitive. If X_L is greater than X_C the circuit will be inductive.

Resonance

There is a special case, called *resonance*, where $X_L = X_C$. X_C totally cancels X_L and the circuit behaves as if the resistance were the only opposition to current flow. The total opposition to current flow is provided by the resistance. The current can then be calculated using ordinary dc Ohm's law, just as if the capacitor and inductor did not exist in the circuit. In a resonant circuit the total phase shift is 0 (zero).

The current in Figure 6–15 can be found by ordinary Ohm's law.

$$I = \frac{E}{R} = \frac{10}{100} = 0.1 \text{ amp}$$

6.12 PARALLEL AC CIRCUITS

Figure 6–16 shows a typical parallel ac circuit, with voltage and current waveforms and the vector diagram. Notice that all elements are connected directly across the ac line in the same way devices are connected to the household power line. The voltage across each component is in phase with the incoming line voltage and the voltage across each is 120 volts. The current through the inductor lags the voltage by 90° and the current through the capacitor leads the voltage by 90°

Because of the phase shift in the inductor and capacitor, we cannot simply add individual branch currents as we do in a dc circuit. Instead we must use vector addition

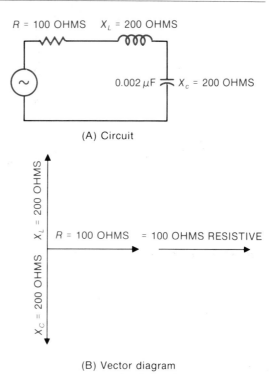

(A) Circuit

(B) Vector diagram

Figure 6-15   Resonant circuit example.

as we did with series circuits. In the parallel circuit, however, our vectors represent currents instead of voltages or impedances.

Example 6–11

Problem: Given the circuit in Figure 6–17, find the total current.

Solution: First, find the current in each branch.

1. $I_R = \dfrac{E}{R} = \dfrac{100}{300} = 0.33 \text{ amp}$

2. $I_L = \dfrac{E}{X_L} = \dfrac{100}{400} = 0.25 \text{ amp}$

3. $I_t = \sqrt{R^2 + X_L^2} = \sqrt{0.33^2 + 0.25^2}$

$$= \sqrt{.1089 + .0625} = \sqrt{0.1714}$$

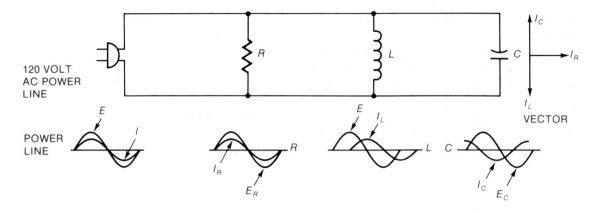

Figure 6-16 Parallel ac circuits.

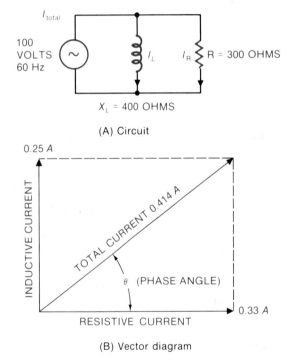

(A) Circuit

(B) Vector diagram

Figure 6-17 Inductance and resistance in parallel.

$$I_t = 0.414 \text{ amp}$$

The vector diagram is shown in Figure 6-17B.

6.13 FINDING THE IMPEDANCE OF A PARALLEL AC CIRCUIT

If we want to find the ac impedance of the circuit in the previous example, we can use the ac Ohm's law form $Z = E/I_{total}$.

Example 6-12

Problem:

$$Z = \frac{100}{0.414} = 241.5 \text{ ohms}$$

In this case it seems that we must know the applied voltage to find the impedance. In a series circuit it was possible to find the impedance directly. However, if we do not know the applied voltage value in a parallel circuit, we can still find the impedance. All that is necessary is to *assume* any arbitrary, convenient voltage.

Example 6-12a

Suppose we take the previous problem and pretend we do not know the applied voltage.

Solution:

1. Let us assume a voltage of 500 volts.

2. Find the current in each branch.

$$I_R = \frac{500}{300} = 1.66 \text{ amps}$$

$$I_L = \frac{500}{400} = 1.25 \text{ amps}$$

3. Find the total current.

$$I_t = \sqrt{R^2 + X_L^2}$$

$$= \sqrt{1.666^2 + 1.25^2}$$

$$= \sqrt{2.775 + 1.56}$$

$$= 2.082 \text{ amps}$$

4. Using ac Ohm's law, find Z.

$$Z = \frac{E}{I} = \frac{500}{2.082} = 240.15$$

The value we got before was 241 ohms. The discrepancy comes about because we didn't carry the values (in either case) out to enough decimal places. For most practical work, both answers are acceptable. Using a calculator capable of square root calculations can verify the results to the desired accuracy.

6.14 PARALLEL RESONANCE

The parallel resonant circuit shown in Figure 6–18 is often called a *tank circuit*. The unique resonant condition provides energy storage in the capacitor that is exactly equal to the energy storage in the magnetic field of the inductor. Assuming the capacitor to be fully charged to start, the capacitor will discharge through the inductor storing the capacitor's stored energy in the inductor's magnetic field. When the capacitor is discharged, the inductor's field begins to collapse, driving its stored energy back into the capacitor. Thus, current will continue to circulate from inductor to capacitor and back again.

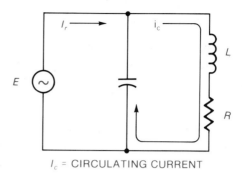

I_c = CIRCULATING CURRENT

Figure 6-18 Resonant tank circuit.

If there were no losses in the circuit, the current would circulate forever. In real circuits there is *always* some resistance and this resistance gradually dissipates the energy in the form of heat. The smaller the resistance (in dotted lines) the faster the circulating energy is dissipated.

"Q" is measured by the relationship $Q = X_L/R$. It can also be written as $Q = X_C/R$ because, at resonance, $X_L = X_C$. A high value of the quality Q means the energy of a tank circuit will circulate longer than it will with a lower value Q.

Impedance of a Parallel Resonant Circuit

Because X_L cancels X_C at resonance, the impedance is simply the resistance if the resistance is in parallel as shown in Figure 6–18. If the resistance is in series, the impedance approaches infinity. The reason for this is the circulating current. The only current demanded by the parallel tank is that which is lost in heat by the series resistance. With a small series resistance and a large value for X_L (and X_C), the current required to maintain the circulating current is very small. A small current means a high impedance. *A parallel tank has a high impedance at resonance.*

Resonant Frequency and Bandwidth

Every parallel inductor-capacitor circuit will be resonant at some frequency. When you examine Figure 6–19, you will see that as the frequency increases, X_L increases and X_C decreases. The X_C curve in the figure is going downward while the X_L curve is going upward. The two curves must inevitably cross somewhere. The point at which they cross (point 0) is the resonant frequency, because at this point $X_L = X_C$. The resonant frequency is designated f_0.

The resonant frequency can be determined for any inductor/capacitor combination by using the following formula:

$$f_0 = \frac{1}{2\pi \sqrt{LC}}$$

Where f_0 is the frequency of resonance
2π is the constant; 2×3.14159
L is the inductance in henrys
C is the capacitance in farads

Curve A in Figure 6–19 is called the *resonant frequency curve*, or *bandwidth curve*. Resonance does not occur at a single frequency because all real inductors have some resistance. The more resistance there is in the circuit, the flatter and wider the curve will be. A narrow, tall curve results when the

Q is high $(Q = X_L/R)$ and will be squat and broad when the Q is low. The bandwidth is defined as those frequencies within the curve where the curve is above 70.7% of the total curve height.

Figure 6–20 shows a high Q and a low Q resonant frequency curve. Note the band of frequencies covered by the low Q curve is wider than that covered by the high Q tank circuit. In many applications, resistance is deliberately added to the circuit to make it respond to a wider band of frequencies. In other applications the resistance is kept small to respond to only a narrow band of frequencies.

The bandwidth of a circuit can be found by the equation,

$$\text{bandwidth } (f_2 - f_1) = \frac{f_0}{Q}$$

Where bandwidth is measured at the 70.7% point on the resonance curve
f_0 = the resonant frequency
Q = the figure of merit of the tank
$Q = X_L/R$, where X_L is the inductive reactance at the resonant frequency, and R is the series resistance in the tank.

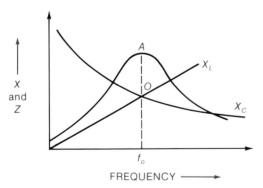

Figure 6-19 X_L, X_C, and the resonant frequency.

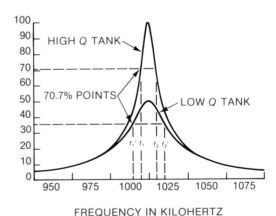

Figure 6-20 Q and bandwidth.

SUMMARY

1. There are 360° in a sine wave curve. The peak voltages occur at 90° and 180°.
2. The frequency of a sine wave is measured in cycles per second. The unit of measurement is the hertz.
3. The period of a sine wave = 1/the frequency.
4. A sine wave's equivalent heating ability is 70% of its direct current equivalent.
5. Rms value of a sine wave is 70% (70.7%) of its peak value.
6. Capacitance in an ac circuit causes a 90° phase shift between voltage and current, with the current leading.
7. Inductance in an ac circuit causes a 90° phase shift between voltage and current, with the voltage leading.
8. The formula for inductive reactance is

$$X_L = 2\pi f L$$

9. The formula for capacitive reactance is

$$X_C = \frac{1}{2\pi f_C}$$

10. Reactances and resistances must be added *vectorially* to find the impedance *(Z)*.
11. In parallel circuits, the capacitive currents, inductive currents, and resistive currents must be added *vectorially* to get the total current. The impedance can then be found by ac Ohm's law.
12. Ac Ohm's law memory aid:

$$\frac{E}{I \quad | \quad Z}$$

13. Impedance may also be found by the Pythagorean method.

$$Z = \sqrt{X^2 + R^2}$$

where X is either X_C or X_L.

14. Resonance occurs when $X_C = X_L$.
15. A capacitive-inductive resonant circuit is often called a tank circuit.
16. The figure of merit of a tank circuit is called Q and is defined as

$$Q = \frac{X_L}{R} \quad \text{or} \quad \frac{X_C}{R}$$

17. A parallel tank circuit has a very high impedance at resonance.
18. A series tank circuit has a very low impedance at resonance.

19. The resonant frequency of a tank circuit is

$$f_0 = \frac{1}{2\pi \sqrt{LC}}$$

20. The bandwidth of a tank circuit is

$$\text{bandwidth} = \frac{f_0}{Q}$$

REVIEWING YOUR ELECTRONICS VOCABULARY

1. Bandwidth
2. Capacitive reactance
3. Impedance
4. Inductive reactance
5. Phase shift
6. Power factor
7. Resonance
8. Sine wave
9. Tank circuit
10. Vector

CHECKING YOUR UNDERSTANDING

1. How does alternating current differ from direct current?
2. How many degrees are there in a sine wave?
3. Where (in degrees) does the peak voltage in a sine wave occur?
4. What is meant by the frequency of a sine wave?
5. What is the formula for capacitive reactance?
6. What is the formula for inductive reactance?
7. Write the three forms of ac Ohm's law.
8. Write the formula for Q when R and X_L are known.
9. Write the formula for bandwidth when the resonant frequency and Q are known.
10. In terms of X_L and X_C, what is the special condition for resonance?

SOLVING ELECTRONIC PROBLEMS

1. What is the resistance of a 660 watt electric soldering iron operated from a 110 volt 60 hertz ac power source?
2. What is the reactance of a 4 microfarad capacitor when it is used in a 60 hertz circuit?
3. What is the current through a 15 microfarad capacitor that has 100 volts at 60 cycles applied?

4. What is the current through a 15 henry inductance with 100 volts at 60 hertz applied to it?

5. What is the equivalent impedance at 60 hertz of a circuit consisting of a pure inductance of 0.5 henry, a 100 ohm resistor, and a 26.5 microfarad capacitor all connected in parallel?

6. An *RF* choke has an inductance of 10 millihenrys and is to be used at a frequency of 1,200 hertz. What is its inductive reactance?

7. In an *RLC* circuit where *L* is 150 microhenrys, *C* is 250 microfarads and *R* is 10 ohms, find the resonant frequency.

8. In a series *RLC* circuit consisting of a 20 microhenry choke, a 20 ohm resistor, and a 0.01 microfarad capacitor with an applied frequency of 550 kHz at 15.5 volts, find the current and the power.

9. A certain resistor dissipates 5 watts of power and has 160 mA of current flowing in it. What is the peak voltage that will appear across it?

10. In a certain *RL* circuit the voltage drops across the *R* and *L* are 30 volts and 40 volts, respectively. Find the applied voltage and phase angle.

CHAPTER 7
Vacuum Tubes

INTRODUCTION

When metals are heated to a high enough temperature, electrons are boiled off. This is called the Edison effect (Figure 7–1).

The electrons given off by a heated wire filament form what is called a *space charge,* a cloud of electrons around the filament.

Electrons emitted by the heated filament are attracted to the positive plate. When the electrons reach the positive plate they flow through the wire, through the meter, and back to the positive side of the power source (see Figure 7–2).

In order to be consistent, we will use

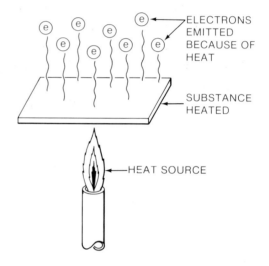

Figure 7-2 Thermionic emission.

electron flow in this text in any discussion of *current* unless otherwise stated.

In Figure 7–3 one battery supplies power to heat the filament and a second supplies power between the filament and plate. This second power source is commonly known as the *plate supply, or B+.*

As long as the filament is heated and B+ is applied to the plate, there is current flow in the plate circuit. Now, if the plate supply voltage is reversed in its polarity then there is a negative charge on the plate that repels electrons, and there will be no current flow from the filament to the negatively charged plate.

Note in Figure 7–3 that there are three

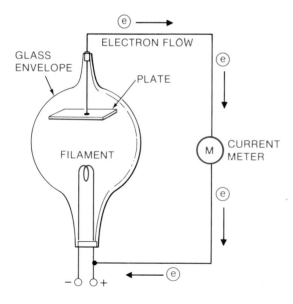

Figure 7-1 The Edison effect.

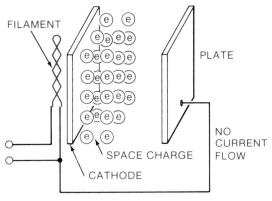

(A) Plate and filament at the same voltage. No current flowing in the plate circuit.

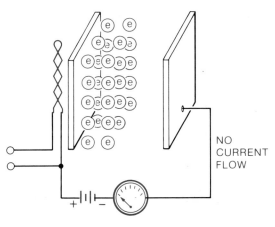

(B) Plate negative with respect to filament. No current flow in the plate circuit.

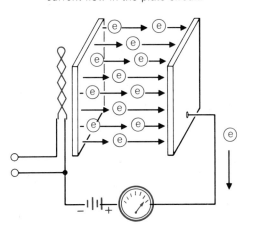

(C) Plate positive with respect to the filament. Current flow in the plate circuit.

Figure 7-3 Current flow due to the Edison effect.

possible combinations of plate voltage polarity with respect to the filament polarity.

7.2 THE DIODE

The Fleming valve, shown in Figure 7–4, was the forerunner of the modern *diode* (two electrodes) tube. Figure 7–5 gives the schematic diagram symbols for the two basic types of diodes, the directly heated and the indirectly heated cathode types.

In the directly heated tube the filament also serves as the cathode, whereas in the indirectly heated version, they are separate elements. Figure 7–6 shows the separation of cathode and filament.

When the indirectly heated cathode (Figure 7–7) is raised to its correct temperature by the filament, it emits electrons just as the filament does. However, it is electrically insulated from the filament and this insulation allows us to place high voltages on a cathode when the circuit requires it.

Figure 7–8 provides some examples of the many types of diode tubes.

If we take a diode tube and supply a variable plate voltage, as shown in Figure 7–9, we can plot the characteristic curve shown in Figure 7–10.

Figure 7–10 has the characteristic plate current (I_p) on the vertical axis and plate voltage (E_p) on the horizontal axis. It can be

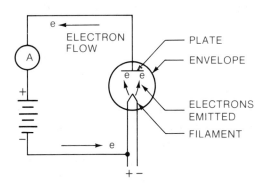

Figure 7-4 Fleming valve.

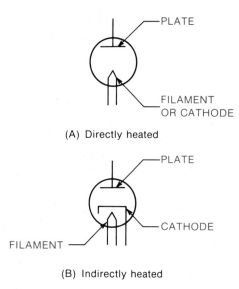

(A) Directly heated

(B) Indirectly heated

Figure 7-5 Diode tube schematic diagram symbols.

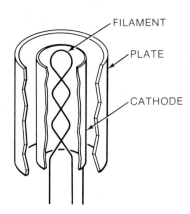

Figure 7-6 Cutaway of a diode tube.

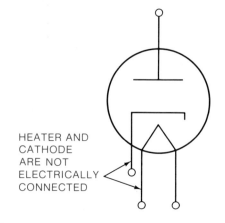

Figure 7-7 The indirectly heated cathode and high voltages.

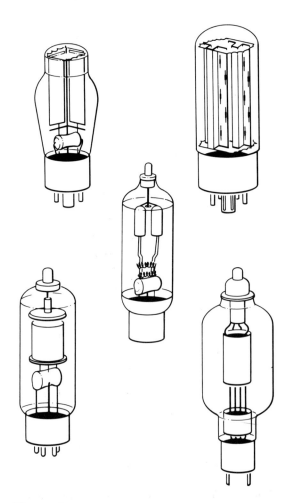

Figure 7-8 Vacuum tube diodes.

seen that I_p is slow to increase at very low voltages, but at higher voltages I_p starts to increase rapidly at almost a linear rate up to a point where further increases in E_p will cause no further increases in current. This point is known as the tube's *saturation point* (see Figure 7–10).

The diode tube acts as a switch, without moving mechanical parts, that allows current to flow only in one direction. If we replace the plate voltage battery in Figure 7–9

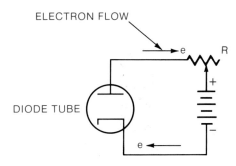

Figure 7-9 Diode circuit.

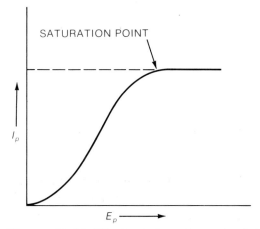

Figure 7-10 Diode tube characteristic curve.

with an ac source, as in Figure 7–11, the plate voltage will be first positive, then negative. See Figure 7–12.

When current flows only during half of the input wave, the action is called *half-wave rectification*. This rectifying action can be visualized by plotting the input and output waveforms on the tube's characteristic curve, as shown in Figure 7–13.

The characteristics of a given diode can be described by four important ratings:

1. *Maximum plate current* (I_{max}). The maximum current that can flow in the tube without damage.

2. *Plate dissipation.* The power loss to heat because of the electron bombardment of the plate.

3. *Peak inverse voltage* (E_{piv}). The maximum voltage that can be applied be-

tween elements of the tube in the off condition without damage.

4. *Plate resistance* (R_p). The internal path resistance of the current within the tube itself. It is found by applying Ohm's law using I_p and E_p, as follows:

$$R_p = \frac{\Delta E_p}{\Delta I_p}$$

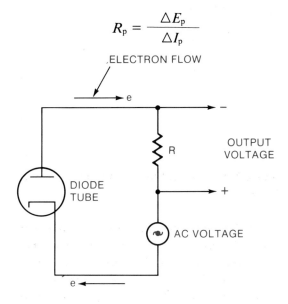

Figure 7-11 AC applied to a diode tube.

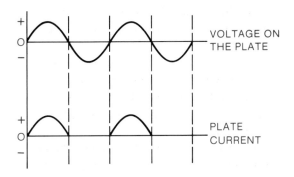

Figure 7-12 Graph of voltage and current in the plate of a diode tube.

7.3 MULTIELEMENT TUBES

There are many tubes with more elements than the diode. For example, the *triode*, de-

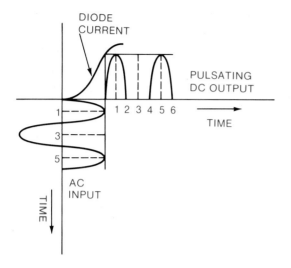

Figure 7–13 Plot of the rectifying action of a diode tube.

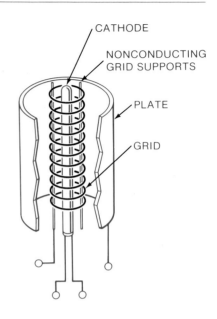

Figure 7–14 Elements of a triode tube, cutaway view.

veloped in 1907 when the American inventor Lee DeForest inserted a third electrode between the cathode and the plate of a diode.

Figure 7–14 shows the elements of a triode tube. Note that the *grid*, as the third element is called, is simply a wire wound in a spiral around the cathode with spacers to keep it at a specified distance.

In the triode the flow of electrons is from the cathode to the plate, as it is in the diode. In the triode this current flow will pass through the grid, and the grid potential can be varied to control the amount of current through the tube. Figure 7–15 illustrates the three possible polarity states that the grid can have.

In part A of Figure 7–15 where the grid has 0 volts, or no charge, the grid has little effect on the current flow in the tube. In part B, the grid's positive voltage has an acceleration effect on the electrons flowing toward the plate. This causes an increase in plate current. A positive grid voltage that is too high may cause the plate to overheat.

In part C of Figure 7–15, where there is a negative grid voltage, the electrons that

would normally flow toward the plate are repelled back toward the cathode. If this grid voltage is negative enough, it causes the tube current to cease and the tube is said to be cut off.

The polarity of the grid voltage is always taken with respect to the cathode. Thus if the cathode is +150 volts, then a voltage of +145 on the grid would be a 5 volt negative grid voltage.

This grid voltage is often called the *grid bias voltage* and is designated by E_c or E_g. (The two terms are used interchangeably in this and most other texts.)

In the triode tube there are three basic quantities of particular interest to us. These are the grid voltage, or bias; the plate voltage (between plate and cathode); and the plate current. If these three values are known we can see how the tube works by plotting the values on a graph described as the set of the tube's characteristic curves.

Figure 7–16 is such a set of curves for a typical triode tube. Our example is the type

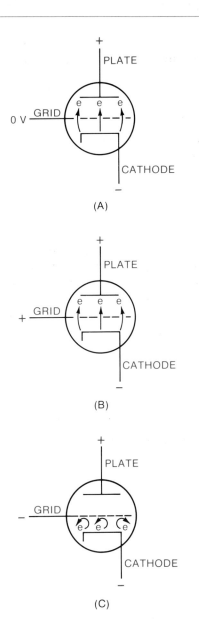

Figure 7-15 Effects of a grid in a triode tube.

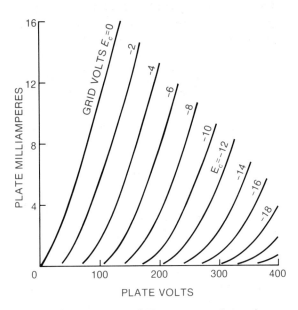

Figure 7-16 6SN7=GT average plate characteristics.

6SN7-GT tube.

The curve in Figure 7-16 designated "grid volts $E_c = 0$" is the curve for the tube connected to act as a diode. Looking back at Figure 7-10, note the resemblance between it and Figure 7-16.

In Figure 7-16 each curve was plotted with a different grid bias voltage. Notice that as the negative bias is increased, the plate voltage must be increased in order to obtain the same plate current. For example, if 4 mA of tube current is flowing with −2 volts of grid bias, the plate voltage is approximately 75 volts. However, if the grid bias is increased to −14 volts, a plate voltage of approximately 325 volts is needed to yield a plate current of 4 mA.

Let us examine the curves of Figure 7-16 a little further. Looking at the −2 volt bias curve at a plate voltage of 100 volts, we see that the plate current is 5.4 mA. Now if we increase the plate voltage to 125 volts and maintain the −2 volt bias, the plate current will become 8.4 mA, an increase of 3 mA. If we maintain the plate voltage and change the bias the plate current also increases, but here a much smaller voltage change is needed for the same amount of plate current increase. For example, assume the plate voltage is 200 volts and the bias is changed from −8 to −6 volts, an increase of +2 volts.

This will cause the plate current to increase from 3.4 mA to 7.6 mA, a plate current increase of only a +2 volt change in grid bias.

This ratio of the change in plate voltage to grid voltage change, if the plate current change in each case is the same, is known as the tube's *amplification factor*, represented by the Greek letter μ. Thus a tube's μ is

$$\mu = \frac{\Delta E_p}{\Delta E_c}$$

The amplification factor describes the effect of the grid bias on the plate current. The value is generally determined by the way in which the tube is constructed. The nearer the grid is to the cathode, the larger its effect will be on the plate current.

Another important factor to consider is that the elements in a tube act as do the plates of a capacitor (vacuum dielectric). Thus by bringing the grid closer to the cathode, the interelectrode capacitance is increased. This capacitance is normally a very undesirable thing, as we will see later in our study.

The small change in grid bias that causes a change in plate current is known as the tube's *transconductance* (g_m). Transconductance is also known as *mutual conductance*. Its value can be determined by the following equation:

$$g_m = \frac{\Delta i_b}{\Delta e_c}$$

The transconductance of a tube is measured in micromhos. The *micro*mho is 0.000001 of a mho.

As an example, a tube that has a 2 mA change (Δ) in plate current for 1 volt of change in grid bias, has a transconductance of 2,000 micromhos.

The three basic parameters of a tube are the grid bias, the plate voltage, and the plate current. The relationship between the three basic parameters of a tube can be expressed as follows:

$$\mu = (g_m)\,(r_p)$$

where g_m is the transconductance, r_p is the plate resistance, and μ is the amplification factor.

Example 7–1

Problem: What is the amplification factor of a tube that has a plate resistance of 7,500 ohms with a 5 mA change in plate current for a 2 volt change in bias?

Solution:

$$g_m = \frac{5\ mA}{2\ volts}$$

$$= 2.5 \times 10^{-3}$$
$$\text{or } 0.0025\ \text{mho}$$

0.0025 is converted to micromhos by pointing off six places to the right, or 0.002 50, to produce 2500 micromhos.

$$= 2,500\ \text{micromhos}$$

$$\mu = (2,500)\,(7,500)$$

This is 0.0025 × 7500 to produce 18.75

$$\mu = 18.75$$

Let us return for a moment to the interelectrode capacitance of a tube. If we allow the capacitance to become very large, any change in plate current will be fed back to the grid by this capacitive coupling. The capacitive coupling can be reduced by the use of an additional electrode placed between the grid and the plate, as shown in Figure 7–17. This tube with an extra grid (screen grid) is known as a *tetrode*.

A screen grid has the undesirable char-

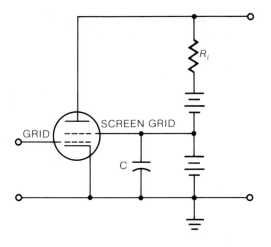

Figure 7-17 Tetrode circuit.

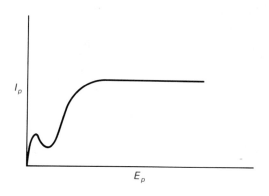

Figure 7-18 $I_p E_p$ curve for a tetrode tube.

acteristic of collecting the electrons knocked off the plate (secondary emission). The collecting of these electrons will cause a dip in the plate current characteristic curve, as shown in Figure 7–18.

This dip can be eliminated by the addition of still another grid called the *suppressor grid*. A tube with a suppressor grid (called a *pentode*) is diagrammed in Figure 7–19. It is inserted between the screen grid and the plate. The suppressor grid is usually connected to the cathode and thus is normally negative with respect to the plate. The suppressor grid is able to repel the secondary emission electrons back to the plate and so prevent a dip in the $I_p E_p$ curve. See Figure 7–20.

In a pentode the amplification factor can have a very high value, often in the order of 1,400 micromhos or greater. The r_p is also very high, in the order of 1.5 megohms. The transconductance (g_m) of the pentode is normally lower than that of a tetrode, but some do have g_m in the order of 8,000 or 9,000.

There are many tubes that have more than three grids, but only the heptode (five grids), known as the pentagrid mixer or converter, is at all common in tube equipment.

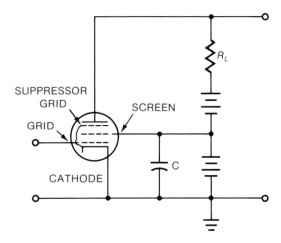

Figure 7-19 Pentode tube circuit.

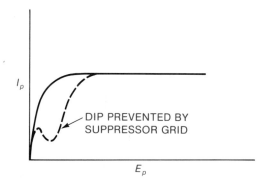

Figure 7-20 $I_p E_p$ curve for a pentode tube.

The schematic symbol for this tube is shown in Figure 7–21.

It is common in tube equipment to have several tubes within one envelope. An example is the 12AX7, which has two triode sections within one envelope.

As a general rule for most tubes, the first digit or two in the type number indicates the filament voltage. For example, the 6BA6 has a 6.3 volt filament and the 12AX7 has a 12.6 volt filament. The final digit is the number of elements contained in the envelope. The 12AX7, for example, has seven elements—two plates, two grids, two cathodes, and one filament. A particular tube is often available with a variety of filament voltages; for example, a 6CD6 and a 12CD6 would be identical except for the filament voltage.

7.4 VHF AND MICROWAVE TUBES

Special tubes are used in the VHF and microwave frequency spectrum that take advantage of the special qualities of cavity resonators or electron transit time resonance. In Figure 7–22 we can see examples of some very-high-frequency (VHF) and microwave tubes that are in common use today.

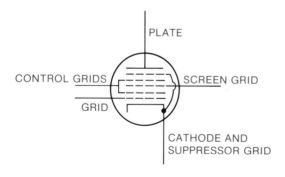

Figure 7-21 Pentagrid tube schematic.

A planar or lighthouse tube is a common VHF or microwave oscillator/amplifier tube used in VHF equipment. It is not often used in new designs because existing technology has provided better devices for the purpose.

Figure 7–22A shows a cutaway drawing of a typical planar triode tube. Note that the tube elements are arranged in parallel planes rather than in the concentric cylinders used in the construction of most other tubes.

Figure 7–22B shows two examples of planar tubes in use today.

The Klystron

One of the most common microwave tubes is the klystron. Figure 7–23 is a picture of a small tunable klystron.

A basic klystron tube consists of four parts: a beam or electron source, a velocity-modulating unit that is usually called a *buncher*, a *drift tube* through which the velocity-modulated beam travels, and a *catcher* that removes the energy from the velocity-modulated beam. These basic sections are detailed in Figure 7–24.

The beam source is a simple electron gun similar to those found in cathode ray tubes (see section 7.5). The electrons making up the beam are emitted from a heated cathode, and flow away from it along converging paths. Note that it looks like a tetrode tube without a plate. The control grid, as usual, controls the number of electrons that will be allowed to move toward the catcher while the accelerating grid speeds up any electrons passed by the control grid. The velocity of the beam of electrons is adjusted by varying the voltage on the accelerating grid. See Figure 7–25A.

A buncher, or cavity and drift space region, is made up of the drift tube and two to four resonant cavities that surround the

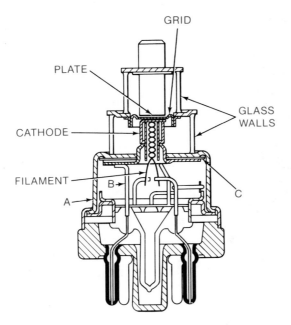

(A) Cutaway view of a planar tube.

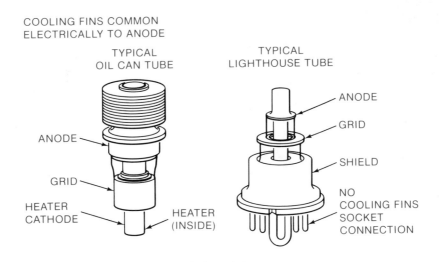

(B) Typical planar tubes.

Figure 7-22 Typical VHF tubes.

Figure 7-23 Klystron tube.

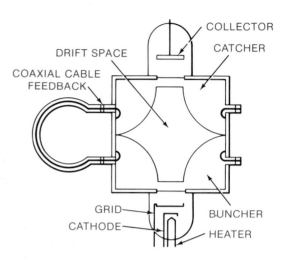

Figure 7-24 Simplified diagram of a klystron showing the major elements.

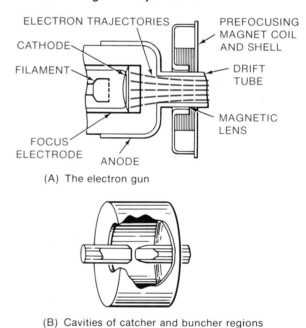

(A) The electron gun

(B) Cavities of catcher and buncher regions

Figure 7-25 Klystron electron gun.

tube at preset intervals along it. The drift tube itself is an axial-interrupted tube in which the electrons are neither accelerated nor decelerated. The drift tube's length to diameter ratio is about 20:1. Each of the interruption points along the tube has an associated buncher cavity constructed so that the drift tube tips in the cavity to become the capacitive loading elements of the cavity. Thus, very large RF voltages will be impressed across them. The cylindrical structure of the cavity forms the inductive element of the cavity.

The final element in the klystron is the collector or catcher. The catcher simply gathers the electrons after their function has been completed and returns them to the beam power supply. The collector must dissipate the large energy content of the spent electron beam; therefore, the collector must be cooled to transfer this energy from the tube. In high power klystrons, the tube is liquid-cooled to dissipate the heat.

In high power amplifier type klystrons a very strong axial magnetic field is used to direct and maintain the electron beam in the drift tube. There will be one magnetic coil per cavity. The high power klystron is shown in Figure 7-26.

When the electron beam leaves the electron gun, it is in one continuous stream and will not produce radio frequency power as it flows through the klystron. As a result, the beam must be varied to be useful. This is accomplished by the drift tube cavity group, which changes the relative velocity of the electrons in the beam.

A special type of klystron, known as the reflex klystron, is shown in cutaway form in Figure 7–27. This klystron has only one cavity, but its principle of operation is the same as other klystrons.

Klystron operation itself is simple. The beam of electrons is fed to the buncher cavities. They are velocity modulated by feeding energy to the cavity. This energy causes the beam electrons to either slow or accelerate, and this causes them to gather in groups or bunches as they progress down the drift tube. When the tube is correctly adjusted, this bunching occurs at the microwave frequency. The bunched electrons then pass through the catcher grids at the microwave frequency. The bunching acts like an ac current between the catcher grids and will excite the catcher. Thus the klystron will act as an amplifier, taking in energy at a low level at the buncher cavity and providing a high level output at the catcher cavity.

If some of the output is fed back to the input, the tube will oscillate.

The Magnetron

Except for the klystron, the magnetron is the most common microwave tube. The magnetron is a device that depends upon resonant cavities within its structure to operate.

Before we proceed with how the magnetron operates, we will take a brief look at how it is built. In Figure 7–28, we see a picture of a small magnetron used in a short range radar. Note that the tube has large magnets attached to the central body.

Figure 7–29 illustrates the anode of the magnetron showing the hole and slot system of resonant cavities in a simple magnetron. Part A of the figure is a view on the axis of the cylinder that shows only the main outline of the anode. Each of the cavities consists of a cylindrical hole joined to the central space by a small slot. Although six cavities are shown, magnetrons with other numbers of cavities are not uncommon. Part B is a sectional view of the anode in perspective. There are no cavity grids in a magnetron. Instead, the electric field generated in the resonant cavity is what modulates the circular electron beam. This field is illustrated in Figure 7–30.

The cathode generating the electron beam is normally placed along the axis of the anode, as shown in Figure 7–31.

Except for the cavities in the anode, a magnetron is a simple diode tube. If there were no magnetic field, the tube would act like any other diode tube. The electrons would travel radially outward from the cath-

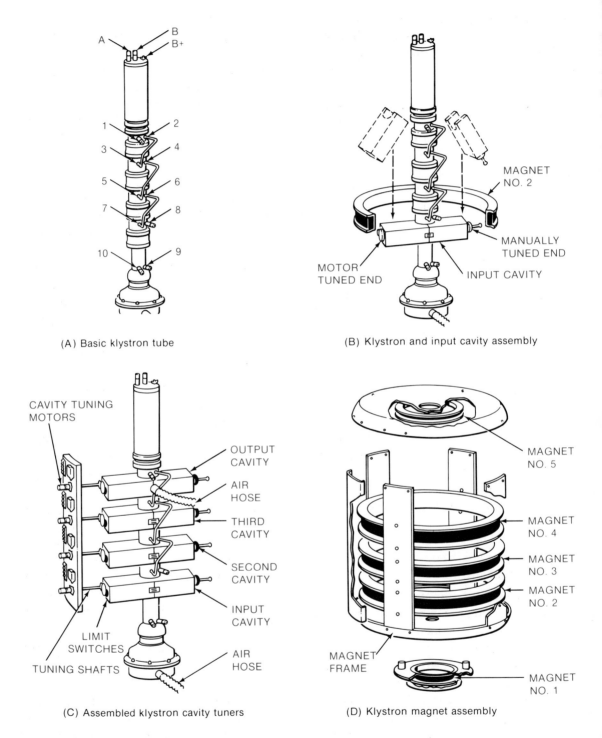

(A) Basic klystron tube

(B) Klystron and input cavity assembly

(C) Assembled klystron cavity tuners

(D) Klystron magnet assembly

Figure 7-26 High power klystron and its magnetic assemblies.

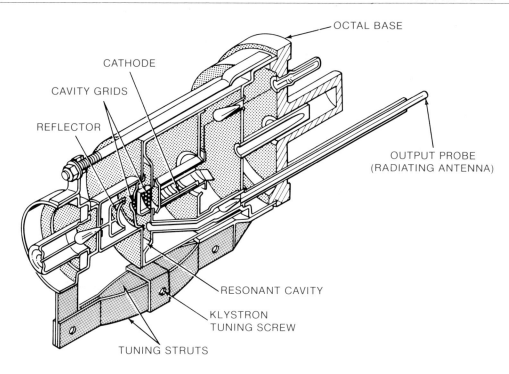

Figure 7-27 Reflex klystron, cutaway view.

Figure 7-28 Magnetron.

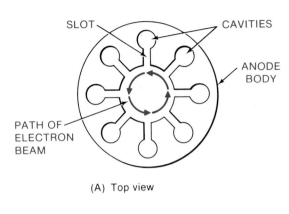

(A) Top view

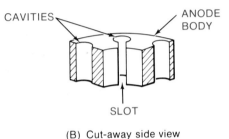

(B) Cut-away side view

Figure 7-29 Hole and slot resonant cavity.

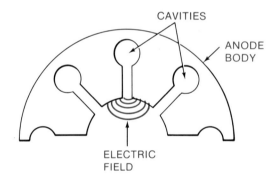

Figure 7-30 Electric field in the slot.

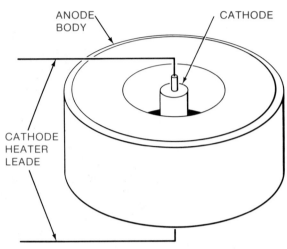

Figure 7-31 Cathode of a magnetron.

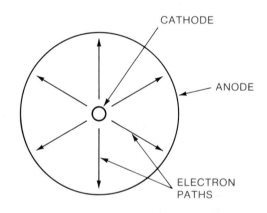

Figure 7-32 Electron paths in a magnetron without a magnetic field applied.

ode to the anode, as shown in Figure 7–32.

In Figure 7–33 we can see how the electron path is affected if a magnetic field is applied to the axis of the anode. In part A we see a very low magnetic field strength and the electron paths are curved slightly. A stronger magnetic field or a lower voltage between cathode and anode will lead to the more sharply curved paths shown in part B. When the correct relation exists between the magnetic field strength and the cathode-anode voltage, the electron paths are like those shown in Figure 7–34A. This is a rather idealized picture, since it neglects all interaction between the electrons and also neglects the effect of the cavities. In practice, collisions between the electrons disrupt the simple path that runs from cathode to anode and back again. The actual path spirals outward so that the electrons ultimately are captured by the anode, as shown in part B.

Correct electron paths can be obtained with almost any anode voltage if the correct magnetic field is used. If the correct voltage is applied to the anode, the possibility of oscillation (transfer of energy from the electrons to the cavities) depends on the relations between electron velocity. Spacing between the various anode cavities, and the resonant frequency of those various cavities. Because of this interaction, the magnetron will oscillate *only* over a very narrow range of magnetic field strengths and anode voltages.

The basic operation of the magnetron is not as involved as it may sound. The magnetic field causes the electrons to pass energy to the cavities as they go by them. The anode removes the electrons from the system as they slow up.

Because of the nature of a magnetron, it can be affected by changes in the output impedance. A change in load will vary not only the power output, but also the frequency. Therefore care must be taken in a magnetron's operation to prevent these changes, which are known as *pulling,* from occurring.

Magnetrons are available in many sizes, up to 10 kilowatts output for pulse work. In pulse service a duty cycle of 1/1000 is common. That is, an output for only about 1/1000 (on for 1 microsecond, and off for 1000 microseconds). There are magnetrons available for high duty cycles and even continuous duty operation, but these are normally lower powered types. In general, as the frequency of the operation is increased, the physical structure of the magnetron is smaller because of the smaller size needed in the resonant cavities. A magnetron is normally about 35 percent efficient. Thus a small physical size will limit the power output because of heat dissipation limitations.

7.5 CATHODE RAY TUBES

The *cathode ray tube,* or *CRT* as it is commonly known, is a special type of tube where the electrons emitted by the cathode are concentrated into a small narrow beam. This beam of electrons is accelerated to a very high velocity before striking a specially treated phosphor screen which, when struck by the electron beam, will glow.

The television picture tube is the most common use for the CRT, but there are many other very important uses.

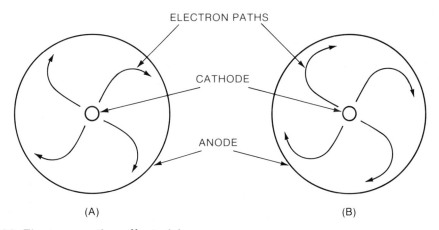

Figure 7-33 Electron paths affected by a magnetic field.

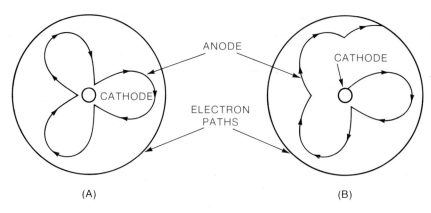

Figure 7-34 Electron paths with correct magnetic field applied.

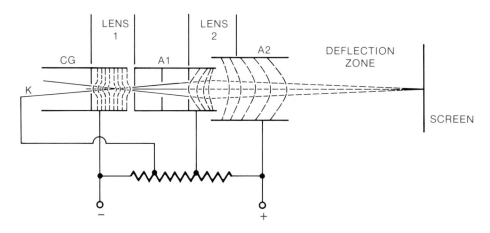

Figure 7-35 Cathode ray tube (CRT).

In Chapters 1 and 2 we saw how an electron beam can be affected by a magnetic field or an electrostatic field. This control of an electron beam can be used to focus it into one spot, and by an additional set of electrostatic or magnetic deflection controls, a beam can be directed to any point on the CRT screen.

In Figure 7-35 we see an example of an electrostatic focusing system for a CRT. This system uses the principles outlined in Chapters 1 and 2 to accomplish the focus-

ing. Figure 7-36 is the optical equivalent of Figure 7-35.

However, operating the basic principle of all CRTs is the same.

Deflection of the electron beam in CRTs is accomplished by either an electric field on deflection plates or by electromagnets called deflection coils mounted outside of the tube. There are several different kinds of phosphors used, varying in chemical structure and thus in persistence (glow time) and color (among other things). Most oscilloscope CRT faceplates are coated with a green-emitting phosphor, because green phosphors are most efficient.

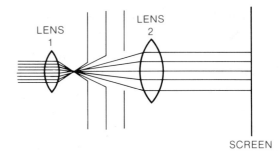

Figure 7-36 Equivalent optical system of a cathode ray tube (CRT).

SUMMARY

1. The vacuum tube is a spin-off from Edison's work with the incandescent lamp.

2. A white-hot filament emits (boils off) electrons. Also, many oxide materials produce electrons when heated by being placed near a hot filament. Both arrangements are used to produce the electron supply in vacuum tubes.

3. A diode tube is a one-way electrical valve. Current can flow from the cathode (or filament) to the plate, but not from the plate to the cathode.

4. When all of the electrons being boiled off the cathode are being collected by the plate, the tube is said to be in saturation. At saturation, an increase in plate voltage does not increase the plate current, because *all available* electrons are being collected at this plate.

5. Important diode ratings are:
   a. maximum plate current
   b. maximum plate power dissipation
   c. peak inverse voltage
   d. plate resistance (the tube's internal resistance from cathode to plate)

6. A three-element tube is called a triode. The triode is capable of amplification. The diode is not.

7. The grid in a triode is the electron control element. The signal to be amplified is applied to the grid and the amplified signal is taken from the plate.

8. Making the grid negative repels electrons, driving some of them back toward the cathode. If the grid is made negative enough, all the electrons will be repelled. There will be no cathode-to-plate current. The tube is said to be cut off.

9. The tube's amplification factor is μ (mu) and is equal to:

$$\mu = \frac{\Delta E_p}{\Delta E_g}$$

10. The figure of merit in a tube is called mutual conductance or transconductance (g_m) and it is the ratio of plate current to grid voltage. Its unit of measurement is the micromho (siemens). The equation is

$$g_m = \frac{\Delta I_p}{\Delta E_g}$$

11. Two elements in a tube form a capacitor with a vacuum dielectric. This interelectrode capacitance causes problems at high frequencies.

12. The addition of a screen grid into the tube (making it a tetrode) was an early solution to the interelectrode capacitance problem. However, this extra grid caused a dip in the tube's operating curve, representing an unstable operating condition.

13. The pentode (five element) tube added still another grid, called the suppressor grid, to remove the dip in the tetrode's operating curve. The pentode made the tetrode obsolete.

14. The first one to three digits in a tube's number define the filament voltage. The final digit tells how many elements are in the envelope. Several tubes are often put into the same glass envelope.

15. At very high frequencies, special vacuum tubes are required.

16. At very high frequencies, the electrons do not have time to get from the cathode to the plate before the ac input signal reverses. To correct for this, the klystron tube places resonant cavities (tank circuits) along the electron path to take advantage of the transit time. As the electron stream passes each cavity, it sets up a circulating current.

17. The magnetron also uses resonant cavities along the electron transit path. In the magnetron the electron stream is forced into a circular pattern by a large magnet. As the electron stream passes each cavity, it causes a circulating current at the cavity's resonant frequency. A cavity is the high frequency equivalent of an inductive capacitive tank circuit.

18. The cathode ray tube (CRT) is a special vacuum tube where the "plate" is a phosphor-coated glass faceplate. When the electron beam strikes the screen, it produces a spot of light. Deflection plates or deflection coils are used to move the beam over the screen. The beam can then be used to trace out pictures for television, for example, or to draw graphs on an oscilloscope.

REVIEWING YOUR ELECTRONICS VOCABULARY

1. Bias
2. Cathode
3. Diode
4. Grid
5. Plate
6. Rectifier
7. Saturation
8. Tetrode
9. Transconductance
10. Triode

CHECKING YOUR UNDERSTANDING

1. Draw a schematic symbols for diode tubes, triode tubes, and pentode tubes. Label each of the parts.
2. What is the Edison effect?

3. Name two basic tube parameters that are direct functions of grid bias.
4. Does a vacuum tube require a negative bias to turn it off or to turn it on?
5. How much plate current flows when a tube is cut off?
6. Describe the rectifying action in a diode.
7. Describe how the control grid works in a tube.
8. Why have screen and suppressor grids been added to some tubes?
9. What is the formula for the μ of a triode?
10. In a 12AX5 tube, how many electrodes are there? How many volts on the filament when it is operating properly?

SOLVING ELECTRONIC PROBLEMS

1. Find the mutual conductance g_m when the

$$g_m = \frac{g_m A}{2 \text{ volts}}$$

2. Find the mutual conductance (g_m) when the plate current $= \triangle$ 10 mA and grid voltage $= \triangle$ 2.5 volts
3. Find μ (mu) when $\triangle$ plate voltage is 42 volts, and a $\triangle$ grid voltage is −2 volts
4. If plate resistance (r_p) is given by the formula:

$$r_p = \frac{\triangle V_p}{\triangle I_p}$$

find the value for r_p when $\triangle$ plate voltage is 82 volts and a $\triangle$ plate current is 12 mA.

CHAPTER 8
Diodes and Transistors

INTRODUCTION

At absolute zero (−273° C), semiconductors would be near-perfect insulators. Above absolute zero, the higher the temperature goes, the better conductors semiconductor materials become.

Within the range of normal earth temperatures, semiconductors range from poor to good conductors. This change in conductivity with temperature is not a simple relationship. For example, in germanium, an increase in temperature of only 10° C will double its conductivity; in silicon, a 10° C increase triples its conductivity.

If a block of silicon is hooked up and heated as shown in Figure 8–1, the current in the circuit will gradually increase as the temperature of the block increases. The current also increases if the voltage is increased. But increasing the voltage increases the current only proportionally, according to Ohm's law, while increasing the temperature increases the current at an exponential rate.

The temperature (over which we have no control) exerts a greater effect on the current than does the voltage, which we do control, in electronics.

There are two ways to cope with this temperature problem and make the current more voltage-dependent than temperature-dependent. One method is to add certain impurities to the semiconductor material. Free electrons are then made available in large quantities. These impurity-produced electrons are not temperature-dependent, but voltage-dependent. The second method of restricting temperature-controlled current involves proper circuit design.

8.1 SILICON CRYSTALS

Two elements, silicon and germanium, are the two most important semiconductors in modern technology. Silicon has largely replaced germanium as processing methods for silicon have matured. Recently, how-

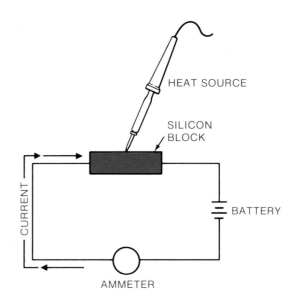

Figure 8-1 Temperature and conductivity in silicon.

ever, there have been some new high-power germanium devices that may rival established silicon devices. Compounds, such as gallium arsenide, are used in special applications such as light emitting diodes (LEDs).

Germanium and silicon each have four free electrons in their outer orbits. When there are many atoms available in their crystalline form, electron-sharing occurs. The result of this sharing behavior is as though the formerly free valence electrons had become tightly bound in their particular places in the crystal. Figure 8-2 is a diagram of this covalent bond. An electron associated with an individual silicon atom would require only a 0.05 electron volt *(e*V*)* to free it from the atom. When a large number of atoms form covalent bonds, they bind the electron to a pair of atoms so tightly that it takes about 0.7 *e*V to break the electron free.

These covalent bonds in semiconductors are still weak enough so that many of them are broken at any temperature above absolute zero. The higher the temperature, the more covalent bonds are broken. Whenever a covalent bond is broken by heat energy, an electron becomes free to be moved by an electric field. When the electron leaves its spot in the crystal, it leaves behind a *dangling bond.* This dangling bond has an attraction for any electron passing by, and will capture it if it comes near. The dangling bond is called a *hole.* Because of its attraction for electrons, it is generally thought of as a positively charged body. The hole is also thought of as able to move through the crystal in the same way as an electron, although hole mobility is really just a convenient fiction. While we may find it difficult to visualize holes moving under the influence of an electric field, we can easily visualize changing concentrations of holes.

Figure 8–3 shows a crystal in which B is an electron whose covalent bond has been broken. The dangling bond A is the hole.

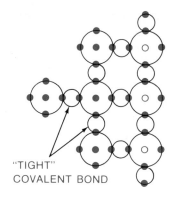

"TIGHT"
COVALENT BOND

(A) Silicon crystal

"LOOSE" BOND OF AN
INDIVIDUAL ATOM

(B) Silicon atom

Figure 8-2 The covalent bond.

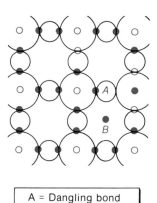

A = Dangling bond
B = Freed electron

Figure 8-3 Bond broken by heat energy.

8.2 CONDUCTION IN SILICON

When there is no electric field, free electrons are evenly distributed throughout the block of silicon. Electrons are also being captured by holes, and each capture results in the destruction of an electron-hole pair. When an electron is captured by a hole, the hole no longer exists and the electron is no longer a free electron. Electron-hole pairs are constantly created and destroyed in about the same numbers.

When an electric potential is applied across the block, electrons are attracted to the positive end of the block. Electron-hole pairs are being formed throughout the block, but because of the electric field, there is a heavy concentration of electrons at the positive end and fewer electrons at the negative end. Those holes at the negative end of the block are not capturing electrons, because there are almost none available to capture. They have moved to the positive end. At the negative end of the block, then, there is an excess of holes. At the positive end of the block there is an abundance of electrons and the holes are filled as soon as heat energy breaks them loose.

We now have a block of semiconductor material with a high concentration of electrons at one end and a high concentration of holes at the other. We can say that electrons have moved to the positive end of the block, while holes have moved to the negative end.

In the pure semiconductor, all available carriers, holes and electrons, are the result of heat-broken bonds. Conduction can be *controlled* by providing controlled amount of electrons (or holes) that do not depend on heat for their freedom.

8.3 N-TYPE SILICON

If a small quantity of some impurity with five valence electrons is introduced into the silicon crystal, there is a gain of one free electron. Figure 8–4 is a sketch that shows this condition.

The atom in the center is called a *donor atom* because it donates one free electron. In addition to having five valence electrons, the donor atoms must fit into the crystal struc-

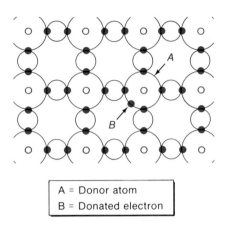

A = Donor atom
B = Donated electron

Figure 8–4 N-type silicon crystal and donor atoms.

ture easily. This restricts available donors to three elements—arsenic, phosphorus, and antimony. One impurity atom is added to each one hundred thousand to one million atoms of silicon.

With one donor atom per million silicon atoms, a cubic centimeter block would have 10^{16} free electrons contributed by the donors. In addition to the donated electrons, there are about 10^{10} electrons that have been freed owing to heat-ruptured bonds. The majority of the electrons available come from the donors and are free at all temperatures above absolute zero. At room temperature there are 10^{16} donor electrons and about one-millionth of that number that are the result of broken bonds. Donor electrons are in the majority, and their number is essentially constant at all usual temperatures ($0.05\ e$V is required to free them). Adding donor atoms, called *doping,* creates a less temperature-sensitive semiconductor. Because there are more electrons than holes, and because the electrons carry a negative charge, a semiconductor doped with donor-type atoms is called *N-type* (N for negative). The N-type semiconductor contains only free electrons at absolute zero, but at normal temperatures heat-ruptured bonds yield electron-hole pairs. The thermally produced electrons simply join the donor electrons. The holes move in a direction opposite to the direction taken by the electrons.

8.4 P-TYPE SILICON

In order to make practical semiconductor devices, we need another type of semiconductor. This complementary type is called the *P-type;* it has only free holes (at absolute zero) and no free electrons. P-type semiconductors are also made by doping the pure silicon. However, the doping atoms have only three valence electrons. These doping atoms are called *acceptors,* because each one contributes a dangling bond (or hole). These holes can accept electrons supplied from outside the block. Figure 8–5 shows the P-type silicon crystal and acceptor atoms.

The P-type dangling bonds (holes) created by the impurity atoms can accept electrons, which must be supplied by an external battery (or power supply) if current is to flow through the P-type crystal. This is true because P-type silicon has no free electrons.

Figure 8–6 describes conduction and nonconduction states for pure silicon, silicon doped with donor impurities, and for silicon doped with acceptor impurities. P-type dopants are aluminum, boron, gallium, and indium.

8.5 THE P–N JUNCTION DIODE

The junction diode is made by joining a block of P-type semiconductor with a block of N-type semiconductor in a continuous crystalline structure.

The manufacturing process starts by diffusing donor and acceptor impurities into a block of pure silicon (or germanium). The diffusion is accomplished at temperatures

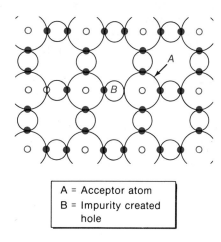

A = Acceptor atom
B = Impurity created hole

Figure 8-5 P-type silicon crystal and acceptor created hole.

near 1000° C. P-type (acceptor) impurities are introduced into one end while N-type (donor) impurities are introduced into the other end of the block. Within the block there is an abrupt transition from P-type to N-type material. This transition is called a *junction.* Figure 8–7 shows the junction diode. The junction diode is essentially a one-way electrical valve, also called a *rectifier.*

Any distinction between diode characteristics and junction characteristics is found only in power, current, and voltage ratings.

The Depletion Zone

When the crystal is formed, electrons begin to diffuse into holes, forming a transition or depletion zone that contains neither free electrons nor holes. The process is self-arresting and ceases on completion of a very narrow transition zone.

In the sketch in Figure 8–8, as the transition zone grows wider, electrons must cross a widening gap where electrons and holes are few and far between. The amount of recombination decreases exponentially

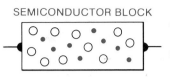

SEMICONDUCTOR BLOCK

• ELECTRON
○ HOLE (DANGLING BOND)
◉ A HOLE THAT HAS CAPTURED AN ELECTRON

CONDITIONS:

1. All carriers, electrons, and holes are heat generated.
2. Electrons and holes are generated in pairs, and are distributed evenly through the block.

(A) Pure silicon with no emf applied.

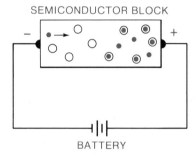

BATTERY

Conditions:

1. All carriers, electrons, and holes are heat generated.
2. Electrons and holes are equal in number because they are always formed in pairs.
3. Free electrons are attracted to the positive end of the block, filling nearly all the holes in the positive end.
4. Electrons in the positive end of the block that have not been captured by holes are returned to the positive end of the battery.
5. Electrons enter the negative end of the block from the battery and move from hole to hole toward the positive end of the block.
6. The amount of current is a function of temperature and increases exponentially as the temperature increases.

(B) Pure silicon with emf applied.

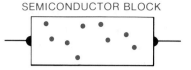

SEMICONDUCTOR BLOCK

Conditions:

1. N-type silicon has only free electrons, no holes.
2. These free electrons are free at most ordinary temperatures, and conduction is not appreciably dependent on temperature when a potential is applied.

(C) N-type silicon with no emf applied.

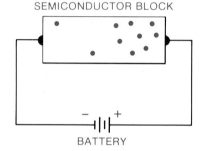

SEMICONDUCTOR BLOCK

BATTERY

Conditions:

1. Electrons are attracted to the positive end of the block. Electrons in the block are supplied by five valent impurity atoms.
2. Conduction is not much influenced by temperature.
3. A few holes, approximately one for each million electrons, exist as the result of heat-ruptured covalent bonds.

(D) N-type silicon with emf applied.

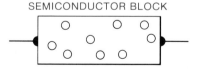

SEMICONDUCTOR BLOCK

Conditions:

1. The P-type semiconductor has only holes, no electrons (at absolute zero). Holes are provided by trivalent impurity atoms.
2. Some electrons exist in the free state owing to heat-ruptured covalent bonds, but the number is very small compared to the number of holes supplied by the donor atoms.

(E) P-type silicon with no emf applied.

Figure 8-6 Conduction in silicon.

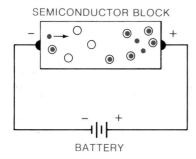

SEMICONDUCTOR BLOCK

BATTERY

Conditions:

1. All the electrons involved in conduction must be supplied from outside the block, in this case by the battery.

2. Electrons injected into the block move freely in and out of available holes.

3. The holes are supplied by trivalent dopant atoms.

   Conductivity is not a function of temperature, except that owing to the small number of additional carriers produced by heat ruptured covalent bonds.

   (F) P-type silicon with emf applied.

Figure 8-6 continued

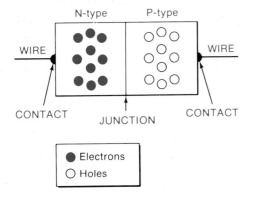

Figure 8-7 The junction diode.

as the distance away from the junction increases. The exponential gradient is shown by the curve in Figure 8–8.

The N and P regions are electrically neutral in the beginning, but as the crystal is formed, electrons diffuse across the junction and fall into holes on the other side. The

N side loses some of its free electrons to holes on the P side, leaving the N side slightly positive. This makes the zone next to the junction on the P side slightly negative because of the electrons that have come from the N side. In silicon a potential barrier equal to approximately 0.6 V is formed. Further movement across the junction is prevented until an external voltage greater than the 0.6 V barrier potential is applied across the diode. The barrier voltage is always 0.6 volts for silicon and 0.25 volts for germanium.

The important thing to remember about the depletion zone is that it sets a minimum threshold potential. Current cannot flow through a silicon junction diode until a potential of approximately 0.6 V is applied across the silicon junction. This critical voltage is sometimes called the *hook voltage* or *potential hill voltage*.

Figure 8–9 shows the diode schematic symbol and outline drawings of several common silicon diode types.

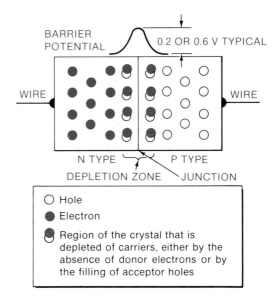

Figure 8-8 The depletion zone.

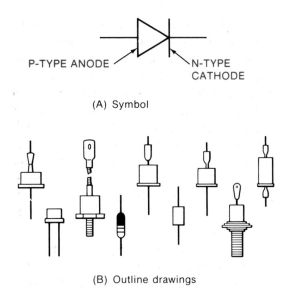

(A) Symbol

(B) Outline drawings

Figure 8-9 Diode symbol and outline drawings.

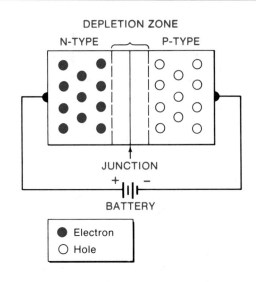

Figure 8-10 The reverse-biased diode.

The Reverse-Bias Diode

The reverse-bias condition is the "off" or nonconduction condition. Figure 8–10 shows the reverse-bias battery polarity and the hole and electron distributions in a reverse-bias junction diode.

As the diagram shows, electrons are attracted to the positive pole of the battery at the right end of the drawing. The holes in the P end of the block are attracted to the negative pole of the battery, shown at the left end of the drawing. The holes and electrons withdraw from the junction, leaving an area that is almost completely depleted of carriers. This area is known as the depletion zone. The higher the reverse-bias voltage, the wider the depletion zone becomes. The depletion zone is essentially an insulator; it has no available carriers. No current flows through the junction area in the reverse-bias condition.

Junction Capacitance

A capacitor consists of two conductive plates separated by an insulating material (dielectric). A reverse-bias diode meets these requirements. It has two areas that are rich in carriers (conductors), separated by the depletion zone, which has no available carriers and is therefore an insulator. The dielectric constant of a silicon depletion zone is approximately 12. The amount of capacitance in a junction diode is small enough so that it becomes important only at high frequencies. Special junction diodes are manufactured in such a way as to provide fairly high capacitances.

These diodes are used as voltage-variable capacitors in oscillator tank circuits and other applications. The capacitance of a reverse-bias junction is varied by varying the bias voltage. Increasing the voltage increases the width of the depletion zone and decreases the capacitance.

The Forward-Bias Diode

The forward-bias condition is the conducting condition. Figure 8–11 shows the battery polarity and the distribution of electrons and holes in the forward-bias connection.

The negative field at the N end of the

device repels the free electrons toward the junction. The positive field at the P end of the block repels the holes toward the junction. The arrows within the block (Fig. 8-11) show the direction of carrier movements within the block. The arrows outside the block show the direction of electron movement. If the battery voltage is higher than the (graphical) hook voltage (0.6 V for silicon), electrons are forced through the transition zone across the junction and into the P region. An electron crossing the junction into the P region is captured by a hole. The electron has left the N region, leaving it one electron short. The N crystal, which was electrically neutral, now becomes one unit positive because the crystal now has one more proton than it has electrons. This positive charge draws an electron from the negative terminal of the battery. One electron has left the battery. At the P side of the block, the electron has dropped into a hole. Once the hole is filled, it is no longer a hole. One hole has been lost while an electron has been gained by the P crystal. The P side of the crystal now has an excess electron and consequently a unit negative charge. The positive terminal of the battery draws an electron out of the right-hand end of the block to restore the charge balance in the P end of the crystal. One electron has left the negative battery terminal, and one electron has returned to the positive battery terminal. If we can visualize some 10^{14} to 10^{19} electrons crossing the junction, we have a rough picture of forward-bias diode action. Forward bias is the conducting condition for a junction diode.

Reverse Bias Leakage Current

An electron that has been freed by heat energy leaves a hole. Heat energy always generates an electron-hole pair. This is true in both P and N ends of the crystal. Figure 8-12 shows a reverse-bias diode with elec-

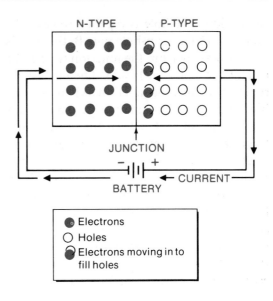

Figure 8-11 The forward-biased diode.

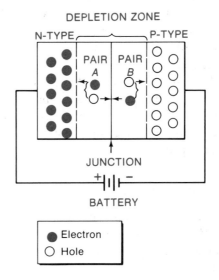

Figure 8-12 Reverse bias leakage current.

tron-hole pairs being thermally generated within the depletion zone.

The arrows in Figure 8-12 show the direction of carrier movement under the influence of the field produced by the battery. If you examine electron-hole pair A, you will see that the electron moves away from the junction to join the rest of the electrons on the N side. The hole is repelled toward the junction. In electron-hole pair B, the hole is attracted away from the junction to join the rest of the holes on P side. The electron is repelled toward the junction, where it combines with the hole from pair A. This upsets the balance in each side of the crystal, and the negative pole of the battery delivers an electron to the P end of the crystal and the positive pole draws one electron from the N side of the crystal. One-half of the electron-hole pair A is forward-biased. These carriers (the electron on the right and the hole on the left in Figure 8–12) constitute a current flow called *leakage current*. The other half of each *pair* is reverse-biased and does not cause any current flow.

This leakage current is the sole current in the reverse-bias direction. It is normally from 1/10,000 to 1/10,000,000 as much as the forward-bias current. The amount of leakage current increases exponentially with temperature.

In a junction diode leakage currents are generally of little importance, but the transistor has the ability to amplify, and leakage currents amplified by a factor of 100 or more can be a problem.

The Diode Conduction Curve

In order to understand the practical ratings of diodes, it is essential to understand both forward and reverse bias voltage/current relationships.

The best way to describe these relationships is to draw a graph, as in Figure 8–13. In the upper righthand quadrant, you will notice that almost no current flows until the hook voltage is reached. The small current that does flow is due to heat-generated electron-hole pairs within the depletion zone. When the hook voltage is reached, a small increase in forward-bias voltage results in a large increase in current. Notice

that the curve is not linear, and that means that the resistance of the junction changes as the voltage across the junction changes.

If the graph had numerical values and we were to calculate junction resistance $(R = E/I)$ at several points along the graph, we would find that the junction resistance *decreases* as the voltage *increases*. This change in junction resistance is of little concern in a junction diode, but when it is the forward-biased junction in a transistor, the small change is magnified many times by the amplification of the transistor.

Notice also that the forward-conduction curve rises steeply and shows no sign of leveling off, indicating theoretically that there is no limit to the current. The practical limit to diode current is internal temperature (junction temperature). The junction literally melts when a sufficiently high current flows through the junction resistance. When the junction melts locally, the diode becomes shorted. Diodes rarely open and any diode failure will likely be a short.

To avoid excessive junction temperature, the manufacturer's instructions concerning maximum voltage, current, and mounting arrangements are extremely important. It is a good idea to operate only up to 80 percent of the manufacturer's maximum ratings. The important points along the forward-bias curve are the hook voltage and the variation in junction resistance (the nonlinearity and slope of the curve.)

The Zener/Avalanche Part of the Curve

Now let us examine the reverse-bias part of the curve in the lower left quadrant of Figure 8–12. Notice that increasing the reverse-bias voltage increases the reverse current only slightly until a critical voltage called the *zener point* is reached. At the zener *knee* of the curve the current suddenly rises from microamperes to milliamperes or amperes.

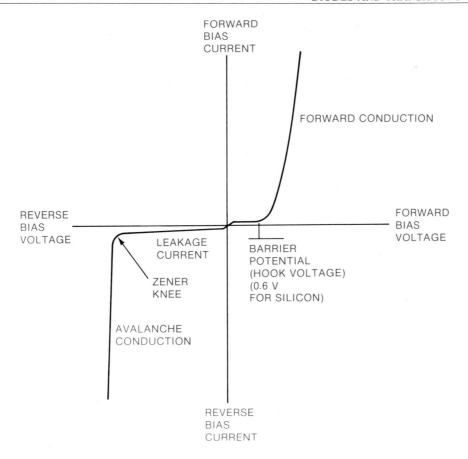

Figure 8-13 The diode conduction curve.

There are two principal mechanisms involved in production of this current: *field emission (Zener's theory)* and *ionization by collision.*

As the voltage is increased in the reverse-bias direction, the depletion zone becomes wider. At some critical point the field is large enough and the path a carrier can travel without colliding with an atom is long enough so that an electron can gain sufficient momentum to strip electrons from atoms with which it collides. The dislodged electrons pick up speed until they collide with other atoms, liberating still more electrons. Figure 8–14 is a sketch of this process. The mechanism is called *avalanche* because

it builds up like an avalanche.

The carriers that initiate the avalanche process are heat-generated minority carriers in the depletion zone.

Special devices such as zener diodes and silicon controlled rectifiers (SCRs) are designed to operate in the zener/avalanche part of the curve. For other diodes (and transistors), operation in the zener/avalanche part of the curve destroys the junction.

Zener diodes can be made with the zener knee at almost any desired voltage, although zeners for over 50 volts are likely to be rare and very expensive. Zener diodes make excellent voltage regulators because, unlike a resistor, the voltage drop across a zener diode is constant over a wide range of currents.

Figure 8–15 shows a typical zener diode regulator circuit.

Junction Switching Times

One of the specifications sometimes given for certain diodes and transistors is recovery time. It takes time to switch a junction from a forward to a reverse-bias condition; that is, from a conducting to a nonconducting state. (The reverse is true also.) This specification is important to computer devices and others whose operations involve rapid turn-on or turn-off.

When a junction is forward-biased, the depletion zone is filled with carriers because of the large number of recombinations (holes and electrons) taking place at the junction. If the bias is suddenly removed, conduction does not cease instantly, because the nonconducting state cannot be obtained until carriers have been cleared out of the depletion zone.

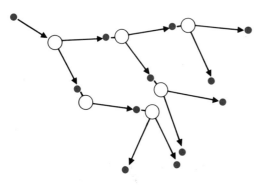

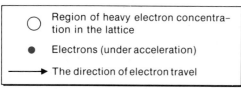

Figure 8-14 Avalanche mechanism.

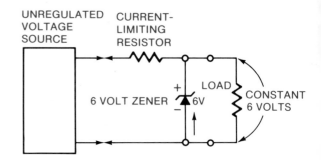

ZENER DIODE SYMBOLS:

Figure 8-15 Zener diode voltage regulator.

This short period of current flow after the bias has dropped to zero is called *storage time.*

There is also time involved in switching from a reverse-bias to a forward-bias state. This delay is due to the fact that the junction capacitance absorbs the initial forward-bias current in the process of taking on a charge. After the charging is "complete," current becomes available for normal conduction.

Forward Bias Junction Resistance

The junction resistance of a forward-bias diode is the effective resistance of the depletion zone. It is dependent not only upon temperature, but also upon the operating current. An empirical equation derived by Shockley gives the junction resistance as

$$R_j = \frac{25 \ (mV)}{I \ (mA)}$$

R_j = junction resistance
25 = a constant
I = current through the diode

The Shockley relationship is only approximate, but it is the only practical evaluation of junction resistance available.

Reverse-bias Junction Resistance

The reverse-bias diode is very nearly an open circuit. The resistance varies from many megohms for diodes to about one megohm for reverse-bias transistor junctions.

8.6 TRANSISTORS (BIPOLAR)

The transistor is a most imprecise device and requires careful circuit design to make it practical. Temperature sensitivity is an important problem in transistors, and one that must be solved by the circuit designer. The problem cannot be solved by the manufacturer.

In this section we will examine these transistor actions, their temperature variations, and some circuits that make them work.

Transistor Construction

The transistor consists of two junctions in a continuous crystal. Placing either a P or an N between two opposite types results in a PNP or an NPN triode transistor. See Figure 8–16. A contact is made to each crystal area, making it a three-terminal device. One "end" block is called the emitter, the middle block is called the base, and the other "end" block is called the collector. The middle section is called the base. The base region of the crystal is very thin, 0.8 microns or less. This thin base region is essential to normal transistor operation, as we shall see shortly. Twenty-five microns is approximately equal to 0.001 inch.

Figure 8–16 diagrams the two transistor types and shows their symbols, one typical structure, and some typical case styles.

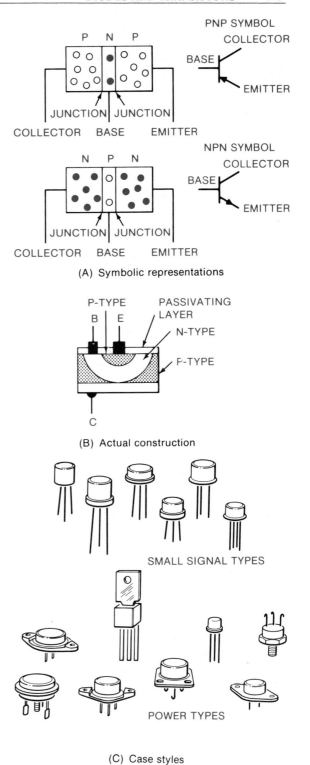

(A) Symbolic representations

(B) Actual construction

(C) Case styles

Figure 8-16 The structure of the transistor.

Transistor Amplification

For the following discussion, please refer to Figure 8–17 and keep the following facts in mind:

1. The base region is very thin and has few available holes (in the example, the base region is the P type).
2. The base is lightly doped, reducing the number of available holes still further.

Assume that the base-emitter bias is less than the hook voltage of the base-emitter junction. The base-emitter junction is therefore reverse-biased, and there is no base-emitter current.

The collector-base junction is reverse-biased by, let's say, 10 V. Thus, there is no collector-base current flowing. There is also no emitter-to-collector current flowing because both junctions are reverse-biased.

So far the transistor has been in the off condition. Now let us bring the emitter-base bias voltage up above the hook voltage, forward-biasing the junction and starting base-emitter current flow. A great many electrons are drawn through the emitter block toward the junction. These electrons arrive at the junction to find that holes are sparse in the base region. Those electrons that find holes in the base region combine with them and result in base current like any forward-biased junction. For each 100 electrons drawn into the base region, there are only enough holes in the base to capture a fraction (one percent or less) of them. The rest of them cannot go back to the emitter, because the field is pushing them away. These un-combined electrons gather near the collector-base junction, where they are attracted by the positive field of the collector battery. They are drawn into the collector, causing an emitter-to-collector current to flow. Electrons leaving the emitter block take two paths. About 1 percent combine with holes in the base to form base-emitter current, while most of them move through the collector block to form an emitter-collector current.

The large emitter-collector current is dependent upon the flow of the much smaller emitter-base current. If the base-emitter voltage is increased slightly, more electrons are drawn into the base region; far more than the base can use. The result is a small increase in base current and a much larger increase in collector current. This current gain is called *beta* (β).

Transistor Parameters

In addition to β, the transistor's current gain, there are several other important parameters and definitions to examine.

Currents

I_c: The collector current

Note: The collector and emitter currents are approximately equal.

I_b: The base current

I_e: The emitter current

I_e: The emitter current

$$(I_e = I_c = I_b)$$

I_c (*max*): The manufacturer's absolute maximum steady-state collector current. Normal operation is at less than 40 percent of this figure.

E_c (*max*): The manufacturer's absolute maximum rating for the reverse-bias voltage across the collector-base junction. Even an instantaneous excess can destroy the transistor.

Current Gains

a. For common collector and common emitter circuits (see Figure 8–18):

β (beta): The current gain of the transistor in the common-emitter and common-collector configurations. Range: 10 to 200.

$$\beta = \frac{I_c}{I_b} \text{ (a simple ratio, no dimension)}$$

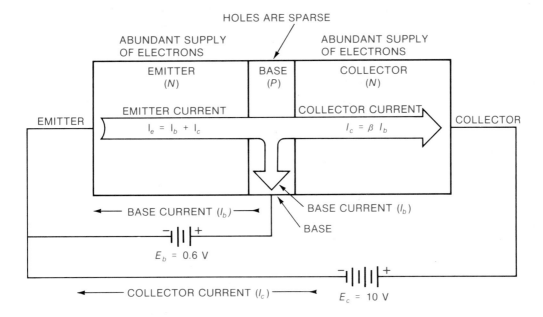

HOLES ARE SPARSE

ABUNDANT SUPPLY
OF ELECTRONS

ABUNDANT SUPPLY
OF ELECTRONS

| EMITTER (N) | BASE (P) | COLLECTOR (N) |

EMITTER CURRENT
$I_e = I_b + I_c$

COLLECTOR CURRENT
$I_c = \beta\, I_b$

EMITTER

COLLECTOR

BASE CURRENT (I_b)

BASE CURRENT (I_b)

BASE

$E_b = 0.6$ V

COLLECTOR CURRENT (I_c)

$E_c = 10$ V

Figure 8–17 Transistor amplification.

Note:

I_g: The current gain of the complete circuit I_g is always less than β.

b. For the common base circuit (see Figure 8–18):

α (alpha): The intrinsic current gain in the common-base configuration. Range: from 0.9 to a limit of 1.

$$\alpha = \frac{I_c}{I_e} \text{ (a simple ratio, no dimension)}$$

Note: The common base circuit is not often used.

Junction Resistances

a. Base-emitter junction:

R_e': The forward-biased base-emitter junction resistance.

$$R_e' = \frac{25\ (mV)}{I_c\ (mA)}$$

(the Shockley relationship)

R_e' is in ohms. Range: 100 ohms to 5,000 ohms

b. Collector-base junction:

The collector-base junction is always reverse-biased and always has a resistance of from one to two megohms.

Leakage Current

I_{co}: The reverse-bias leakage current of the collector-base junction. Because the leakage current results from thermally produced carriers, the temperature is normally stated as part of the parameter. The emitter is not connected. The symbol I_{cbo} is sometimes used instead of I_{co}.

8.7 TRANSISTOR CIRCUIT CHARACTERISTICS

There are three basic transistor circuits; common emitter, common collector, and common base. The common emitter circuit (Figure 8–18A) is the most popular and the one most often used.

The common collector circuit (Figure 8–18B) is a special circuit and is used only where a high input resistance and low output

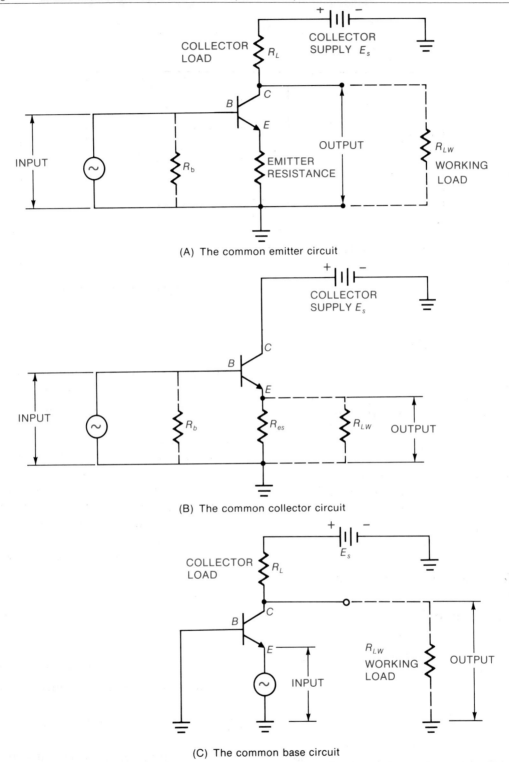

(A) The common emitter circuit

(B) The common collector circuit

(C) The common base circuit

Figure 8-18 The three transistor amplifier configurations.

resistance is required. It does not provide any voltage amplification.

The common base circuit is rarely used because of its extremely low input resistance. Its use is generally restricted to those circuits where the input can be driven by a transformer. This is too costly for most applications.

Circuit Current Gain

Because of the heat sensitive nature of the base emitter junction, and of beta, it is necessary to provide resistance in the base and emitter circuits to stabilize the transistor. The addition of these reduces current gain to between 1 and 10. Except in the common collector circuit, no effort is made to use the current gain if there is any. In order to see why stabilization is necessary, suppose we examine how beta and the junction voltage vary. Beta variations are the ratio of collector current to base current:

$$\beta = \frac{I_c}{I_b}$$

Beta varies with collector current and temperature, and from transistor to transistor of the same type number.

Beta increases with temperature at the rate of about 1% per degree C rise in temperature. This is illustrated in the curve in Figure 8–19A. Beta is also different for different collector currents as shown in Figure 8–19B.

Because beta is completely undependable, we must generally ignore current gain and concentrate on voltage gain. There are but few instances where we cannot use amplification in the form of voltage gain as satisfactorily as current gain. We can, in those rare cases, fall back on the com-

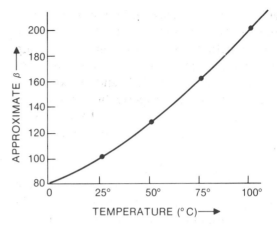

(A) Variations in beta with temperature

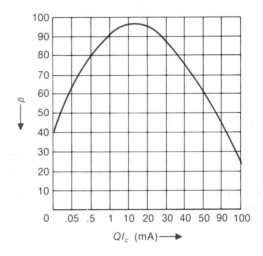

(B) Variations in beta with collector current

Figure 8–19 Variations in beta with temperature and collector current.

mon collector (often called *emitter-follower*) circuit.

Voltage Gain in the Common Emitter Circuit

The transistor can be used as a voltage amplifier because of the large collector supply voltage. The base-emitter circuit requires a range of only a few tenths of a volt to vary the base-emitter junction current from zero to maximum. The collector-base junction may be capable of handling a voltage of from 10 to 50 V (sometimes more). In Figure 8–20A and B, we see a transistor that is properly biased and has a collector supply voltage of 10 V (a typical value) and a collector load resistor of 1 $k\Omega$.

In Figure 8–20A, there is 0 V of base-emitter bias voltage. This means that there is no base-emitter current, and consequently no collector current. Under these conditions there is no voltage drop across the collector load resistor (R_L). (Assume a second fixed bias voltage that is within a millivolt of overcoming the barrier potential.)

$$E = IR; E = 0 \times 1\ k = 0\ V$$

Therefore, the output voltage will be equal to the supply voltage, in this case 10 V.

For Figure 8–20 assume that increasing the base bias battery voltage from 0 V to 0.6 V causes enough base-emitter current to flow to result in 10 mA of collector current. These figures are fairly typical.

With 10 mA of current flowing through the 1 $k\Omega$ collector load resistor (R_L), Ohm's law tells us that the voltage drop across R_L is 10 V:

$$E = IR; E = 1.0\ k \times 10\ mA = 10\ V$$

If the entire supply voltage is dropped across the collector load resistor, the voltage drop across the transistor, and consequently the output voltage, must be 0 V. The voltage gain is equal to the change in output voltage divided by the change in input voltage.

$$\text{Voltage gain} = \frac{\Delta\ \text{output voltage}}{\Delta\ \text{input voltage}} = \frac{\Delta E_o}{\Delta E_{in}}$$

In this example the change in input voltage is 0.6 V, $\Delta E_{in} = 0.6$ V.

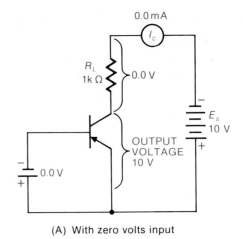

(A) With zero volts input

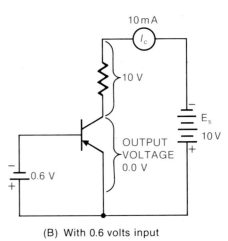

(B) With 0.6 volts input

Figure 8-20 Voltage gain.

The voltage gain of the circuit is

$$V_g = \frac{\Delta E_o}{\Delta E_{in}} = \frac{10\ V}{0.6\ V} = 16.66$$

Practical voltage gains range from 2 to several hundred, depending upon the circuit design.

This discussion pertains to the voltage gain of the common-emitter circuit. It is also valid for the common-base circuit (the common-collector circuit always has a voltage gain of about 1).

Input Impedence

The input impedance is equal to the emitter to ground resistance multiplied by the current gain (beta) of the transistor. Calculated input impedances are only approximate because of the normal uncertainty about the true value of beta. As a rule, the estimate given by the following formula is adequate for practical purposes:

$$Z_{in} = \text{beta } (R_e{}' + R_e)$$

Where: $R_e{}'$ is the base-emitter junction resistance; $R_e{}' = 25 \text{ mA}/I_c$; and R_e is any external emitter resistance, as shown in Figure 8–21. A capacitor is shown by dotted lines in Figure 8–21. Because input impedance is an ac value, a high-value capacitor (10 to 500 µF) effectively shorts the external emitter resistor. The equation for the circuit with the bypass capacitor connected becomes

$$Z_{in} = \text{beta } (R_e{}')$$

Calculating Voltage Gain

The base-emitter circuit is the input and the collector-emitter circuit is the output. The general formula for voltage gain is

$$V_g = \frac{E_{out}}{E_{in}}$$

or

$$A = \frac{V_{out}}{V_{in}}$$

If the same current flows through two resistors, the voltage drop across each is proportional to their resistance, whatever the actual current (Ohms law, series circuits).

Note: Both A and V_g are used for voltage gain. Either V or E may be used for volts. Because collectors and emitter currents are

always equal (approximately), we can calculate the voltage gain by the simple formula

$$\text{Voltage gain} = \frac{\text{Collectors resistance}}{\text{Emitter resistance}}$$

For an unbypassed circuit line, like that in Figure 8–21, the equation is

$$V_g = \frac{R_L}{R_E}$$

The external emitter resistance is so much larger than $R_e{}'$ in a properly designed circuit that it is convenient to omit $R_e{}'$ from the equation. When the external resistor $R_e{}'$ is shorted for ac by the bypass capacitor (C_{bp}), $R_e{}'$ becomes the only emitter resistance in the circuit and the equation must be written as

$$V_g = \frac{R_L}{R_e{}'}$$

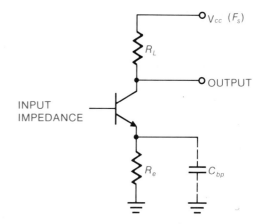

Input impedance	Voltage gain
(A) Unbypassed	(A) Unbypassed
$Z_{in} = \text{beta} \times R_e$	$V_g = R_L/R_e$
(B) Bypassed	(B) Bypassed
$Z_{in} = \text{beta} \times R^1{}_e$	$V_g = R_L/R^1{}_e$

Figure 8-21 Circuit for input impedance and voltage gain explanation.

Bias and Stability

Any practical circuit must be biased to a particular idling collector current. The circuit must also be stabilized against beta variations and changes base-emitter junction voltage.

Figure 8–22 shows the practical circuit for the two most common bias and stability schemes. In Figure 8–22A R_{b1} serves as the bias resistor. R_{b2} and R_e are the stability resistors. R_e must have at least 1 volt drop across it. When the transistor is operating, the higher this voltage drop is the more tolerant the circuit will be of base-emitter junction voltage variations caused by temperature changes.

The resistor R_{b2} stabilizes against beta variations. The measure of the circuit's ability to compensate for changes in beta is called the *stability factor (S)*.

$$S = \frac{R_{b2}}{R_e}$$

If the circuit is to be stable the value of S cannot exceed 10.

In Figure 8–22B, resistor R_e serves as both the bias resistor and the junction voltage stability resistor. In this circuit the stability factor is also $S = R_{b2}/R_e$. Again S cannot exceed 10 and is generally 1 or less. This bias scheme requires two power supplies, and because of that extra cost it is restricted to specialized circuits.

Input Impedance of the Complete Circuit

The addition of R_{b2} in Figure 8–22 lowers the input impedance because it is effectively in parallel with (beta $\times$ R_e). The input impedance equation with R_{b2} added is

$$Z_{in} = R_{b2} \parallel (\text{beta} \times R_e)$$

($\parallel$ means "in parallel with")

or

$$\frac{R_1 \times R_2}{R_1 + R_2}$$

The Voltage Mode Circuit

Figure 8–23 shows a variation of the common emitter circuit. The stability factor in this case is

$$S = \frac{R_{b1}}{R_L}$$

The voltage gain and input impedance of the circuit in Figure 8–23 are approximately the same as for the fully bypassed circuit in Figure 8–21. R_e must have at least a 1 volt drop for junction voltage stability.

Figure 8–24 shows practical common collector and common base circuits. The stability factor in both circuits is the same as for the common emitter circuit.

The voltage gain for the common base circuit is the same as that of the common emitter circuit ($V_g = R_L/R_e'$). The voltage gain of the common collector circuit is always equal to 1 (unity).

The input impedance for the common collector circuit is the same as for the common emitter circuit, $Z_{in} = R_{b2} \parallel (\text{beta} \times R_e)$. The input impedance for the common base circuit = R_e', typically 25 to 50 ohms. This is much too low for most applications.

8.8 FIELD EFFECT TRANSISTORS

Field effect transistors (FETs) find their application where very high input impedances are required but where relatively low voltage gains can be tolerated. They are often found in measuring instruments, TV tuners, and in other places where very high input impedances are essential.

Like bipolar transistors, the FET must

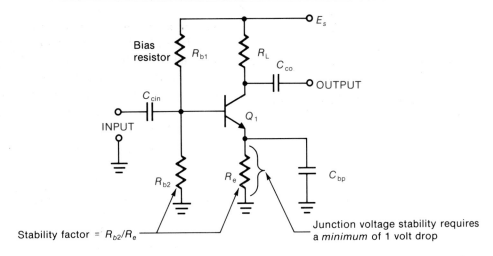

(A) Base bias (common emitter).

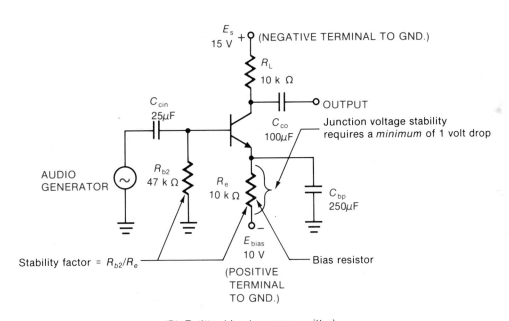

(B) Emitter bias (common emitter)

Figure 8-22 Bias and stability.

also be stabilized against variations in its parameters. There are two types of FET devices in current use, *junction field effect (JFET)* and *metal oxide semiconductor (MOSFET)*.

Junction Field Effect Transistors

Junction-type FETs are formed as a thin bar of silicon called the *channel* and a diffused-in diode called the *gate*. As shown in Figure 8–25, the channel is reduced to a narrow gate region by diffusing-in a diode

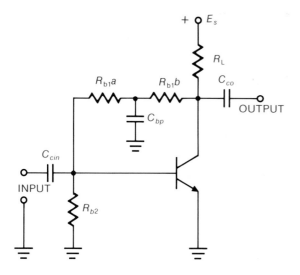

Figure 8-23 The voltage mode circuit.

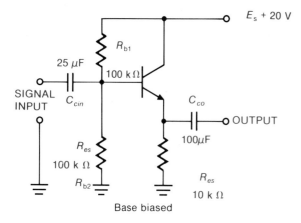

Base biased

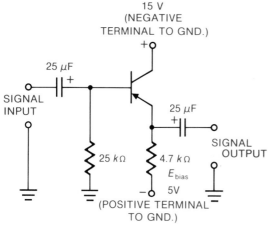

Emitter biased

(A) Common collector circuits

on opposite sides of the channel.

Junction FETs are made as either N-channel or P-channel devices. The symbols are shown in Figure 8–26. A voltage is applied that reverse-biases the gate diode and creates a field capable of pinching off current flow through the channel. Because the gate diode is reverse-biased, the device has a high input impedance. The FET can be operated without any bias unless the peak input signal forward drives the gate by more than 0.6 V. For higher voltage input signals, we must bias the device at the expense of reduced voltage gain.

P-channel and N-channel devices require opposite polarities. We can remember the drain polarity by noting that the arrow on the symbol points in to a positive drain and away from a negative drain.

MOSFETs

Metal oxide semiconductors (MOSFETs) are similar to the junction FETs except that the gate is a small, high-quality capaci-

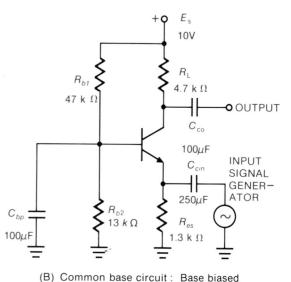

(B) Common base circuit : Base biased

Figure 8-24 Common base and common collector circuits.

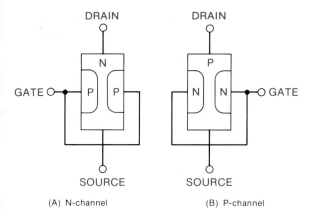

(A) N-channel

(B) P-channel

Figure 8-25 The junction FET.

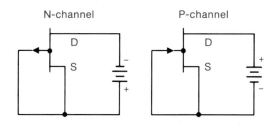

Figure 8-26 Junction FET symbols and polarities.

tor that controls the current flow in the channel without the usual leakage problems of a gate diode. To control the channel current by an electric field, the capacitor must have small dimensions and the silicon dioxide dielectric must be a very thin layer. It consequently has a low breakdown voltage (about 30 V). The gate capacitance is low, and leakage resistance so high, that the gate is easily charged to a voltage above the zener knee.

Gate damage is prevented by using a grounded soldering iron and by protecting the gate from static charges. Insulated-gate FETs should be handled by the case rather than by the leads. The leads should be shorted together during shipping or storing by foil, a wire loop, or conductive styro-

foam. Some MOSFETS have built-in Zener diodes to protect the gate, but precautions are still required in the use of MOS devices.

MOS devices are available in two forms, *depletion mode* and *enhancement mode*. The depletion mode device is normally conducting through the channel and a gate bias voltage must be applied to reduce or cut off the channel current. The enhancement mode device is normally off, and a gate bias voltage is required to start current flowing through the channel. Figure 8–27 shows the construction of a depletion mode MOSFET. The construction of the enhancement mode device is similar, except that no channel exists until the gate field draws carriers up out of the substrate to form one.

Common Source FET Amplifier

Figure 8–28 shows a basic common source depletion mode amplifier circuit. The common source circuit in FETs is the equivalent of a common emitter circuit in the bipolar transistor discussed earlier. The circuit includes typical values and produces a voltage gain of (approximately) 10 with

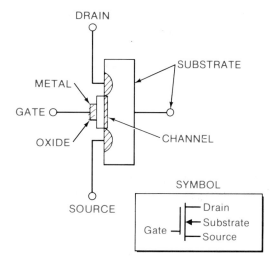

Figure 8-27 The depletion mode MOS-FET.

the bypass capacitor connected.

The input impedance of the FET in Figure 8–28 is so high that the 1 megohm resistor determines the input impedance. This resistor can be increased by a factor of 10 without effecting the rest of the circuit.

Voltage Gain

The voltage gain with the bypass capacitor connected is

$$V_g = G_m R_L$$

where G_m is the mutual conductance (transconductance) obtained from the manufacturer's data manual; the G_m for the 2N3086, for example, is from 400 to 1,200 μ mhos. This wide variation is typical of FET devices.

The voltage gain without the bypass capacitor connected is

$$V_g = f_b \times \frac{R_S}{R_L}$$

where f_b = the feedback factor.

Feedback Factor and Stability

In order for the circuit in Figure 8–28 to be stable, the feedback factor must be 0.75 (75%) or greater.

The feedback factor equation is

$$f_b = \frac{R_S}{R_L}$$

Enhancement Mode Amplifier

The enhancement mode FET is connected in the voltage mode bias circuit. The voltage gain is:

$$V_g = G_m R_L$$

See Figure 8–29 for schematic diagram.

The feedback factor required for stability is again 0.75 or more. The feedback factor is given by the equation,

$$f_b = \frac{R_f}{R_L}$$

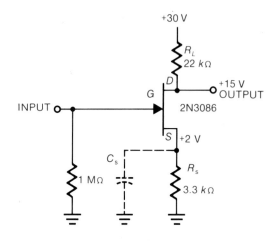

Figure 8-28 FET amplifier (common source).

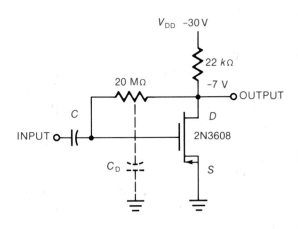

Figure 8-29 Enhancement mode common source amplifier.

SUMMARY

1. Silicon and germanium have four valence electrons.

2. Three valent dopants form a silicon (or germanium) crystal called P-type. Five valent dopant atoms form a silicon (or germanium) crystal called N-type.

3. A P-type crystal has no free electrons (at absolute zero) and the electrons that make up current flow must come from outside the crystal.

4. An N-type crystal has many free electrons contributed by the dopant atoms.

5. Vacancies in the crystal where electrons are missing are called holes. Electrons flow from hole to hole.

6. The simplest practical semiconductor device is a junction diode. The diode is a continuous crystal, part of which is P-type and part N-type.

7. The point of transition in the crystal from P-type to N-type is called a junction. An area around the junction that is free from both holes and electrons is called the depletion zone.

8. Forward-bias is the conducting condition in a junction diode. Reverse-bias is the nonconducting condition.

9. The amplifier figure of merit for bipolar transistors is beta (β). β = collector current divided by base current.

10. The three layers of the bipolar transistor may be arranged as either NPN or PNP.

11. The base region is very thin and lightly doped. Emitter and collector are much larger and more heavily doped.

12. In normal operation, the base-emitter junction is forward-biased and the collector-base junction is reverse-biased.

13. The collector current is always beta times the base current.

14. Because of temperature sensitivity and broad manufacturing tolerances, transistor specifications (parameters) are approximate.

15. Bias is a voltage or current that establishes an idling (quiescent) emitter-collector current.

16. The actual bias point is carefully selected by the circuit designer. Once it is selected, it must be maintained very close to that value.

17. The designer-selected bias point tends to vary with temperature and from transistor to transistor (of the same type number) because of large manufacturing tolerances.

18. The junction field effect transistor consists of a thin channel of N-type (or P-type) and a pair of P-N junctions with the channel forming the N (or P) part of both junctions.

19. In a field effect transistor, the power input element is called the *source*. The control element is the *gate*. The output element is the *drain*.

20. Current through the N-type channel is varied by increasing or decreasing the reverse bias on the two junctions.

21. The off condition of the JFET is called *pinch-off*.

22. The MOSFET consists of a substrate, a channel, and an insulated metal "plate." The metal plate serves as the control element (gate).

23. Control is accomplished by placing a negative charge on the gate that drives electrons out of the channel into the substrate. As electrons are pushed out of the channel, channel current decreases.

REVIEWING YOUR ELECTRONICS VOCABULARY

1. Doping
2. Majority carrier
3. Minority carrier
4. Depletion zone
5. Forward bias
6. Junction capacitance
7. Junction potential
8. Reverse bias
9. Shockley relationship
10. Zener region
11. Base bias
12. Common base
13. Common collector
14. Common emitter
15. Emitter bias

CHECKING YOUR UNDERSTANDING

1. Which factor primarily governs the amount of current flow through a pure semiconductor material?
2. List the common dopant elements.
3. Electron-hole pairs are produced by what kind of energy?
4. What is a dangling bond?
5. List the two ways in which semiconductor circuits can be made less dependent on temperature.
6. What are the most important electrical ratings of a junction diode?
7. How does temperature affect the amount of reverse current in an operating junction-diode circuit?
8. How does temperature affect the amount of forward current in an operating junction-diode circuit?
9. How does voltage affect the amount of current through a reverse-biased junction diode?
10. How does reverse bias influence the junction capacitance?
11. What is the stability factor and what is its maximum value for a stable circuit?
12. Write the input impedance equation for a common emitter, emitter biased, bypassed.
13. Write the input impedance equation for a common collector, emitter biased, not bypassed.

SOLVING ELECTRONIC PROBLEMS

Describe the forward-bias condition of a P-N junction according to the following directions:

1. Make a sketch showing the distribution and direction of travel of the carriers in a forward-biased P-N junction. Show bias potential as applied to the N and P ends of the block.

2. Draw a graph showing the relationship between current (vertical axis) and voltage (horizontal axis). Draw the graph to show conduction in both reverse and forward-bias directions. Label each area of the curve and each point where the curve makes an abrupt change in direction.

CHAPTER 9
Power Supplies

9.1 INTRODUCTION

Almost all electronic equipment operates on direct current (dc). The required dc is often derived from an ac power source such as a commercial power line. The ac line voltage must be rectified, filtered, and often regulated, in order for it to be usable by the equipment. The circuit used to convert ac into suitable dc is known as a *power supply*. The battery in Figure 9–1 is one of the oldest and still common dc power sources. Figures 9–2 and 9–3 show a simple ac power line to a dc power supply output.

In most electronic equipment the power supply is one of the major considerations in making equipment operate properly. Power supply trouble can make the equip-

ment useless or even dangerous.

Figure 9–4 is a block diagram of a power supply that converts ac to dc, then regulates it to a specific constant voltage.

The ac line in Figure 9–3 is fed to the transformer, which changes the 117 volt ac line voltage to the voltage required by the circuit in question. The rectifier then converts the ac source voltage to a pulsating dc. This pulsating dc is fed to the filter where the pulsation levels out. At this point the filtered dc can be used in most types of electronic equipment. When more exact voltage or current is required, a regulator circuit must be added.

9.1 TRANSFORMERS

A transformer is an electrical device that utilizes electromagnetic induction to transfer electrical energy from one electrical circuit to another. Figure 9–5 provides examples of several different types of transformers.

Figure 9-1 A battery power supply.

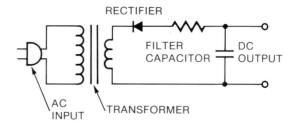

Figure 9-2 Simple power supply.

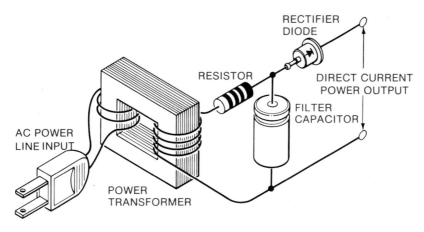

Figure 9-3 Power supply components.

Figure 9-3 Power supply components.

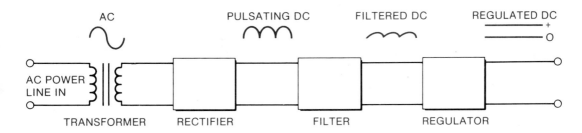

Figure 9-4 Block diagram of a power supply.

Transformers are not limited to voltage step-up or step-down applications. Transformers also can be used as impedance matching devices such as *RF/IF* transformers and audio output transformers.

Isolation

Transformers in power supplies also serve the vital safety function of providing electrical isolation for power-line operated equipment. Some line operated equipment does not use a transformer in its power supply. This results in a shock hazard for anyone working on the equipment. The transformer isolates the equipment from the power line earth ground, greatly reducing the danger of electrocution. There is a special transformer type called an *isolation transformer* that has the same input and output voltages. An isolation transformer should be used when servicing any equipment that is line operated, but uses no power line transformer.

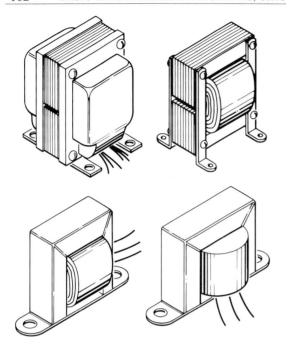

Figure 9-5 Transformer types.

A transformer is used with ac only, except in very special cases. No voltage will be induced in the secondary when a steady dc voltage is applied to the primary. If dc is placed on the primary of a transformer, there will be a voltage induced in the secondary only for the time that the magnetic field is building to maximum and the time when the field is falling after the dc is removed.

There are basically two types of transformers, one with some type of core and one without a core. An air core transformer is normally a radio frequency transformer, and one with a core is an intermediate frequency, audio frequency, or power transformer.

9.2 RECTIFIER CIRCUITS

A rectifier can be either a tube or a semiconductor device. Its function remains the same; to convert the ac input to a pulsating

dc voltage. All rectifiers are rated according to voltage and current capacities.

There are many variations of power supply rectifier circuit arrangements, but they can be generally classified as either low voltage, medium voltage, or high voltage circuits. Within each classification there are three basic rectifier circuit designs; half-wave, full-wave, and bridge rectifier circuits.

The diode vacuum tube has a high internal voltage drop due to fairly high plate resistance values, which limits its use where high values of current are needed. (See Figure 9–6.) The internal resistance can be overcome through the use of solid state diodes. Semiconductors also have internal resistance, but it is much smaller than that of a vacuum diode.

Half-Wave Rectifier Circuits

Figure 9–7 shows two of half-wave rectifier circuit configurations. Part A is a simple diode tube rectifier, and part B is a comparable solid state rectifier circuit.

In the tube type half-wave rectifier shown in part A, when the positive alternation of the input is present at the place of V_1, it makes the plate positive with respect to

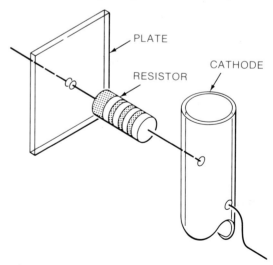

Figure 9-6 A tube has resistance.

the cathode. Thus a pulse of current will flow as shown by the arrows. On the negative alternation of the input waveshape, the plate of the tube is negative. There will be no current flowing, and thus no output voltage, as shown in the output waveshape. As long as there is an input voltage, the tube will continue to conduct on alternate halves of the input cycle. Because current flows only when the plate is positive with respect to the cathode, only one-half of the input voltage is delivered to the output; thus the name half-wave rectifier.

The solid state version of the half-wave rectifier, shown in part B of Figure 9–7, will operate exactly as does the tube version. The diode will conduct only when the anode of D_1 is positive with respect to the cathode.

In our study of ac theory we learned how to determine the peak, output and approximate average voltages. In order to find the peak dc output voltage in a half-wave rectifier circuit. Consider the dc output pulse as follows:

$$E_p = 1.414 \times E_{rms}$$

The voltage is referenced to the bottom of the secondary winding of the transformer.

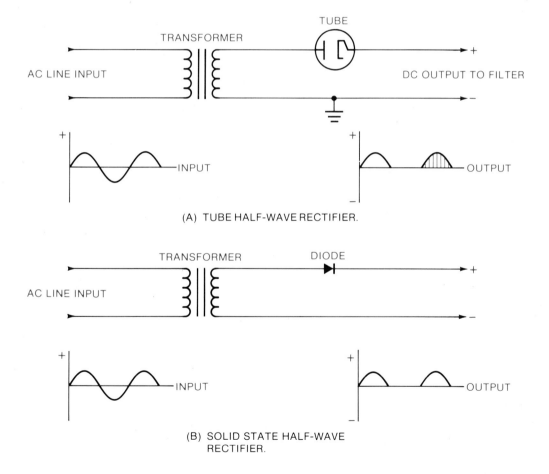

(A) TUBE HALF-WAVE RECTIFIER.

(B) SOLID STATE HALF-WAVE RECTIFIER.

Figure 9-7 Half-wave rectifier.

Example 9–1

Problem: Determine the peak output voltage of a half-wave rectifier circuit with 375 volts rms applied.

Solution:

$$E_p = 1.414 \times 375$$

$$= 530.25 \text{ volts}$$

Now in order to determine the average voltage, we must also use the ac equation,

$$E_{av} = \frac{E_p}{3.14} \quad (E_p = \text{peak voltage})$$

Example 9–2

Problem: Determine the average output voltage of a half-wave rectifier circuit with 375 volts rms applied.

Solution:

$$E_{av} = \frac{530.25}{3.14} = 168.87 \text{ volts}$$

Remember that the voltages found in example 9–2 apply only *before* filtering.

Full-Wave Rectifier

The full-wave rectifier is simply two half-wave rectifiers that function on opposite halves of the input cycle. Another full-wave rectifier circuit, called a *bridge rectifier,* uses a total of four rectifier diodes, working two in opposite directions, one on each half cycle of the input waveform.

Figure 9–8 is the schematic diagram of a full-wave rectifier with a center-tapped transformer using solid-state diodes. When the anode of D_1 is positive with respect to its cathode, it will conduct. This condition exists on the first cycle shown in the waveform in the figure. When conduction occurs, current will flow through D_1 and the load. Because of the negative voltage on the anode of D_2 while D_1 is conducting, D_2 is cut off (not conducting). However, when the second half of the input cycle occurs, D_1 will be cut off and D_2 will conduct. It can be seen that there is conduction through the load during the full cycle of the input waveshape. With the full-wave rectifier circuit using a tapped transformer, we get an output voltage of only half the full secondary voltage. Half-wave circuits provide the total transformer secondary voltage. At first it looks as if there is no advantage to the full-wave rectifier because for the same total secondary transformer voltage, the output voltage is approximately the same as it is in the half-wave rectifier. The major advantage of the full-wave circuit is that the output frequency for the full-wave rectifier is twice that of the half-wave. With this higher frequency the pulses can be smoothed out (filtered) with much smaller filter capacitors, and at a much lower cost.

With four diodes connected as shown in figure 9–9, we have the other popular type of full-wave rectifier. This type is known as a bridge rectifier.

Looking at the wave forms of Figure 9–7 we can see that as the upper end of the transformer goes positive with the ac input line, diodes D_1 and D_3 are both biased into conduction and current will flow (as shown by the arrows) through the diodes and the

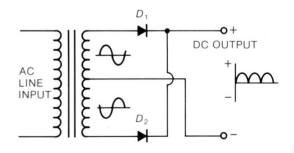

Figure 9–8 Full-wave rectifier.

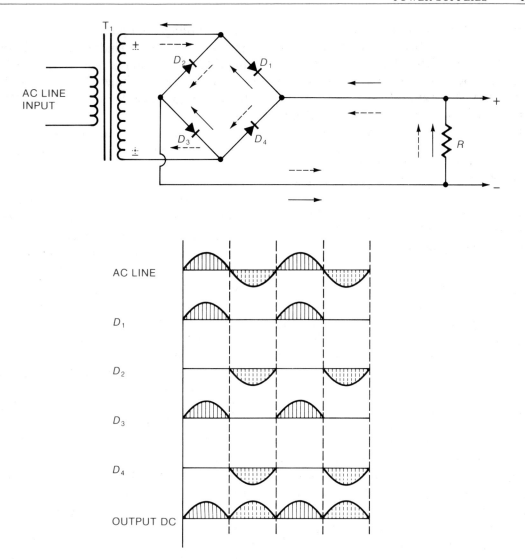

Figure 9-9 Full-wave bridge rectifier.

load. As the ac line changes polarity, D_2 and D_4 are biased into conduction with D_1 and D_3 cut off. Thus current continues to flow through the load, but on this half of the cycle, through different diodes.

It is evident that current flows through the load throughout the full ac line input cycle, but in the same direction through the load. Thus the name *full-wave*. The bridge full-wave rectifier has the same output wave-

form as that of the center-tap full-wave circuit. Both have a ripple (unsmoothed dc pulses) with a ripple frequency of twice the applied frequency.

The major consideration in selecting rectifier diodes is the *peak inverse voltage* (*PIV*). The PIV rating of a diode is the voltage that it must be capable of standing when it is not in the conduction condition. In the half-wave rectifier a capacitor is placed across the output to filter (smooth out) the pulsating dc. The effect is shown in Figure 9–10. For very high voltages, two or more diodes can be placed in series to get a high enough PIV. The total PIV is the sum of the individual diode peak inverse voltage ratings. Diode PIV must be 2.8 × the ac rms value.

In the full-wave bridge circuit shown in Figure 9–11, the output voltage is approximately 1.41 times E_{rms}. The PIV and the voltage applied to the load are the full secondary peak voltage. This PIV can be found by the equation,

$$E_{piv} = 1.414 \ E_{rms}$$

A very important thing to note is that the PIV for a bridge is equal to the peak secondary voltage and not twice the secondary voltage as in the half-wave rectifier.

9.3 POWER SUPPLY FILTERS

Power supply filters fall into two classes, depending upon which component is the input element. If the first filter component is a capacitor, the filter is a capacitive-input filter. And conversely, if the first component is an inductor, the filter is an inductive-input filter. Capacitive-input filters have a high output voltage with respect to the trans-

former voltage, but poor voltage regulation. In contrast, choke (inductor) input filters provide better voltage regulation, but have a lower output voltage than a capacitive filter would have from the same transformer.

Regulation is a measure of how constant the output voltage remains in the face of changes in current demanded by the load. The load is whatever device, circuit, or system the power supply is intended to operate. Very few real loads draw a constant amount of current. Some loads can tolerate varying output voltage (poor regulation), while other loads require a very constant output voltage (good regulation).

Choke (inductor) input filters are not very common today because of the high cost, large physical size, and weight of the choke. Filter circuits using filter chokes are fairly rare because of the availability of inexpensive semiconductor regulator circuits that do a far better job of regulating than a choke.

Figure 9–11 is a graph showing the variation of output voltage with load for a choke and a capacitor input filter. This curve shows the effect of a varying load on a power supply output voltage.

The frequency and magnitude of the rectified pulse voltage are the major factors in determining just how much filtering is needed. The question is how much ripple

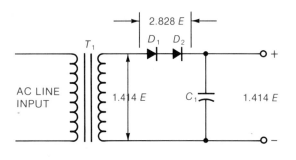

Figure 9-10 Half-wave rectifier showing series diodes for higher PIV.

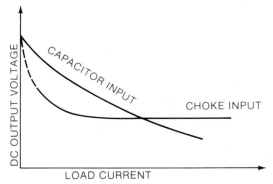

Figure 9-11 Comparisons of filters showing voltage versus current.

the equipment being powered can tolerate. The following equation shows how to determine the percentage of ripple:

$$\text{Percent of ripple} = \frac{E_{rms} \times 100}{E_{dc}}\ \%$$

Figure 9–12 illustrates the three major types of power supply filters.

Pi (π) Filter

Because the pi (π) filter is the most common of the three, we will cover it more completely than the other types. Figure 9–13 is the diagram of a π filter showing the waveforms of the input and the voltages across C_1 and C_2. The voltage waveshape across C_2 is also the output voltage of the filter. We have used a half-wave rectifier to provide the input voltage for the filter circuit in Figure 9–13.

When the first half-wave pulse appears across capacitor C_1, current will be flowing and capacitor C_1 will begin to charge. C_1 will charge to the *peak* voltage of the input pulse during the time the pulse is present. During the time that the half-wave rectifier delivers no output voltage, C_1 discharges into the load through L. C_1 will recharge to peak voltage, and again when the rectifier produces no output voltage, C_1 again will discharge into the load. If C_1 is made large enough, it will store enough electrons during the half-wave rectifier's output pulse to provide current to the load during the rectifier's off time without too great a discharge. The discharging of C_1 will produce an output waveform similar to that shown in the figure.

The inductor L functions to retard any *change* in *current* flowing through it. Thus, when the rectified current pulse is applied to the choke L, it tends to retard the change in current through it. This retarding of the current has an effect similar to C_1 but acts on current variations. Because of the action of C_1 and L, the current applied to C_2 is flowing much more steadily than at the input to the filter. Capacitor C_2 charges and discharges

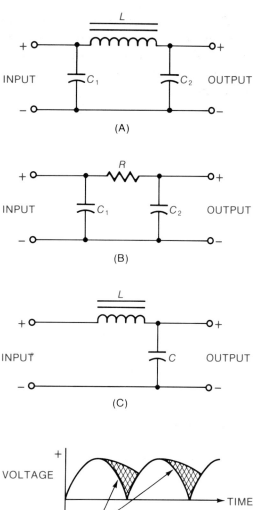

(A)

(B)

(C)

VOLTAGE

The capacitors supply the current during the period shown by the crosshatch area.

(D)

Figure 9-12 Basic filter circuits.

like C_1, providing additional filtering to provide nearly pure dc for powering electronic equipment.

In Figure 9–13B the choke L is replaced by a resistor. The resistor adds a time delay between the charging and discharging of a single larger capacitor, but not as effectively as does a choke filter.

Choke type filter circuits are being replaced by modern solid state regulators that not only regulate, but also provide a great deal of electronic ripple reduction (electronic filtering).

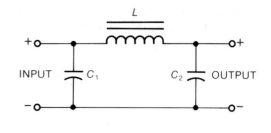

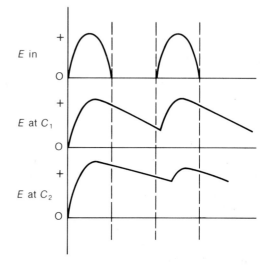

Figure 9-13 Pi (π) filter circuit and waveshapes.

SUMMARY

1. The power transformer steps the power line voltage up or down to the value required by the equipment to be powered.

2. The power transformer also isolates the equipment from the power line to prevent electrical shocks and to protect the equipment from power line ground problems.

3. When working on line-operated equipment that does not use a transformer, a special isolation transformer should be used.

4. The diode rectifier (vacuum tube or semiconductor) allows current to flow through it in only one direction.

5. The filter capacitor smooths out the humps in the pulsating dc from the rectifier.

6. A series resistor is often included to protect the rectifier from surges when the power is first turned on.

7. Rectifiers are classed as half-wave or full-wave.

8. The bridge rectifier is a full-wave circuit.

9. Full-wave circuits are superior to half-wave circuits because they are easier to filter.

10. Choke type filters provide better regulation than capacitor-only filters; but choke type circuits have been largely replaced by electronic regulators.

11. Diode rectifiers must be rated for the ac peak voltage, not the rms value.

REVIEWING YOUR ELECTRONICS VOCABULARY

1. Bridge Rectifier
2. Filtering
3. Full wave
4. Half wave
5. Peak voltage

6. Pi filter
7. Power supply
8. Regulation
9. Ripple
10. RMS voltage

CHECKING YOUR UNDERSTANDING

1. What is the oldest dc power source still in use today?
2. What are two basic functions of a transformer in a power supply?
3. What will occur in a transformer if dc is applied to it?
4. Name two basic types of transformers.
5. Draw a diagram of a basic half-wave rectifier power supply.
6. What would be the average output voltage of a half-wave rectifier circuit with 198 volts rms applied?
7. Draw a diagram of a full-wave bridge rectifier and show the direction of the current on each ac input cycle.
8. What is the name of the power transformer that has the same input as output voltage?
9. What are the three major reasons for not using a choke input filter in a basic nonregulated power supply?
10. Draw a diagram of pi filter and the waveshapes for it.

SOLVING ELECTRONIC PROBLEMS

1. Design a 120 vac to 400 vdc power supply with a bridge rectifier, dual pi filter with a −100 vdc bias supply included.
2. What is the peak voltage if the rms voltage is 120 vac?
3. What is the applied rms voltage to a half-wave rectifier to give an average output voltage of 200 volts?
4. What is the PIV of a full-wave bridge rectifier with an output voltage of 350 volts dc?
5. What is the average output voltage from a full-wave rectifier with the transformer output of 400-0-400?

CHAPTER 10
Voltage Regulators

INTRODUCTION

A voltage regulator is an electronic device connected in the output of a power supply to maintain the output voltage at a constant value. A regulator will react automatically to correct any voltage variations within its rated limits. A good regulator will maintain its specified output voltage despite large variations in current demand.

A voltage regulator can be a very simple device or it can be an extremely complex thing. Generally, more complex circuits provide better regulation than simpler circuits.

10.1 VOLTAGE REGULATORS

A manual voltage regulator is shown in Figure 10–1. In this regulator a simple variable resistor is connected in series with the load. As the voltage changes we can change the resistor to maintain the voltage at the desired value. Most series regulators work on this principle. A less frequently used circuit is shown in Figure 10–2. This shunt regulator places a resistance in parallel with the load and the resistance is adjusted to maintain a constant effective load resistance. The parallel combination of R and the load resistance is maintained at a fixed value by adjusting R. If the load resistance decreases, R is increased to restore the original parallel equivalent resistance. If the load

value increases, the equivalent resistance is restored by lowering the value of R.

Poor regulation in a power supply is the result of the power supply's internal resistance. It is impossible to avoid internal resistance altogether, although every effort is made to keep the internal resistance low. There is a voltage drop across the internal resistance and this voltage drop subtracts from the final output voltage. In addition, the voltage drop across the internal resistance increases as the load draws increased current.

Whenever a regulator is used, the power supply must be able to provide approximately twice the voltage required out of the

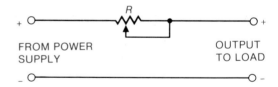

Figure 10-1 Voltage regulator.

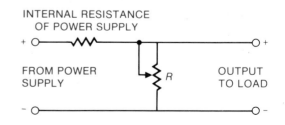

Figure 10-2 Shunt regulator.

regulator for a series regulator. For shunt regulators extra current availability is required. In general, series regulators are more economical because there is less power wasted and because it is cheaper to build a transformer with a higher voltage capability than with a higher current rating.

One of the more common tube regulators is the glow tube type. It is a cold cathode tube filled with an inert gas. Tubes can be used in series in order to increase the voltage at which they will regulate, but they have a very limited current capability. Because of this, tubes have only limited use.

Solid state devices have taken over almost all of the work formerly done by tubes. The complex solid state regulator is a combination of several simple circuits. To begin with, we need a device across which we can vary the voltage. This device is controlled by a voltage that is a sample of the output voltage, which tells it how much voltage it must drop to maintain the required output voltage. The control voltage is derived by comparing the output voltage with a standard or reference voltage and measuring the difference. This *difference* in voltage is used to vary the voltage drop across the control device. The control device adjusts its voltage drop and corrects the deviation from the desired voltage output. A block diagram of an electronic voltage regulator is shown in Figure 10-3. Nearly all voltage regulators contain the blocks (shown in the diagram) in one form or another.

In order to analyze the circuit in more detail, we will start with the variable voltage source. This element can be either in series or in shunt (parallel) with the load. We can use a transistor as the control element, where the voltage across it is the collector-to-emitter voltage. The voltage drop across the transistor can be controlled by the base emitter voltage by sampling the output

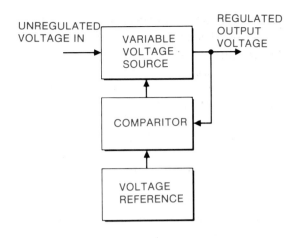

Figure 10-3 Regulator block diagram.

voltage. The circuit in Figure 10-4 shows such a circuit.

The next element we need in the circuit is a voltage reference, something that we can assume to be accurate and with which we can compare the regulated output voltage. Zener diodes and batteries are the most common reference standards. For all applications here, we will use a zener diode, but this does not preclude the use of a battery. Batteries are less often used simply because they demand periodic attention.

The last circuit we need is one that will produce a signal that is proportional to the difference between the output voltage and the reference voltage. This difference or *error* voltage is used to "adjust" the control

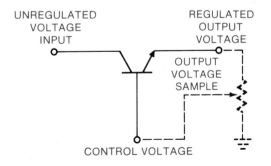

Figure 10-4 Control transistor.

element voltage drop because this is a differential signal; we can use a differential amplifier for this circuit (single-ended circuits are sometimes used).

In the simple regulator circuit shown in Figure 10–5 the component parts are labeled to conform to the block diagram in Figure 10–2. The Zener diode CR_1 is the voltage reference. Resistor R_1 biases the transistor and serves as the zener dropping resistor as well.

The zener reference diode is connected to the base of the control transistor. The power supply output voltage is applied to the collector of the transistor.

If we decrease the load resistance, drawing more current, the emitter voltage becomes less positive. Because the base is held at a fixed voltage by the zener diode, this is equivalent to making the base go more negative, which increases the transistor's conduction. An increase in conduction means a lower voltage drop across the collector-emitter part of the transistor.

Because the control transistor and the load (Figure 10–5) are in series, part of the voltage output of the power supply will be dropped across the transistor and the rest will be dropped across the load.

If the control transistor is caused to reduce its voltage drop, the voltage across the load must increase. And conversely, an increase in transistor voltage drop reduces the voltage. *Note:* The control transistor is

often called the *pass transistor* or *error corrector transistor*.

A more complicated regulator is shown in Figure 10–6. The reference voltage drop is provided by the zener diode (CR_1) voltage drop. R_1 supplies current to keep the zener operating. The voltage divider R_2 and R_3 produces an output sample voltage to compare with the zener reference voltage. The comparing is done in the base-emitter junction of Q_1 since the base is connected to $R_3 / R_1 + R_2$ (V_0) and the emitter is connected to the zener voltage. Thus the current through Q_1 is proportional to V_{be} of Q_1.

The current flowing through R_4 determines the collector voltage of Q_1 and the base voltage of Q_2. The emitter voltage of Q_2 will be approximately 0.6 V less than this base voltage.

If the load resistance R_L is increased, it tends to increase the output voltage, which raises the base voltage of Q_1. Since the emitter of Q_1 is fixed at V_z, this tends to increase V_{be} and thus increases I_{C1}. An increase in I_{C1} flowing through R_4 will lower V_{C1} and V_{B2}. Lowering the base voltage of Q_2 will lower the emitter voltage which is the output voltage. This would tend to compensate for the original voltage change.

Next let's analyze Figure 10–7, a regulator that uses a differential amplifier. In this circuit, the zener diode and R_4, which supplies current to the zener and to Q_2, are the voltage reference. R_1 and R_2 divide the output voltage down to where it can be compared with the zener voltage. The comparison circuit is the differential amplifier. The collector voltage of Q_1 is the base voltage of Q_3. The output voltage is two base emitter voltage drops less than the collector voltage of Q_1. Q_3 and Q_4 is a compound transistor circuit that keeps the transistors from loading R_5 and decreasing the gain of the differential amplifier.

If no regulator were present, a change in load would cause a change in the output

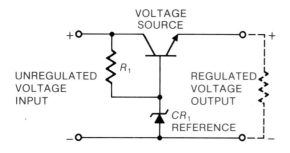

Figure 10-5 Simple regulator.

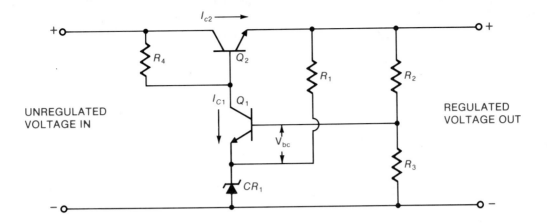

Figure 10-6 Regulator.

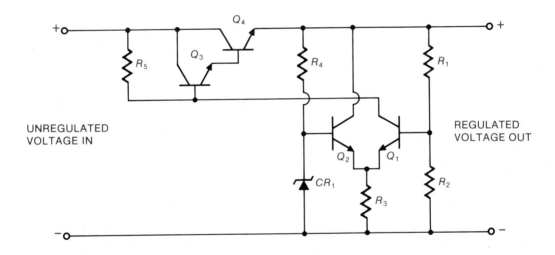

Figure 10-7 Regulator with differential amplifier.

voltage. If a regulator is present, these changes are drastically reduced.

Shunt Regulator

Figure 10–8 is a shunt regulator circuit. The reference element is, again, a zener diode. The comparison element is the base-emitter junction of the transistor. The variable voltage source is the control transistor and R_3. Part of the current flows through R_L and part flows through Q_1 and CR_1.

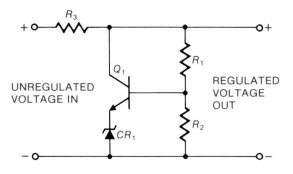

Figure 10-8 Shunt regulator circuit.

If we increase R_L, we decrease the current and increase the voltage out. This in turn increases the voltage on the base of Q_1. Since the emitter voltage is constant (the zener voltage), it forward-biases the transistor, thus increasing the collector current I_C. This current must flow through R_3, lowering the collector voltage which is the output voltage. An increase in the load resistance (R_L) will produce an opposite compensation.

The Zener Diode

The zener diode regulator is a very simple low voltage, low current device. Its operation depends entirely upon the zener diode's operational characteristics; zener voltage point and wattage are the most important characteristics.

A simple regulator circuit using a zener diode is shown in Figure 10-9. The input voltage can be unregulated or regulated, but the input voltage must be higher than the needed output voltage. The load must be

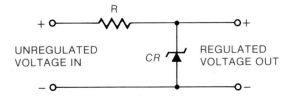

Figure 10-9 Zener diode regulator.

such that the voltage is never reduced below the zener voltage point or the zener will no longer regulate.

Integrated Circuit Regulators

When a simple efficient regulator is needed, we can use one of the integrated circuit (IC) regulators that are on the market. They are available for a wide range of voltages. With the addition of an external control transistor, they can operate at higher currents.

Figure 10-10 is a low-voltage self-contained IC regulator. The resistive divider from V_{ref} is used to provide attenuation of the output voltage to prevent overdriving the input of the comparison amplifier. The frequency compensation capacitor C_1 is placed to ground to prevent instability of the regulator. The resistors R_1 and R_2 are selected to provide the desired output voltage. An example is $R_1 = 750$ ohms, $R_2 = 2.2 \text{ k}$ ohms, to give an output of +5 volts.

Figure 10-11 shows an example of IC regulators.

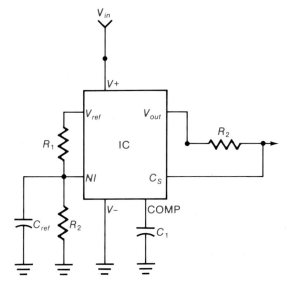

Figure 10-10 Diagram of integrated circuit voltage regulator.

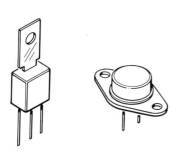

Figure 10-11 Integrated circuit regulators.

10.2 DC TO DC CONVERTERS

Converters are devices that will convert one dc voltage to another. They can be mechanical, such as a motor generator mechanical vibrator, or an electronic circuit. Almost all mobile electronic equipment in vehicles now uses transistor dc-to-dc converters.

Figure 10–12 shows a simplified converter circuit. In this circuit all the inductors are wound on one toroid core such as those shown in Figure 10–13.

When the current first begins to flow in the circuit, the current in either L_1 or L_2 will be slightly larger than that in the other. Each of the transistors is forward-biased by R. Let us say, for the purpose of this discussion, that L_1 has the slightly higher current.

If the base windings L_3 and L_4 are wound as shown, the extra current in L_1 will induce a voltage in L_3 that will forward-bias Q_1 more and reverse-bias Q_2. These biases will make the current in L_1 even greater. This in turn turns Q_1 on and Q_2 off (Q_1 saturates quickly and Q_2 is cut off). Now the full voltage of ($B+ - V_{ce/sat}$) is applied to L_1. This is a constant voltage. The voltage across an inductor is proportional to the rate of change of current through it. Thus, for a constant voltage across L_1, the current will increase

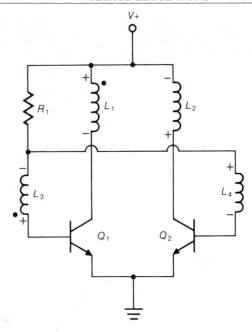

Figure 10-12 Simplified inverter.

linearly. *When the core saturates,* it cannot carry any more magnetic flux, and, thus, the inductance drops to that of an air core coil.

Figure 10–14 shows a graph of the current against time for the inverter transformer's core.

When the saturation occurs, the induced voltage in L_3 drops to approximately zero. With this voltage zero, Q_1 is no longer as forward-biased. The collector current in Q_1 will therefore decrease. When the current in an inductor changes there will be an induced voltage (in the base inductor). This induced voltage will turn Q_1 off and Q_2 on. This will decrease the current in Q_1 even further.

Thus Q_2 will quickly saturate and the current I_{C2} will begin increasing linearly. The transistors will alternately turn on and off, the frequency being determined by the time required to saturate the core.

When the core is saturated the inductance value goes to approximately zero, and the inductor acts like a short circuit. There-

Figure 10-13 Examples of transformer cores.

MAGNETICS, INC.

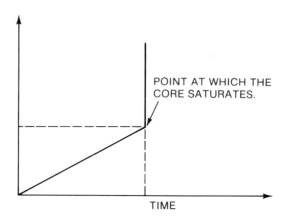

POINT AT WHICH THE CORE SATURATES.

TIME

Figure 10-14 Current/time plot.

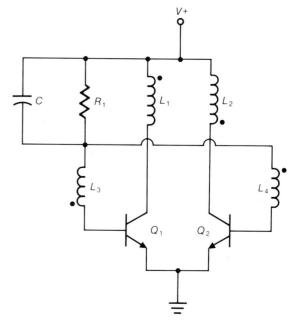

Figure 10-15 Inverter with capacitor.

fore the collector current will begin to rise very rapidly. In order to limit this current spike it is necessary to turn the transistor off. If the capacitor clamps one end of L_3 when the voltage across L_3 goes to zero, it will pull the base voltage down. Thus the capacitor will help limit current spikes.

Figure 10–16 shows a typical converter diagram. This circuit operates exactly like that shown in Figure 10–15. In the converter, the stray capacitance in L_1 and L_2 will cause the square wave collector voltage to try to oscillate. This is known as *ringing* (see part A of Figure 10–17). The ringing can be considerably decreased by placing a small capacitor in series with a resistor between the collectors of the two transistors as shown by R_2 and C_2 in Figure 10–16.

Figure 10–17B is a plot of I_c, showing the two major variations in it due to the time required to saturate the transistor and that variation caused by the saturation of the toroid core.

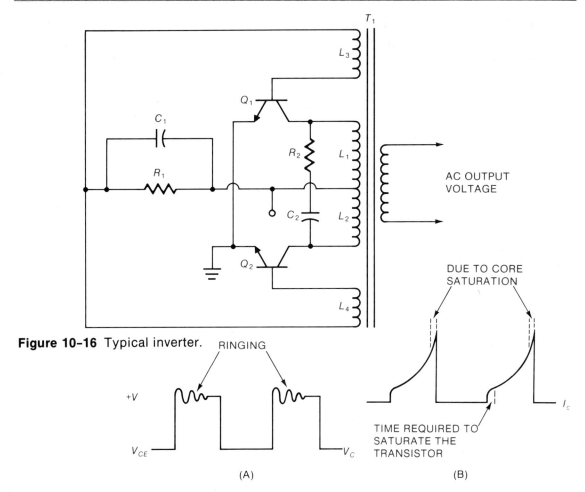

Figure 10-16 Typical inverter.

Figure 10-17 V_c and I_c waveforms for the inverter in Figure 10-16.

SUMMARY

1. A voltage regulator maintains a constant output voltage in spite of variations in power-line voltage, internal power supply resistance, and varying load currents.

2. The regulator is connected to the output of a power supply.

3. Most voltage regulators contain the following elements:
   a. Control or pass transistor.
   b. Reference voltage device (often a zener diode).
   c. An amplifier transistor.
   d. A circuit to compare a sample of the output voltage with the reference voltage (often the comparison operation is carried out in the amplifier itself).

4. An error voltage is the difference between the reference voltage and the sample of the output voltage.

5. The error voltage is amplified and used to vary the control (pass) transistor current to correct any error.

6. Regulators can be either shunt or series types. The series circuit is most common.

7. In a shunt regulator the control transistor is in parallel with the load. In the series regulator the control transistor is in series with the load.

8. Complete voltage regulators are available in integrated circuit packages. Many can have their output voltages set externally. The current ratings can usually be extended to almost any desired level by adding external power transistors.

9. Converters (inverters) convert direct current into a chopped direct current and step the voltage up to the desired voltage with a transformer. The output may be rectified and filtered like any other power supply. An outboard regulator may be attached if required.

REVIEWING YOUR ELECTRONICS VOCABULARY

1. Control (pass) transistor
2. Differential amplifier
3. Internal resistance
4. Inverter
5. Load
6. Reference voltage
7. Regulator
8. Series regulator
9. Shunt regulator
10. Zener diode

CHECKING YOUR UNDERSTANDING

1. Name two types of voltage references used in electronic regulators.
2. High internal resistance in a power supply will cause the power supply to have characteristic?
3. What is one of the major advantages of a series regulator over a shunt regulator?
4. What is another name for the control transistor in a solid state electronic regulator?
5. Why is a differential amplifier used in a regulator?
6. What will occur to the regulation in a zener voltage regulator if the voltage is reduced below the zener diode's zener point?
7. What is an inverter?
8. List the major building blocks in a regulator circuit.
9. How can the regulation of a differential amplifier regulator be improved?
10. Does the core in an average dc to dc inverter saturate?

SOLVING ELECTRONIC PROBLEMS

1. Draw a diagram of a simple zener regulator.
2. Draw a block diagram of a regulator using a differential amplifier.
3. Draw a diagram of a high current IC regulator using at least two external transistors.
4. Draw the diagram of a simple dc to dc inverter.
5. Draw the diagram of a variable output voltage regulator.

CHAPTER 11
Amplifiers

INTRODUCTION

There are amplifier circuits for almost any electronic task. In this chapter several of the most common amplifier types will be discussed. We will examine the characteristics of single-stage transistor amplifiers and the methods of coupling one stage to another. Negative feedback and its effect on amplifiers will also be covered. We will also deal with the operational amplifier, an integrated circuit multi-stage amplifier that can do the jobs of many of the specialized transistor circuits.

11.1 COUPLING NETWORKS

The coupling network between each amplifier stage is almost as important as the amplifier itself. Coupling networks fall into four basic classifications. They are direct (or dc) coupling, resistor/capacitor (or RC) coupling, impedance coupling, and transformer coupling.

Figure 11–1 shows an example of RC coupling.

The network itself is composed of resistors R_2 and R_3 and capacitor C_1. In most circuits, the coupling resistors also form part of the transistor's load and bias circuit. In Figure 11–1, R_3 is the base resistor for Q_2 and R_2 is the collector resistor for Q_1.

The signal from Q_1 that is developed across R_2 is coupled through C_1 to the base of Q_2. At very low frequencies, X_c tends to attenuate the signal, but at high and mid frequencies X_c decreases and the attenuation is minimal. This type of coupling is common in audio amplifiers.

An example of direct coupling can be seen in Figure 11–2. This type of coupling is subject to the problem of thermal instability. When temperatures change, the first stage bias drift due to the temperature change is amplified through all stages. This is not a common type of coupling, but does have its uses.

Impedance coupling is very similar to RC coupling in appearance, except that one (or more) of the coupling resistors, as shown in Figure 11–3, is replaced by an inductor.

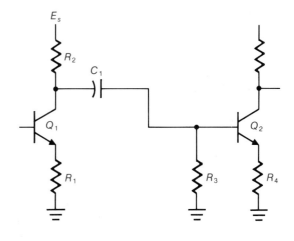

Figure 11-1 RC coupling.

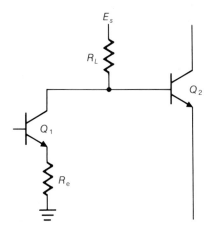

Figure 11-2 Direct coupling.

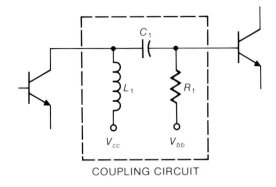

Figure 11-3 Impedance coupling.

This type of coupling is often used in VLF (very low frequency) and MLF (medium-low frequency) applications.

Figure 11–4 illustrates the final common type of coupling, the transformer coupling. In this circuit, the primary of the transformer provides the collector load for Q_1 and the secondary provides the base resistance for Q_2.

There are several variations of this type of coupling, enabling coupling from audio to UHF frequencies. One of the important variations is shown in Figure 11–5. Link coupling is used extensively in the coupling of *RF* transmitter stages.

11.2 AF AMPLIFIERS AND EMITTER FOLLOWERS

An audio amplifier is one that is designed to amplify frequencies in the range of 20 hertz to 20 kilohertz. It is often difficult to obtain equal amplification throughout this wide range.

Figure 11–6 is a typical two stage audio amplifier. This circuit uses a transformer input and output, with *RC* coupling between the two NPN transistor stages.

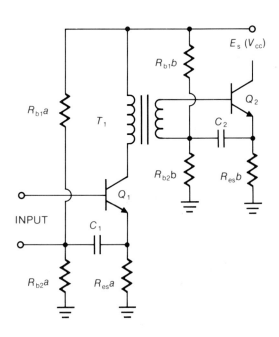

Figure 11-4 Transformer coupling.

The input transformer transforms the low transistor input impedance to a higher circuit input impedance. The *RC* interstage coupling provides isolation between relatively high dc collector voltage and the relatively low voltage required on the base of the second transistor.

The coupling capacitor C_4 is selected to have very little X_c at the lowest frequency of

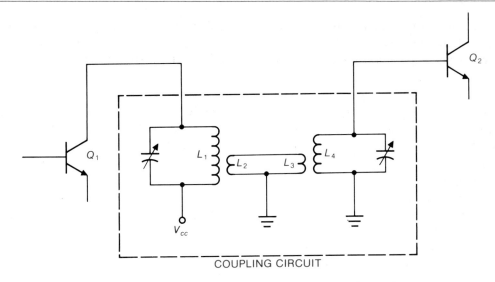

Figure 11-5 Link coupling.

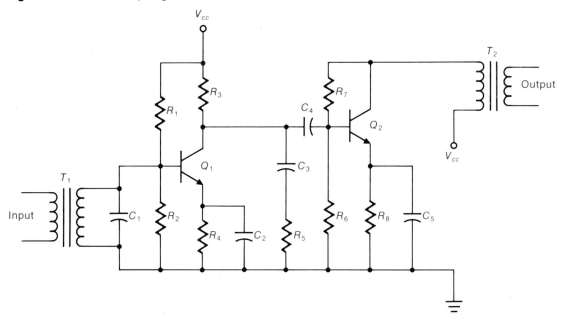

Figure 11-6 Audio Amplifier.

interest, so that the signal passes freely between stages.

The combination of C_3 and R_5 provides a low impedance path to ground for noise. With proper selection of values, this same network can *appear* to boost the bass response of the amplifier by reducing the treble somewhat. If the resistor R_5 is made variable, the network becomes a simple tone control.

The transformer in the last stage transforms the relatively high transistor output impedance down to the generally much lower impedance of a load such as a loudspeaker. The output transformer is called an *impedance matching transformer* and is necessary to transfer the maximum power to the load.

A single output transistor is often unable to produce the power output needed. When higher power levels are needed, a circuit similar to that shown in Figure 11–7 is often used.

In the circuit of Figure 11–7, the two transistors are a matched set; that is, their values are very close to the same. The circuit is a common emitter type.

The circuit shown will cause some distortion of the output waveshape, due to the zero bias point and the 0.6 V junction potential of the base-emitter junction. Figure 11–8 shows a sine wave input and the distorted output. Note the distortion of the output at the zero crossover point where both transistors are turned off for a time. This distortion can be corrected by using an offset positive bias on each transistor to bias them so neither transistor ever completely turns off.

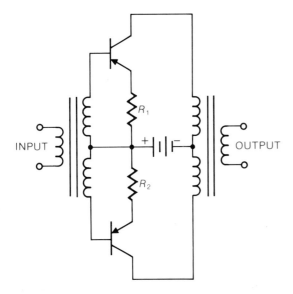

Figure 11-7 Push-pull amplifier.

The small positive bias will cause both transistors to conduct slightly with no input signal. A circuit that will provide this small positive bias is shown in Figure 11–9A.

In this circuit, when there is a signal applied to the input Q_1 will be cut off and Q_2 will conduct. This will reverse on the next alternation, with Q_1 on and Q_2 off, but at the crossover point before the conducting transistor cuts off, the nonconducting one is turned on by the bias. Thus, there is no both-transistors-off condition at the crossover point.

Complementary Symmetry Audio Amplifier

A popular circuit in high fidelity equipment is the *complementary symmetry audio amplifier*. The schematic for a workable version is shown in Figure 11–9B. The circuit shown will deliver 12 watts rms to an 8 ohm speaker (about 25 watts of music power). The circuit is similar in function to that of Figure 11–9A, except that the weak link of the audio world, the transformer, has been eliminated.

It has been a long-term goal for engineers to do away with output transformers in audio amplifiers. It was never done successfully in vacuum tube circuits, but it has proved relatively simple with modern transistors. Output transformers of adequate quality for audio service prove to be very large, heavy, very expensive, and not very efficient. Lesser quality transformers produce distortion and limited frequency response.

In the circuit in Figure 11–9B, resistor R_5 prevents loading of the feedback circuit (R_{b1} and R_{b2}).

Q_1 is a common emitter voltage mode driver. The voltage feedback for Q_1 is taken from the emitters of Q_4 and Q_5 to help stabilize the power stage (Q_1, Q_3, Q_4, Q_5).

The diodes, D_1, D_2, and D_3, provide the

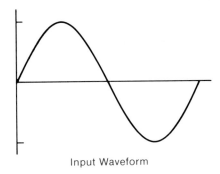

Input Waveform

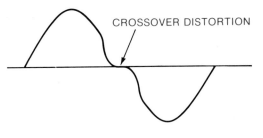

CROSSOVER DISTORTION

Distorted Output Waveform

Figure 11-8 Crossover distortion.

bias to overcome crossover distortion.

R_La and R_Lb are the collector load resistors for Q_1.

C_{bs} provides positive feedback to increase the output power.

The power stage consists of two darlington pair emitter followers, one NPN (Q_2, Q_5) and one PNP (Q_3, Q_4). Only one of the darlington pairs works on each half cycle of the input signal.

C_{co} couples the circuit to the speaker and its stored energy supplies power to Q_2 and Q_5 during the half cycle that they work.

R_{c1} sets the amount of crossover bias and sets the voltage between the junction of the emitters of Q_4 and Q_5 and ground to one-half the supply voltage.

Power transistors Q_4 and Q_5 must be mounted on an adequate heat sink, with at least 4 square inches of aluminum for each transistor. The following transistor types or their equivalents can be used:

Q_1: MPS 6566 (NPN)

Q_2: MPS 6553 (PNP)

Q_3: MPS 6530 (NPN)

Q_4: 2N 4921 (NPN)

Q_5: 2N 4918 (PNP)

$D_{1, 2, 3}$: 1N645

11.3 VIDEO AND PULSE AMPLIFIERS

Video amplifiers are used to amplify complex signals. These signals are used to form a picture on a television or radar screen. The required bandwidth is from 3 to 12 megahertz. One way to extend the bandwidth of an amplifier is to add negative feedback. We will discuss feedback in a later section.

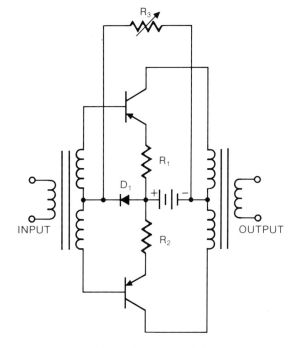

(A) Transformer coupled

Figure 11-9 Power amplifiers with anti-crossover-distortion bias.

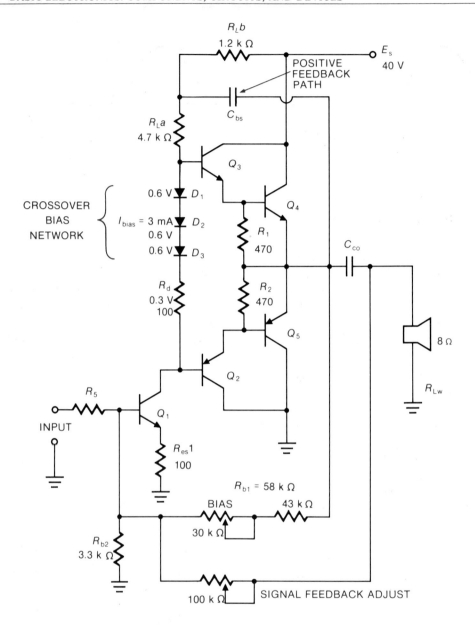

(B) Complementary symmetry power amplifier with
anticrossover - distortion bias.

Figure 11–10 shows the kind of signal that a video amplifier is required to handle. Most modern video amplifiers for television are special wide band versions of the operational amplifier. Figure 11–11 is a typical video amplifier bandpass (frequency response) curve.

Square Wave Pulse

A pulse amplifier must also handle a large

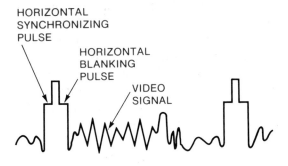

Figure 11-10 Typical television video signal.

bandwidth, although it is strictly an on/off signal. The square wave pulse is composed of a large number of multiples of the base or fundamental frequency. Harmonics are multiples of the fundamental frequency. The square wave contains only odd numbered harmonics (e.g., 3 times, 5 times, 7 times, and so on). Other waveshapes, such as the sawtooth, contain both even and odd multiples (harmonics). All of the harmonics in a waveform, whatever its shape, are sine waves. The shape of the waveform depends upon the number of harmonics, their amplitudes, and the distribution of odd and even harmonics.

Figure 11-12 shows how a square wave results from its harmonic content (only two harmonics are shown in the figure; otherwise it would become too complex to visualize easily). The more odd harmonics added to the waveform, the more nearly perfect the square wave becomes.

Pulse Amplifier

The pulse amplifier, or line driver, is used to increase the driving capabilities of a pulse. A pulse amplifier may also be used to increase the amplitude of a pulse, or to correct a pulse width that has become excessive.

Figure 11-13 shows a schematic diagram of a typical pulse amplifier. The circuit consists of one transistor (Q_1), connected in a common-emitter configuration to amplify the signal and give the necessary power gain. The circuit also contains a pulse transformer, T_1, used to bring the output signal in phase with the input signal and to determine the pulse width of the output.

At quiescence, the input is at ground potential. Q_1 is cut off and therefore the output is also at ground potential. When a negative pulse is applied to the input, Q_1 becomes forward-biased and turns on. Current starts to flow from the -12 volt supply through the transistor to the emitter. The current flow in the collector circuit (T_1 and R_3) causes the

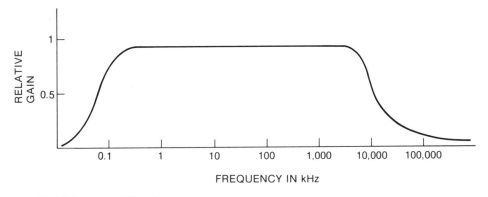

Figure 11-11 Video amplifier frequency response (band pass) curve.

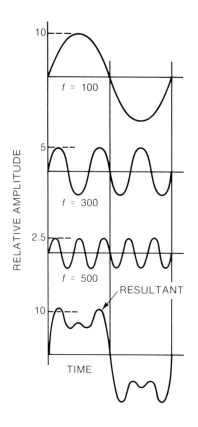

Note: The addition of more odd harmonics will form a perfect square wave:

Figure 11-12 Components of a square wave.

collector to rise from −12 volts toward 0 volts. The changing current in the primary transformer T_1 produces an expanding magnetic field that induces a voltage in the secondary. This voltage is increased by the turns ratio of the transformer and produces

a negative pulse in the secondary. The output will be an increasing negative potential as long as the current through the primary of the transformer is increasing. When the current flow through the primary of the transformer drives the core of T_1 to saturation, the voltage induced in the secondary decreases rapidly to 0 volts. Since the induced voltage in the secondary will fall off before the end of the input pulse, the width of the output pulse is not dependent on the width of the input pulse. Therefore the pulse amplifier may be used to narrow a pulse whose width has become excessive. Current will continue to flow in the transistor as long as the negative voltage is applied to the input. However, the output will remain at 0 volts as long as the transformer core remains in saturation. When the input returns to ground potential, current will cease being drawn through the primary of the transformer by the conduction of Q_1, the magnetic field will collapse, and the circuit will once again be in the steady state.

The current flow through the primary would not normally reach maximum immediately, because Q_1 is not fully conducting at the first instant. The hysteresis of the transformer also has considerable effect. The addition of C_2 in this circuit causes the circuit to reach its maximum more rapidly. When the current in the secondary starts to change, the resultant voltage produces a feedback to the base of Q_1 through C_2 and puts Q_1 into saturation, thus resulting in a faster rise time. When Q_1 is cut off by the input, the magnetic field in T_1 collapses and causes a negative spike in the primary. The diode CR_1 across the primary prevents the negative spike from appearing at the collector of Q_1. CR_1 conducts through R_3 and the primary of T_1 and thus dampens out this unwanted spike. The collapsing field also induces a positive pulse in the secondary. CR_2 limits this positive pulse to 0 volts.

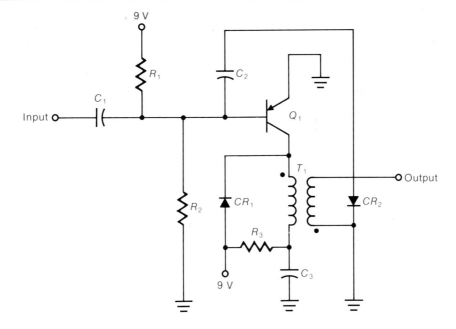

Figure 11-13 Pulse amplifier and shaping circuit.

11.4 RF/IF AMPLIFIERS

Almost all radio frequency (RF) or intermediate frequency (IF) amplifiers have some type of tuned circuit as part of the coupling network between stages. There is a type of so-called "untuned" RF amplifier that we will cover later in the section.

Figure 11-14 is a block diagram of a radio receiver showing where RF and IF amplifiers fit into the system. An IF amplifier is a fixed frequency RF amplifier designed for high gain and selectivity.

A transmitter also uses RF amplifiers, as shown in Figure 11-15. A transmitter often has several stages of RF amplification. In high power transmitters, the final amplifier is sometimes a tube rather than a transistor. This is not to say that a transistor cannot do the job, but with present technology, a tube can sometimes do high power RF work better.

Figure 11-16 is the schematic of a typical tuned RF amplifier of the kind used in a radio receiver.

The bias for the stage is obtained from the voltage divider, R_3, R_4. Capacitors C_2 and C_6 are RF bypass capacitors to keep the RF from feeding back to the power supply. The inter-element capacitance of the transistor is corrected by the capacitor C_4.

The two transformers are tuned by capacitors to the required resonant frequency. Most RF transformers are air core such as the one shown in Figure 11-18, or powdered iron core transformers like the one shown in Figure 11-17.

The transformers help to control unwanted signals by rejecting frequencies outside of their limited bandpass. A tuned transformer has a bandpass similar to that shown in Figure 11-19. A signal that is outside of the bandpass of the tuned transformer is rejected and not amplified.

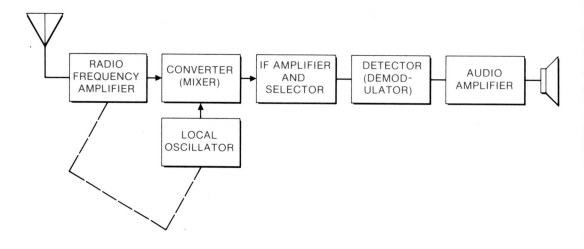

Figure 11-14 Block diagram of a receiver.

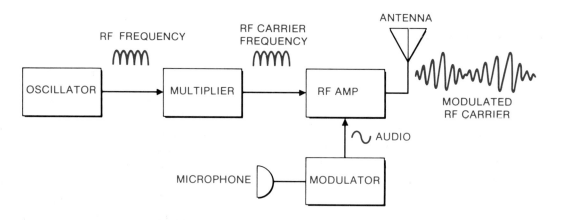

Figure 11-15 Block diagram of a transmitter.

The IF amplifier normally operates at a lower frequency than the RF amplifier. Thus, it normally utilizes a powdered iron or ceramic core transformer and is tuned by moving the core in or out. If the core is fixed, the capacitor can be varied in order to tune the transformer (a movable core is generally cheaper). Figure 11-20 shows examples of IF transformers commonly used in radio receivers.

An untuned RF amplifier is one that is very broad banded, but it is not an all-frequency amplifier. The gain of an untuned amplifier is usually low, as is necessary for such bandwidth.

11.5 DRIVERS

Drivers are special amplifiers used for data transmission or display. Generally, lamp and relay drivers will be acting on a pulse of relatively long duration. Under ordinary conditions, the circuit will be either fully on (saturated) or it will be cut off. Sometimes

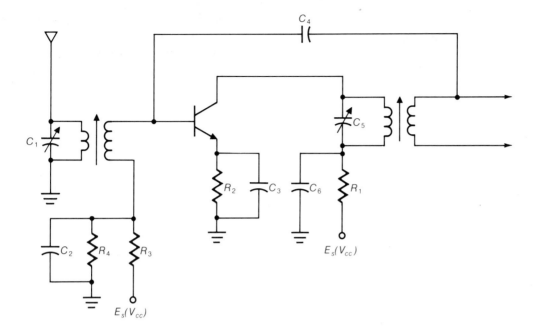

Figure 11-16 Tuned RF amplifier circuit.

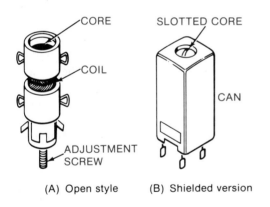

(A) Open style   (B) Shielded version

Figure 11-17 Powdered iron core RF transformer.

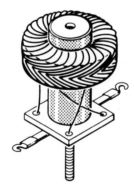

Figure 11-18 Air core RF coil.

a line driver that is a special case will be partially on.

Lamp Driver

A lamp driver is used to control a lamp, that is, to switch it on when a signal appears at its input, and to switch off the lamp when the signal is removed. Such lamps give visual

indications of the state of the circuits in the equipment. These indications can be of value to both the operator and the maintenance technician. Figure 11–21 shows the circuit for a sample lamp driver. Notice that one terminal of the lamp is connected to -12 volts, and the other terminal is connected to the collector of transistor Q_2. This makes the lamp the collector load of transistor Q_2.

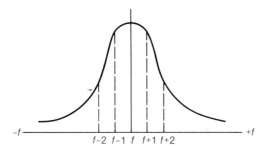

Figure 11-19 Typical bandpass curve for a tuned RF transformer.

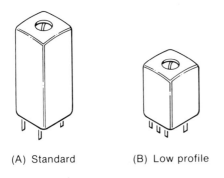

(A) Standard   (B) Low profile

Figure 11-20 Intermediate frequency transformers.

The dotted line is used to indicate that the driver and the lamp are not necessarily at the same physical location.

In the quiescent state, Q_1 and Q_2 are biased at cutoff through the voltage dividers consisting of R_1 and R_2, R_3 and R_4, and CR_1. In the quiescent condition the lamp is off. When a -12 volt signal is applied to the input, Q_1 is forward-biased and conducts through R_3 and R_4. This, in turn, forward-biases Q_2. Q_2 now conducts and switches the light on. When the signal returns to 0 volts, Q_1 is reverse-biased and cuts off. With no current through R_3 and R_4, the base of Q_2 returns to ground, or 0-volt potential. This effectively cuts off current flow in Q_2 and thereby switches the lamp off.

Diode CR_1 limits collector leakage current by effectively reverse-biasing the base-emitter junction.

When critical information is to be displayed by the lamp, a slight modification to the lamp driver can give an indication if the lamp fails. See Figure 11-22. This circuit provides an automatic indication upon lamp failure. If the lamp fails, the neon indicator that is directly across the normal incandescent indicator lamp will no longer be shorted out by the filament in the incandescent lamp, and will therefore fire. The holding current for the neon lamp is supplied from a separate -70 volt line via R_2. The diode CR_1 will isolate the lamp driver and the -70 volt supply.

Many variations exist for lamp drivers, but most are simple and can often be included in the lamp socket.

Relay Driver

The relay driver is used to energize a relay or other electromechanical device, which, in turn, can be used to control many other actions. Relays are often used when very high currents or voltages must be turned on or off.

Figure 11-23 is the schematic diagram of a relay driver. The circuit is a common-emitter amplifier. With the input to the driver at ground level (0 volts), Q_1 is turned off, presenting a high impedance. No current flows in the circuit, and therefore the relay is not energized. When the input is switched to a negative level, Q_1 becomes saturated and presents a low-impedance path to the flow of current. As current flows through the relay coil, the relay becomes energized and the contacts are closed, performing the switching function. A closed contact could equally well be employed; then the operation of the coil would open rather than close a circuit. CR_1 is used as a spike suppressor to limit the negative overshoot from the relay coil's collapsing field.

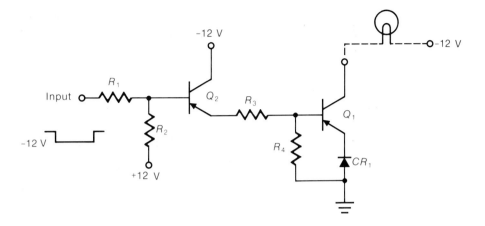

Figure 11-21 Simple lamp driver.

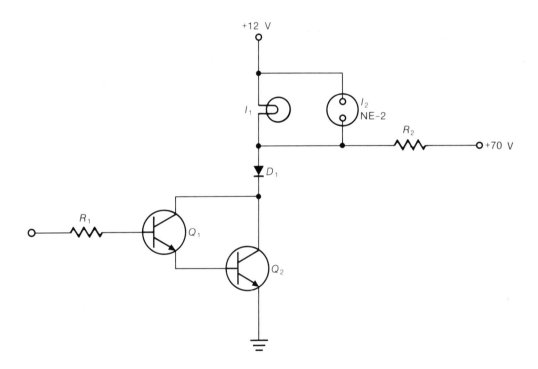

Figure 11-22 Fail safe lamp driver.

11.6 THE DARLINGTON PAIR

The two transistors connected as shown in Figure 11–24 are a super beta compound transistor known as the Darlington pair.

The circuit provides a very high input impedance because there are two betas in tandem. The input impedance formula for the pair is:

$$Z_{in} = \text{beta}_1 \times \text{beta}_2 \ (R_L)$$

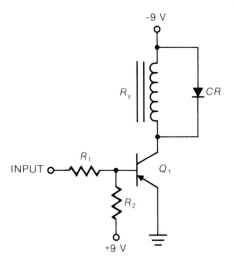

Figure 11-23 Relay driver.

The circuit cannot be expanded into more than three stages because of the amplified temperature drift associated with any direct coupled circuit.

The Darlington pair is used only in the common collector (emitter follower) con-

figuration. Small signal Darlingtons must be purchased as a commercial unit. The combination of a small signal transistor driving a power transistor can be made from any conveniently available transistors.

11.7 THE DIFFERENTIAL AMPLIFIER

The differential amplifier is the nearest thing to a universal amplifier stage yet devised. It forms the basic amplifier stages for the operational amplifier to be discussed in the next section.

The differential amplifier is the most stable and versatile of available circuits. It features exceptionally good stability, and good voltage gain from dc to several megahertz. There are two available inputs, one of which is inverted 180° at the output and one without inversion.

The basic circuit shown in Figures 11–25A and B shows the same basic circuit

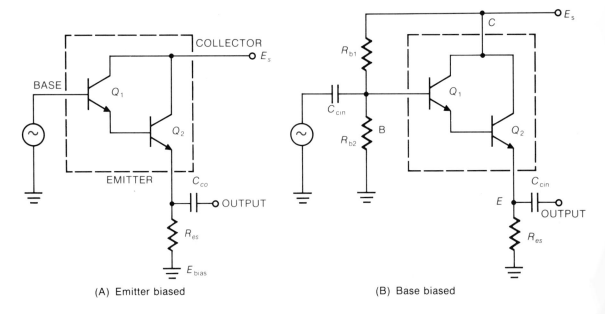

(A) Emitter biased

(B) Base biased

Figure 11-24 The Darlington Pair.

with a transistor used to replace the shared emitter resistor.

The circuit in Figure 11-25A has two inputs, one 180° inverting input and one noninverting input. The two inputs can be used separately with the unused input grounded, or both inputs can be used to amplify the algebraic *difference* between the two signal voltages.

There are also two outputs, either of which can be used separately, or, in special cases, both at the same time. Because of the balanced bridge-like circuit, signal voltages cancel out in the emitter resistor. Ideally there should be no CMS (common mode signal) output voltage. Significant

CMS signal is a good indication of a circuit malfunction or of badly matched transistors. The CMS signal is measured across the common-emitter resistor.

Transistors must be matched very closely if the circuit is to live up to the performance expected of it.

The circuit in Figure 11–25B uses a transistor to simulate the approximately 1 megohm emitter resistance that is often desirable in input stages of direct coupled differential multistage amplifiers. A 1 megohm resistor at 1 mA of current would require a 2,000 volt bias supply. The transistor simulates this high value resistance, but requires only a few-volt bias supply.

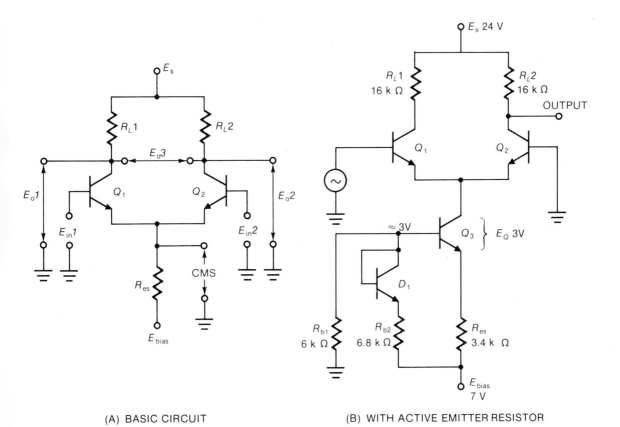

(A) BASIC CIRCUIT   (B) WITH ACTIVE EMITTER RESISTOR

Figure 11-25 The differential amplifier.

11.8 FEEDBACK IN AMPLIFIERS

Adding negative feedback to an amplifier reduces distortion and increases the amplifier bandwidth. The price paid for these advantages is a loss in gain. If an amplifier has gain to spare, feedback can be used to great advantage. With adequate feedback the gain can be predicted with great accuracy, which is seldom the case in nonfeedback amplifier designs.

In Figure 11-26 a fraction of the output signal is fed back to the input 180° out of phase with the input signal. The two signals are added at the input, canceling part of the input signal. Any distortion generated in the amplifier is also fed to the input, where it adds a kind of *predistortion* to the signal that is mixed in the amplifier and tends to cancel the distortion being generated there. The actual signal reaching the input of the amplifier (see Figure 11-26) is the algebraic sum of the signal from the generator and the feedback-fraction signal being returned from the amplifier output. $E_{total\ in} = E_{in} - F_f E_o$, where F_f is the feedback fraction, E_{in} is the signal from the generator, and E_o is the amplifier output voltage.

Voltage Gain Relationships

Voltage gain without feedback:

$$V_g = \frac{E_o}{E_{in}}$$

Voltage gain with feedback (V_g'); the total input signal as seen at the amplifier input:

$$E_{total\ in} = E_{in} + F_f E_o$$

The voltage gain with feedback is:

$$V_g' = \frac{E_o}{E_{in} - F_f E_o}$$

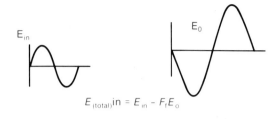

$$E_{(total)}in = E_{in} - F_f E_o$$

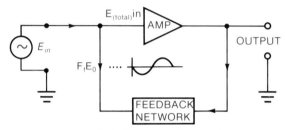

F_f IS THE FEEDBACK FRACTION

Figure 11-26 Negative feedback in an amplifier.

E_o = output voltage

E_{in} = input voltage

F_f = feedback fraction

V_g' = voltage gain with feedback

With a little algebraic manipulation, the formula can be rewritten in a more convenient form

$$V_g' = \frac{V_g}{1 - V_g F_f}$$

V_g' is the voltage gain *with* feedback

V_g is the voltage gain *without* feedback

F_f is the feedback fraction.

In the case of high gain amplifiers, such as the operational amplifier to be discussed in the next section, a still simpler formula can be used.

Table 11-1 The operational amplifier. The operational amplifier is an almost universal amplifier.

Table of Open-Loop and Closed-Loop Voltage Gains

Open-loop Gain, V_g	Feedback Factor, F_f	(The complete formula)	(The simplified formula)
200	0.1	11.1	10
400	0.1	10.2	10
800	0.1	10.1	10
1,000	0.1	10.1	10
10,000	0.1	10.01	10

$$V_g' = \frac{1}{F_f}$$

V_g' is the voltage gain with feedback

F_f is the feedback fraction.

Table 11–1 shows that the higher the gain of the amplifier, the more accurate the simplified equation becomes.

When the feedback fraction is determined by two resistors as it is in the operational amplifier, the voltage gain is determined solely by the resistance ratio. Call the two resistors R_{in} and R_f.

$$V_g' = \frac{1}{\dfrac{R_{in}}{R_f}} = \frac{1}{F_f}$$

which reduces to

$$V_g' = \frac{R_f}{R_{in}}$$

We will see the importance of all of this in the next section.

11.9 THE OPERATIONAL AMPLIFIER

The operational amplifier is an almost universal amplifier. It can be made to have any desired voltage gain by adding two external resistors. Its properties as an amplifier are almost ideal. (See Table 11–1).

Operational Amplifier Characteristics

1. High input impedance.
2. Low output impedance.
3. Very high (open loop) voltage gain (1,000,000 or more).
4. Provision for external feedback to set the voltage gain to any desired value.
5. Very good stability.
6. Capable of a frequency response from dc to some high frequency.
7. One 180° (−) input and one zero degree (+) input.

The operational amplifier (op-amp) is made up of several differential amplifier stages, sometimes with an FET input, and an emitter follower output stage. A simplified op-amp circuit is shown in Figure 11–27.

Figure 11–28 shows several typical op-amp circuits. The triangle-shaped symbol represents a complete op-amp package.

Figure 11–28B is a voltage follower, the op-amp equivalent of a super emitter follower.

Figure 11–28C is a basic amplifier for

any purpose with the voltage gain and input impedance under external control by simply selecting values for R_{in} and R_f. The amplifier provides 180° phase inversion and is roughly equivalent to a super common-emitter circuit.

Figure 11–28D is a noninverting amplifier with approximately the same voltage gain as the inverting amplifier in B. There is no single stage transistor equivalent for this circuit. It features the high voltage gain of a common emitter transistor circuit, combined with the very high input impedance and no phase inversion of the pedance and no phase inversion of the

emitter-follower transistor circuit. Again, the voltage gain controlled by two external resistors.

The circuit in Figure 11–28E is a perfect rectifier, even at voltages so low that they would not turn on a solid state diode, and would produce a distorted half-wave pulse with a vacuum tube diode. It is a popular circuit for ac millivolt ranges in digital multimeters.

The op-amp circuits presented here are only a small sample of those in common use. There are several books devoted entirely to op-amp circuits.

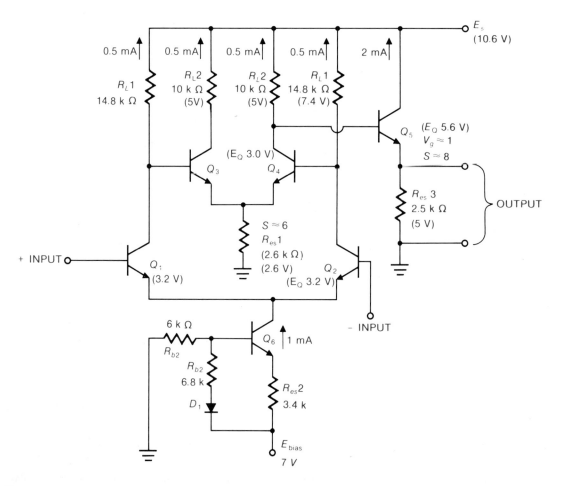

Figure 11-27 Simplified operational amplifier schematic diagram.

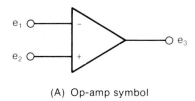

(A) Op-amp symbol

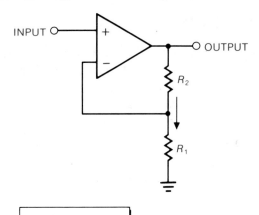

$$V_g = 1 + R_2/R_1$$
$$Z_{in} = \text{Very high}$$

(D) Noninverting amplifier.

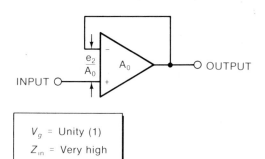

$$V_g = \text{Unity (1)}$$
$$Z_{in} = \text{Very high}$$

(B) Voltage follower

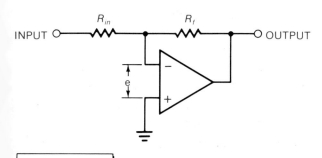

$$V_g = R_f/R_{in}$$
$$Z_{in} = R_{in}$$

(C) Inverting amplifier

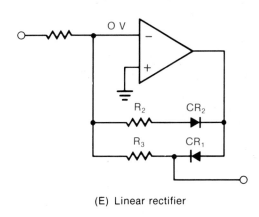

(E) Linear rectifier

Figure 11-28 Op-amp circuits.

SUMMARY

1. There are several methods of coupling amplifier stages:
   a. Resistor/capacitor(RC) coupling
   b. Impedance coupling
   c. Direct coupling
   d. Transformer coupling

2. RC coupling is most commonly found in audio amplifiers.

3. Impedance coupling is used for low frequency circuits, particularly those designed to operate at 60 hertz; servo amplifiers, for example. It is also sometimes used in video amplifier circuits.

4. Direct coupling is restricted to use with very stable transistor circuits such as the differential amplifier.

5. Transformer coupling can be used at any frequency, but is preferred for radio frequencies and intermediate frequencies. Transformers are used in tube type audio equipment, but rarely in quality transistorized equipment.

6. The emitter-follower circuit is used as an impedance transformer. It has a voltage gain of 1 and no phase shift.

7. Complementary symmetry amplifiers are preferred for audio power stages and for output stages in pulse amplifiers.

8. Crossover distortion will occur in a complementary symmetry amplifier unless some fixed bias is applied. Crossover distortion is not important in pulse amplifiers, but is unacceptable in audio systems.

9. An inverter is a common emitter amplifier used in pulse amplifier circuits.

10. Pulse amplifiers require a broad bandwidth. The pulse amplifier amplifies a square wave, which consists of a large number of odd harmonics. Harmonics are multiples (two times, three times, four times, and so on) of the base or fundamental frequency sine wave. A narrow band amplifier will reject some of the harmonics, distorting the waveform.

11. Video amplifier signals contain all the information necessary to produce a television or radar picture on a cathode ray tube (CRT) screen. If the amplifier does not have enough bandwidth, picture detail will be lost.

12. A wide band amplifier must usually sacrifice voltage gain for bandwidth. The greater the bandwidth, the less gain the amplifier stage will be able to produce.

13. Negative feedback is often used in video amplifiers to increase the bandwidth at the expense of gain.

14. Nearly all radio frequency and intermediate frequency amplifiers use tuned (tank circuit) transformer coupling. The tuned transformers provide coupling, and, at the same time, reject unwanted frequencies.

15. Drivers provide power gain to turn on lamps and actuate relays.

16. The Darlington pair is a two-transistor direct coupled transistor that has a very high compound beta. It is particularly useful in the emitter-follower circuit.

17. The differential amplifier is a nearly universal amplifier stage. It features high gain, high stability, inverted and noninverted amplification, and a wide bandwidth.

18. An operational amplifier is a complete amplifier system in a package. It uses several differential amplifier stages and an emitter-follower output stage. Provisions for external feedback are provided for easy gain control.

REVIEWING YOUR ELECTRONICS VOCABULARY

1. Audio amplifier
2. Darlington pair
3. Direct coupling
4. Distortion
5. Impedance coupling
6. Intermediate frequency amplifier
7. *RC* coupling
8. RF amplifier
9. Video amplifier

CHECKING YOUR UNDERSTANDING

1. List four methods of coupling amplifier stages.
2. What is the most common coupling method in audio amplifiers?
3. Why are transformers often avoided as coupling devices in high quality audio equipment?
4. Why are transformers the preferred coupling method at radio and intermediate frequencies?
5. In what kind of circuit is crossover distortion a problem?
6. Of what frequency components is a square wave composed?
7. What kinds of cores are used in RF and IF transformers?
8. List at least four outstanding characteristics of the differential amplifier.
9. What is the purpose of replacing the emitter resistor in a differential amplifier with a transistor?
10. List seven important characteristics of an *operational amplifier*.

SOLVING ELECTRONIC PROBLEMS

1. Draw the schematic diagram of an *RC* coupled, two-stage transistor amplifier. Use the common emitter circuit.
2. Draw the schematic diagram of a Darlington pair amplifier.
3. Draw the schematic diagram of a differential amplifier circuit.
4. Draw the schematic diagram of an operational amplifier inverting amplifier with a voltage gain of 10.
5. Draw the schematic diagram of an operational amplifier noninverting amplifier with a voltage gain of 11.

CHAPTER 12
Signal Generation and Waveshaping

INTRODUCTION

An oscillator, by definition, is a device that generates a signal at a frequency determined by certain components within its circuit.

Oscillators are classified as *relaxation* types or *sinusoidal* types. The relaxation oscillator depends on a resistor-capacitor timing circuit and a switching device to discharge the capacitor at a critical threshold voltage.

There are two basic types of *sinusoidal oscillators,* those that produce a sine wave output. The first type is a two-terminal oscillator that has a resonant circuit to determine the frequency and a negative-resistance device to maintain the oscillations. The second basic type of sinusoidal oscillator is the much more familiar feedback type, which is basically an amplifier with some type of network to feed some of the output back into the input. The common techniques for altering the waveshapes produced by both kinds of oscillators will be examined.

12.1 RELAXATION OSCILLATORS

The tunnel diode has the quirk of having an unstable current-voltage characteristic, as shown in Figure 12–1A. When we drive this negative-resistance device with a voltage source, it will become stable. If you examine the curve of Figure 12–1A, you can see that the tangent of the negative-resistance portion of the curve is approximately tangent to the positive or normal section of the curve. Therefore the amplitude of the output of the oscillator will be determined by the area over which the lines coincide. Figure 12–2 is a tunnel diode oscillator; note its simplicity.

We can get a rough idea of how the circuit works by visualizing a ball sitting on the unstable part of the curve in Figure 12–1A. Noise in the system causes the ball to roll down into the valley of the curve, where it tends to roll back and forth as shown in Figure 12–1B. As the ball rolls back and forth, circulating current is excited in the tank circuit, which, in turn, keeps the ball rolling in step with the resonant frequency of the tank.

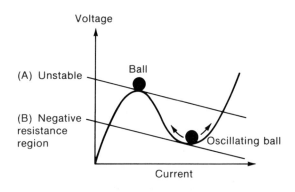

Figure 12-1 Negative resistance curve.

200

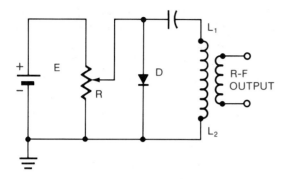

Figure 12-2 Tunnel diode oscillator circuit.

Another simple relaxation oscillator is the four-layer diode oscillator. The circuit is shown in Figure 12–3.

How It Works

The capacitor charges slowly through the resistor. The four-layer diode behaves as an open circuit until a critical voltage of about 8 volts is placed across it. When the capacitor reaches a charge of 8 volts, the diode suddenly turns on, becoming a near short across the capacitor. The capacitor is rapidly discharged, until at about 1 volt the diode shuts off and remains off until the capacitor again charges to 8 volts. The output waveform is not a sine wave.

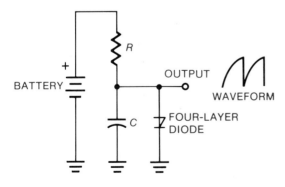

Figure 12-3 Four-layer diode oscillator circuit.

12.2 FEEDBACK OSCILLATORS

A feedback oscillator is simply an amplifier with some type of network that will feed some of the output of the amplifier back to its input in the correct phase. A block diagram of a basic feedback oscillator is shown in Figure 12–3. Because of the ability of tubes and transistors to amplify, they can generate oscillations that will be sustained as long as we maintain power to the circuit. In order for oscillation to occur, a part of the oscillator must be shock-excited into oscillation by a *change* in current flowing through the tank. When the LC circuit begins to oscillate (ring), the oscillations of this LC circuit will be amplified by the amplifier (transistor). From the output of the amplifier a small part of the signal is fed back to the original shock-excited circuit section, which will make up for any losses in the circuit and thus maintain the oscillations as long as power is applied.

The feedback in an oscillator may be inductive or capacitive, or a combination of the two. In this chapter we will try to cover the more common types of oscillators and the principles of their operation. But before we begin our study of oscillators, we will study the important subject of *waveshaping*. Waveshaping circuits are common in many types of oscillators. We will also cover the kindred subjects of *clippers, clampers,* and *limiters*. Some types of oscillators utilize

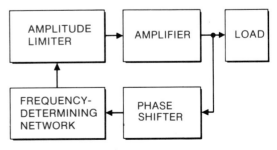

Figure 12-4 Block diagram of a feedback oscillator.

clippers or limiters to generate or shape the output in order to obtain the type of waveform desired.

12.3 WAVESHAPING CIRCUITS

We have already studied *RL* and *RC* time constants. This section will present a quick review, but will show in addition how the time constant circuit can be put to good use to reshape a waveform or establish a dc reference for a signal.

The Differentiation Network

The differentiation network is a very simple circuit, and, with proper selection of its component values, the shape of a waveform can be altered.

The circuit shown in Figure 12–5 is a differentiator, shown with its input and output waveshapes. The sudden application of the leading edge of the square wave input signal will cause maximum current to flow in *R*, since the capacitor has no voltage charge on it and can offer no opposition to the input voltage. The voltage drop across *R* will rise very rapidly to a maximum shown as point A in the figure. By selecting values of

R and *C*, we can establish a very short time constant as compared to the input signal's period. The capacitor *C* will charge rapidly and the voltage drop across *R*, and thus the current through *R*, will drop in direct proportion to the charge on capacitor *C*, which will offer opposition to the input voltage. The capacitor will charge to full charge long before the end of the input waveform. This action is shown as point B in Figure 12–5. From point B to point C in time, no current will flow because of the charge on the capacitor. At time point C the input waveshape drops to zero volts, thus the capacitor no longer has a voltage driving it. Therefore, it will send a surge of current of the opposite polarity through *R*, from time point C to time point D. With a short time constant the capacitor will discharge fully in a very short period, as shown by the waveform from time point D to point E. From time point E to time point F the voltage across *R* will remain at zero volts because there is no input nor is there a charge on capacitor *C* to produce an output. Thus a complete cycle of the input signal gives two output pulses, one positive (charging) and the other negative (discharging).

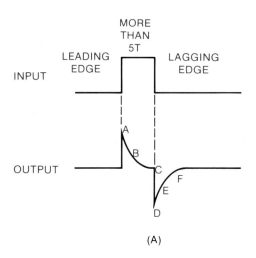

(A)

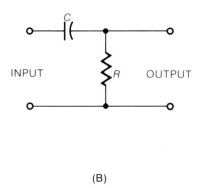

(B)

Figure 12–5 Differentiator.

Integrator Circuit

An *RC* circuit may be constructed, so that the charging time is short and the discharge time is long. A circuit that has these characteristics is shown in Figure 12–6. The short time for charging permits the capacitor to charge to full input voltage long before the input signal's first half-cycle, as shown in the waveshapes of the figure. When the input signal reaches its second half-cycle time, as shown in Figure 12–6, the capacitor will begin to discharge toward zero volts.

   A good example of this type of circuit is the television vertical integrator. A time constant on the order of about 100 microseconds is common. This time constant can be obtained as follows:

$$T = RC$$

$$T = (100,000)\ (.001\ \mu F)$$

$$T = 100,000 \times 0.000000001$$

$$T = 0.0001\ \text{seconds}$$

$$T = 100\ \text{microseconds}$$

Figure 12–7 shows a typical TV vertical sync integrator. The pulses fed into the integrator are of various widths, as shown in the input waveshape of the figure. Note that there are also differently timed intervals between the pulses. The integrator, because

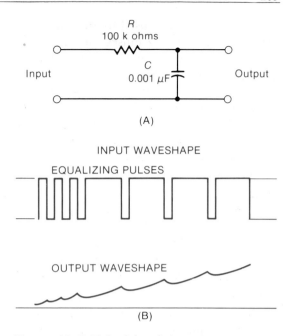

(A)

INPUT WAVESHAPE

EQUALIZING PULSES

OUTPUT WAVESHAPE

(B)

Figure 12–7 Television integrator.

of its time constant, will ignore the short pulses, called equalizing pulses, and will begin to recognize the wide pulses as the pulses it is designed to see. The capacitor will charge only to a very low voltage during the time the equalizing pulses are present and will almost fully discharge between them. But when the wider vertical pulses appear, with the much shorter time between them, the capacitor will charge during the pulses and discharge very little between, thus giving a stepping increase charge to the

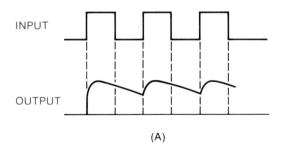

(A)

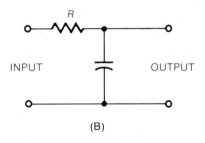

(B)

Figure 12–6 Integrator.

capacitor that can be used by the television receiver to sort 60 Hz pulses out of a composite waveform that contains both 60 Hz and 15,750 Hz pulses.

The integrator circuit can be used to generate a triangular waveshape. If the capacitor is allowed to charge through a high resistance, it will develop a long exponential charge curve by gradually building the charge on the capacitor over a long time period.

The capacitor will discharge much faster than it charges because the discharge occurs through the output load of the circuit, which is of much lower resistance than the charging resistance. This type of circuit is widely used in electronic circuits. Some oscillators such as the 4-layer diode oscillator depend upon the time constant of the RC charge-discharge time to establish their operating frequency.

12.4 DIODE CLAMPING AND LIMITING

Often the dc reference level of a signal must be changed or set to a certain dc value despite input signal variations. The circuit shown in Figure 12–8 can be used to accomplish this. The circuit will not distort the input signal's waveshape if the time constant of the RC network is long compared to the time period of the input signal. Because of the circuit's ability to pass a signal without distortion, the circuit can be used with complex input signals. The capacitor blocks the incoming dc level so the signal will swing around a ground (zero) reference level. In the example (Figure 12–8) the resistor is reference to ground. This will cause the average dc output to be zero. The shaded area in Figure 12–8 shows that the positive alternation equals the negative alternation. As can be seen, the signal is not a symmetrical square wave. It has a narrower, but

higher, positive pulse as compared to the negative portion. If the input were a symmetrical square wave, the positive and negative swings would be of equal amplitude. A signal's peak value, with respect to its reference, depends upon its waveshape. Also, the peak value will vary directly with the signal strength. Although the capacitor establishes a dc reference for the output, the output, is not clamped to a specific voltage.

By employing a diode in conjunction with a capacitor and resistor, the input signal can be clamped to any dc reference voltage. This clamping can be easily accomplished by biasing the circuit to the desired level.

Clampers

A clamper is a circuit that permits the voltage of a waveform to rise or fall only as far as a specific reference voltage. Clampers may have a negative or positive reference voltage.

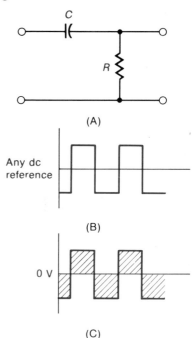

Figure 12-8 Clamper.

Positive Diode Clamper It can be seen in Figure 12–9 that the output from each circuit is clamped to a dc voltage reference. The output of the positive diode clampers are always *above* the reference, whatever it may be. As with the circuit of Figure 12–8, the waveshape and the peak-to-peak amplitude of the input are left unchanged by the circuit. The output end of the capacitor is kept charged above the clamping reference level by approximately the peak voltage of the input signal by the rectifying action of the diode. Because of this, the output signal rides on top of the dc clamping refer-

ence voltage. As an illustration, let us apply a symmetrical sawtooth waveshape to the input of a diode clamper with a signal dc reference of 0 volts and a peak-to-peak voltage of 8 volts. If we have a clamper bias of −2 volts, the reference for the clamper is thus −2 volts. The output signal will therefore be a symmetrical sawtooth waveshape that varies from −2 volts to a +6 volts with a peak-to-peak voltage of 8 volts, the same as the input signal.

Negative Diode Clamper In the negative diode clampers shown in Figure 12–9, the

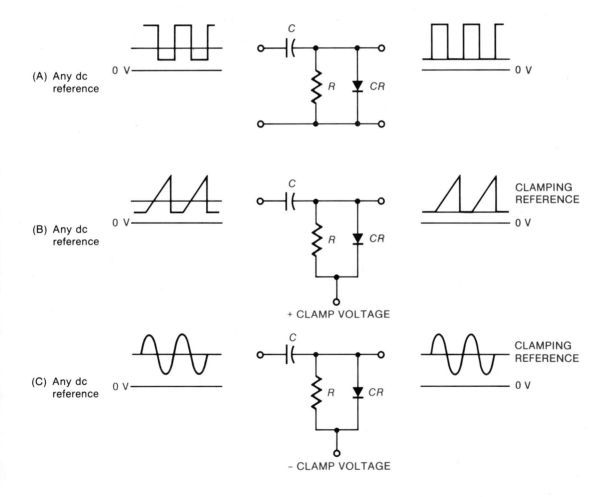

Figure 12-9 Positive diode clampers.

cathode of the diode in each circuit is connected to the reference rather than the anode as in the positive clamper. With the diode thus connected, it will keep the capacitor charged below the clamping reference by an amount equal to the peak voltage of the input signal. Because of this diode action, the output rides *below* the reference clamp voltage in negative clampers.

A quick method for identifying the type of clamper (positive or negative) is to note the arrow direction on the diode. If it points *toward* the bias or ground, the clamper is a negative clamper. Check the circuits of Figures 12–9 and 12–10 to verify this.

Limiters

A circuit that limits the amplitude of either the positive or negative excursion or both is known as a *limiter*, (sometimes called a *clipper*), because it limits or clips the positive peak, negative peak, or both of the input signal. This clipping or limiting will flatten the peaks of the input waveshape in doing its job.

Limiters are used extensively in pulse waveshaping. A sine wave can be limited or clipped to almost a square wave. The output of oscillators can be improved and distorted pulse shapes can be corrected. A limiter can also be used to prevent unwanted amplitude variations and to help eliminate system noise.

Series Limiter A series limiter is formed by placing a diode in series with the load. The circuit also has a resistor to a bias voltage or to ground as needed. For this version of the circuit, the diode is reverse-biased by the input signal. The limiting is, of course, not perfect because of the reverse current flow. To get the best limiting action, it is necessary to make the resistor as small as possible

compared to the reverse resistance of the diode.

The circuit shown in Figure 12–11 is called a *positive limiter*, because it will limit the upward swing of the input signal. The basic circuit is unbiased and will therefore limit at 0 volts. It is a simple half-wave rectifier, with only the negative alternation appearing across the resistor. By utilizing a positive bias, only part of the positive alternation is clipped. The clipping reference in Figure 12–11 is +E and the diode conducts until the input signal reaches this +E voltage. When the input signal reaches the +E voltage value, it will reverse bias the diode, which then becomes a very high resistance. This high resistance virtually blocks the input, thus giving an output of +E as long as the amplitude of the input exceeds the +E bias level.

When a –E bias is used, a larger amount of clipping occurs. The fact that a negative bias causes more clipping of the input signal, and a positive bias causes less clipping, is the secret of the series diode limiter.

Negative Series Limiter To get a negative series limiter, all we have to do is to reverse the diodes in the circuit just discussed. A negative series limiter is shown in Figure 12–12. By reversing the diodes, we get the opposite type of clipping as the rectification action occurs in the opposite direction from the positive limiter. In Figure 12–12 a polarity opposite to that of Figure 12–11 is shown. The negative alternation is clipped. If less clipping is desired, a negative bias is applied. If more is wanted, a positive bias is applied.

Shunt Limiter Another type of diode limiter is shown in Figure 12–13. This limiter design is known as the *positive shunt limiter*. Its limiting action is similar to the positive series limiter in the way bias affects its operation. However, in this circuit the ohmic value of the series resistor should be very small compared to the load resistance. The series resistor and the load form a voltage divider and thus the series resistor causes some attenuation. Therefore, the smaller the series resistor is made, the less the output voltage attenuation. This type of limiter, because of the shunting diode, is considered an open circuit, and the small series resistance works best with a high resistance load.

The reversal of the diode provides limiting of the opposite polarity part of the waveform.

The major advantage of the shunt limiter is illustrated in Figure 12–14. With shunt limiters one may combine a positive and a negative limiter into a single unit.

Zener Limiter As you will recall, a zener diode is a diode that operates in its breakdown region. As shown in Figure 12–15, by selection of the zener's operation voltage the clipping point can be selected without a bias supply. Also as shown, a positive/negative clipper/limiter can be made with a single symmetrical Zener diode.

12.5 SCHMITT TRIGGER

The Schmitt trigger is another circuit designed for pulse shaping. If *any* waveshape of sufficient amplitude is applied to the input of the circuit, the output will be

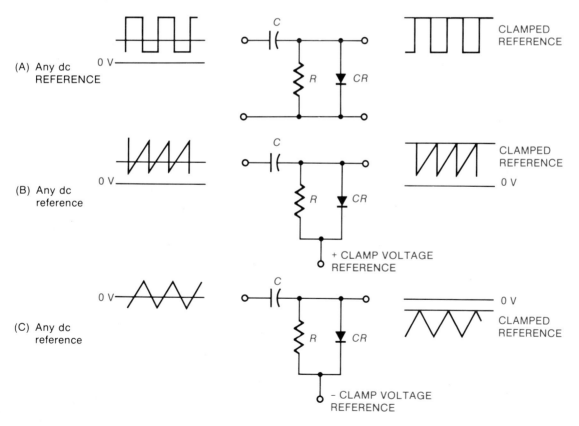

Figure 12-10 Negative diode clampers.

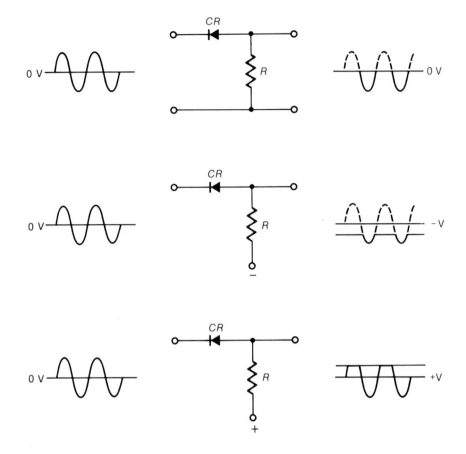

Figure 12-11 Positive series limiter.

a rectangular waveshape.

The Schmitt trigger circuit is a device that produces an output only when the input signal has reached a desired amplitude. In order to develop an output, the input signal must overcome the bias on the circuit. Since the bias is adjustable, it is possible to control the amount of signal required to trigger the circuit.

The only time there is an output is when the signal input overcomes the reference level (see Figure 12–16B). No particular signal waveshape is required as long as the amplitude is high enough. The output is always a rectangular waveshape of constant amplitude. The width of the output pulse depends upon how long the input is equal to or above the reference level. The amplitude of the input signal necessary to develop an output is determined by the reference level.

A transistorized Schmitt trigger of conventional design is shown in Figure 12–17. In the quiescent state, transistor Q_1 is at cut-off, with the collector voltage approximately equal to $-V$. This negative voltage is coupled to the base of transistor Q_2 through resistor R_3 and the base voltage of transistor Q_2 is equal to the voltage drop across resistor R_5.

Current flow from the emitter of transistor Q_2 through common emitter resistor

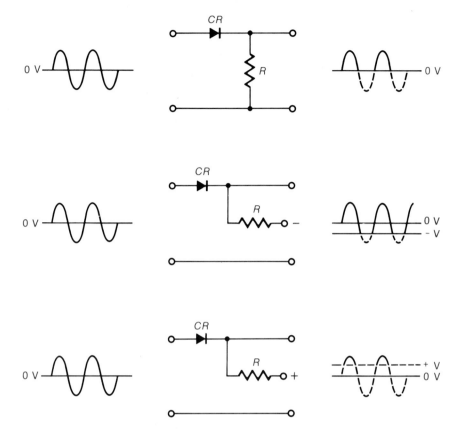

Figure 12-12 Negative series limiter.

R_4 maintains the emitter of transistor Q_1 at a negative potential. The reverse bias now developed between the emitter and the base of transistor Q_1 maintains the cutoff condition. A sufficiently high negative voltage at the base of transistor Q_2 produces forward bias for the emitter base junction and drives it into saturation.

A negative signal of sufficient amplitude applied to the base of transistor Q_1 will overcome the reverse bias and cause transistor Q_1 to conduct. The potential at the collector decreases; that is, becomes less negative. This change is coupled to the base of transistor Q_2. The emitter current of transistor Q_2 decreases, lowering the potential across resistor R_4. The emitter of transistor

Q_1 becomes less negative, reducing the reverse bias and increasing collector current. This regenerative action continues until transistor Q_1 is operating in the saturation region and transistor Q_2 is at cutoff. The output voltage is a maximum negative voltage as shown in the output waveform in Figure 12-17.

This stable condition continues until the input begins to rise to become more positive. The positive-going input decreases the base potential of transistor Q_1 and increases the reverse bias, causing the collector voltage to increase (become more negative), the emitter current to decrease, and the potential across R_4 to decrease, simultaneously. The increasing (negative) voltage at the col-

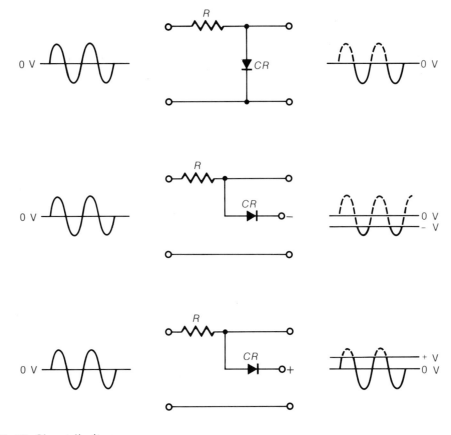

Figure 12-13 Shunt limiter.

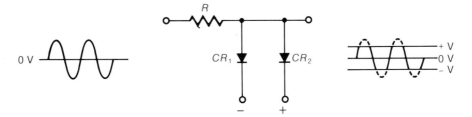

Figure 12-14 Positive/negative shunt limiter.

lector of transistor Q_1 is coupled to the base of transistor Q_2, driving it negative, and the decreasing voltage of resistor R_4 causes the emitter of transistor Q_2 to go more positive. Both actions reduce the reverse bias of the emitter-base junction and transistor Q_2 again operates at saturation, cutting off

transistor Q_1 and thus returning the circuit to its original operating conditions. The output is a minimum negative voltage, as shown in Figure 12-17.

The rise and fall time of the output waveshape of this circuit is shorter than that of conventional bi-stable multivibrators,

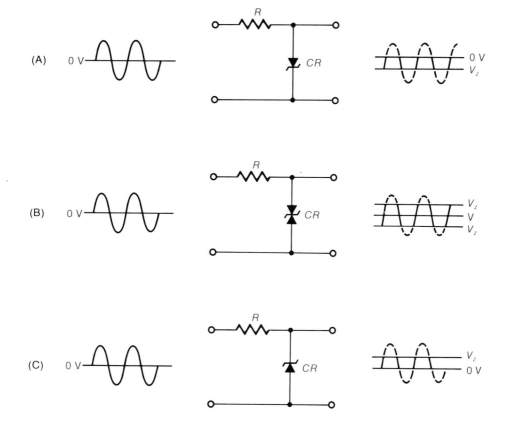

Figure 12-15 Zener diode limiters.

which we will cover later in this chapter. The shape of the Schmitt output waveshape does not depend upon the shape of the signal input waveshape.

12.6 INDUCTANCE-CAPACITIVE OSCILLATORS

In Chapter 6 we covered the basic *LC* circuit (Figure 12–18) and most of its characteristics. As you will recall, such a circuit will tend to oscillate; that is, the capacitance will charge when the magnetic field collapses in the inductor. The capacitor then discharges through the inductor, causing another magnetic field to build in the inductor. When the capacitor is discharged, the magnetic field in the inductor

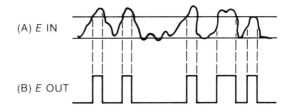

Figure 12-16 Schmitt trigger waveshapes.

begins to collapse, thus starting the cycle over again. Because all circuits have some resistance, some of the energy in the circuit during this cycling will be lost as heat. Therefore, each cycle will have less and less amplitude, as shown in Figure 12–19, until the energy is finally reduced to zero.

Figure 12–20 is the circuit diagram of a

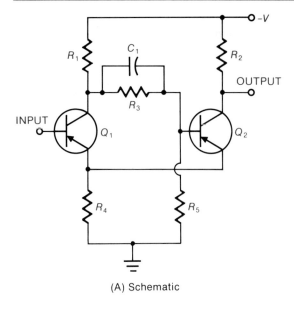

(A) Schematic

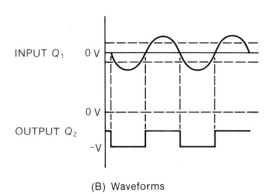

(B) Waveforms

Figure 12-17 Schmitt trigger circuit.

Figure 12-18 LC circuit.

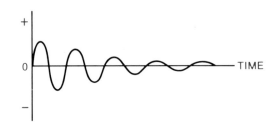

Figure 12-19 Oscillations in a tuned circuit.

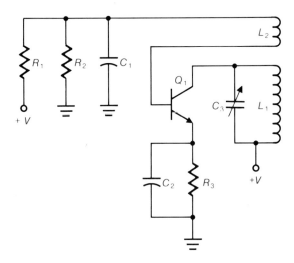

Figure 12-20 LC oscillator.

very simple LC oscillator. In this circuit L_1 is coupled to, and phased with, L_2, and thus any voltage induced into L_1 will be coupled to the base of the transistor. No external signal is required to start or excite this type of oscillator. Oscillations will continue to occur as long as power is applied to the circuit. When power is first applied to the circuit, any random voltage variations (usually noise) in the circuit will be amplified. The voltage variations that occur at the resonant frequency of the tuned circuit in the collector of the transistor will be amplified more than any other frequency. The voltage variations that occur at this resonant frequency will become dominant very quickly due to the feedback energy supplied by the amplifier output. The dominance of the resonant frequency in the collector circuit will cause the circuit to operate at this frequency and to maintain an output as long as power is applied to it.

In our example, positive inductive feedback is utilized to sustain the oscillations, but capacitive or even resistive coupling could also be utilized to establish the feedback required by the circuit.

Frequency

The frequency of the oscillator is determined by the resonant frequency of the *LC* tank circuit. We can approximate the frequency of the oscillator from the following equation:

$$f = \frac{0.159}{\sqrt{LC}}$$

or

$$f_0 = \frac{1}{2\pi \sqrt{LC}}$$

Now that we know how an *LC* oscillator works, let us analyze several basic types.

The Armstrong Oscillator

The Armstrong oscillator is the one we covered in our example. Figure 12–21 is an Armstrong oscillator with *L* and *C* variable to permit variation of the frequency of oscillation. The output can be taken from either plate or collector circuit, or it may be taken from grid or base. However, an output from plate or collector is by far the best, as it has less effect upon the frequency of oscillations.

The Armstrong oscillator in Figure 12–21 is called a *series fed* oscillator because of the way in which the plate or collector current flows through the feedback coil in series with the plate or collector of the tube or transistor.

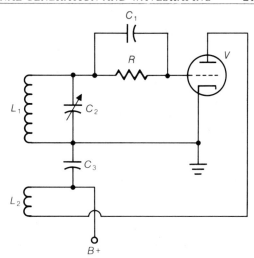

Figure 12-21 Armstrong oscillator.

The Hartley oscillator is a very close relative of the Armstrong oscillator, but there are two basic differences. First, the feedback coil is moved from the plate or collector circuit and placed between the cathode or emitter and ground. This puts the feedback coil at a much lower voltage point in the circuit and thus lower voltage rated *LC* components can be used. Second, instead of the two separate coils used in the Armstrong oscillator, the Hartley uses only one coil (autotransformer) which is taped near the ground end as seen in Figure 12–22. The coil in combination with the capacitor forms a resonant tank circuit, which determines the frequency of oscillation.

The Hartley oscillator can be either series fed, as shown in Figure 12–22, or shunt fed, as shown in Figure 12–23. The output can be taken from either the collector or the base in the shunt fed Hartley or from the base in the series fed design.

Colpitts Oscillator

The Colpitts oscillator, shown in Figure 12–24, is very similar to the Hartley, except that two variable capacitors are used in the

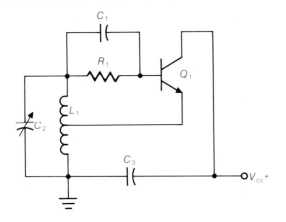

Figure 12-22 Hartley oscillator, series fed.

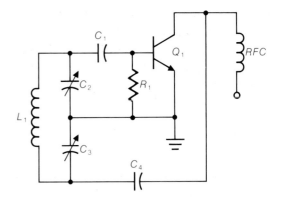

Figure 12-24 Colpitts oscillator.

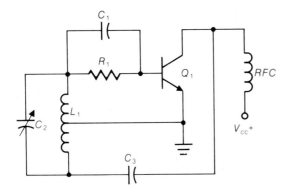

Figure 12-23 Hartley oscillator, shunt fed.

tank circuit instead of the tapped coil. Feedback of this type is known as *capacitive feedback*. The ratio of the values of the two capacitors determines the amount of feedback. The feedback is obtained by coupling the ac collector current through C_2. The frequency of the oscillator can be varied by adjusting C_1, C_1 and C_2 or L. The output from the oscillator can be taken from either the base or the collector circuits.

12.7 RESISTOR-CAPACITOR (RC) OSCILLATOR

Resistor-capacitor *(RC)* oscillators are principally low frequency, audio oscillators.

They do not use an LC tank circuit for frequency control, but instead utilize the principle of phase shift in the feedback network. There are three major types of RC oscillators: the phase-shift, the Wien bridge, and the bridged T.

Phase Shift Oscillator

The phase shift oscillator shown in Figure 12-25 is frequency-selective because only one set of R and C will provide the 180-degree phase shift (at one particular frequency) necessary to maintain oscillations. Any other frequency will provide feedback with incorrect phasing to maintain oscillations. Because of this, the circuit will operate at the frequency where there is phase shift of exactly 180 degrees in the RC network. The oscillation frequency can easily be changed by adjusting either C or R in the RC feedback network. The frequency is inversely proportional to the R and C values in the network.

Wien Bridge Oscillator

The Wien bridge oscillator utilizes an RC bridge network to provide the feedback with proper phase shift. The oscillator shown in Figure 12-26 uses two transistors in the

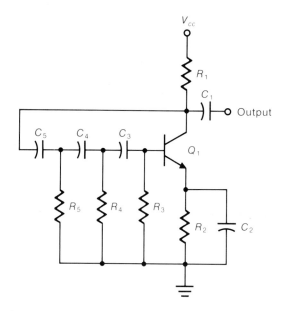

Figure 12-25 Phase-shift oscillator.

common emitter configuration. Transistor Q_2 functions as an amplifier and phase inverter to deliver the correct phase voltage to the feedback network. Some degeneration (negative feedback) is also used in the oscillator to provide frequency stability and reduce distortion in the output signal.

The oscillator's feedback is developed from the collector of Q_2 and ground. From Q_2, the feedback is passed by C_3 to the bridge network. In the bridge, the voltage on C_2 will be passed on the base of Q_1. Because of the *RC* bridge network, the feedback will be in phase at only one frequency. This is due to the phasing relationship of the bridge components. The phasing of the signals across R_1, C_1 and RB_1 and C_2 vary in opposite directions as the frequency changes. At the operating frequency, the phase shift is zero. As the frequency shifts up or down, the feedback decreases. Only the correct phase feedback voltage will be enough to sustain oscillation.

In the Wien bridge oscillator of Figure 12–26, the negative feedback is obtained by

omitting any bypass capacitors across the emitter resistors of the transistors. Some of the feedback voltage is also applied through R_2 to the emitter of Q_1. This negative feedback, or degeneration, is fixed because it is developed across resistors and its amount is determined by the value of R_2. By making R_2 a variable resistor, the amplitude of the output can be controlled.

The frequency of the oscillator is determined by C_1 and C_2 in connection with R_1 and RB_1. The equation for the output frequency is

$$f = \frac{1}{2\pi\ R_1 C_1 RB_1 C_2}$$

The equation could be reduced further if RB_1 and R_1 are equal and C_1 is equal to C_2. Then we can restate the equation as follows:

$$f = \frac{1}{2\pi\ R_1 C_1}$$

The oscillator can be made variable by making either C_1 and C_2 or R_1 and RB_1 variable in a step function.

Both Q_1 and Q_2 are biased and stabilized similarly. The thermistor RT_1 and resistors RB_1, RC_1 and RF_1 provide the bias for Q_1. Resistors RB_2, RC_2 and RF_2 make up the biasing resistors for Q_2. Capacitor C_c is a coupling capacitor between Q_1 and Q_2. The output of the oscillator is taken through C_c to the load.

Example 12–1

Problem: Find f, when R_1 is 100,000 ohms and C_1 is 0.1 microfarad.

Solution:

$$R_1 = 100,000\ \Omega$$

$$C_1 = 0.1\ \mu F$$

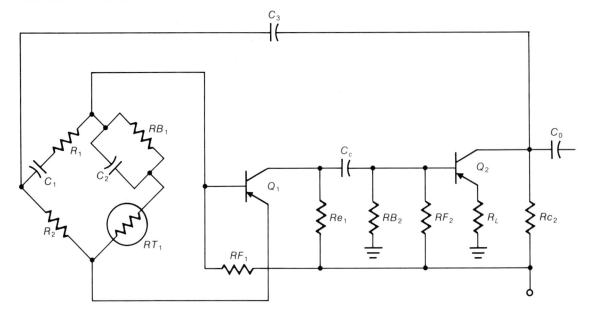

Figure 12-26 Wien bridge oscillator.

$$f = \frac{1}{2\pi R_1 C_1}$$

$$= \frac{1}{6.28 \times 100,000 \times 0.0000001}$$

$$= \frac{1}{.0628}$$

$$= 15.92 \text{ hertz}$$

Bridged T Oscillator

The bridged T oscillator, as shown in Figure 12–27, uses an RC notch type feedback network filter to determine the oscillator's frequency. The bridged T filter network can be made variable to allow the frequency of the oscillator to be varied.

12.8 CRYSTAL OSCILLATORS

The frequencies of the oscillators we have covered so far are affected by changes in load, temperature, and supply voltages. When we want to maintain exactly a certain frequency over a long period, a *crystal controlled oscillator* can do the job. A full dis-

cussion of crystals is not within the scope of this text. However, we should understand some of their capabilities and characteristics.

Crystal oscillators operate on a principle known as the *piezo-electric effect*. This is the ability of some crystalline materials to change their shape when voltage (emf) is applied to the crystal. Some piezo-electric crystals are utilized in phonograph pickups and other places where a mechanical motion is to be converted into an electrical signal.

In an electronic oscillator, a small slab of quartz crystal is mounted between a pair of electrodes. The physical measurements of the slab are such that it will vibrate mechanically at a frequency very close to the desired oscillator frequency. The driving force for oscillation of the crystal is an applied voltage. The velocity of the crystal, as it is deformed mechanically, will lead the applied voltage by angles up to 90 degrees at frequencies below resonance and will lag behind the applied voltage by angles up to 90 degrees at frequencies above resonance. In addition, for a given velocity at various fre-

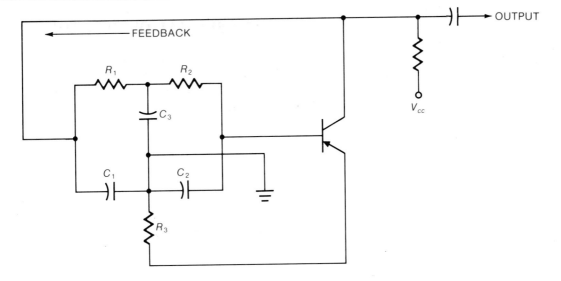

Figure 12-27 The bridged "T" (or twin "T") oscillator.

quencies, the applied voltage will be a minimum at resonance.

Figure 12–28 shows what occurs when a voltage is applied across a crystal. In part A of the figure, voltage has been applied but the crystal has not yet begun to deform. The applied voltage, E, is in the direction indicated by the arrow. As the crystal begins its deforming process, it will develop a counter voltage, shown as F in part B of the figure. Because of F, the voltage applied to the crystal must be increased in order to maintain the same voltage across the crystal. The current flow to the crystal holder plates is proportional to the rate at which the charge is increased, and this, in turn, is proportional to the rate at which the crystal is distorted, the *crystal velocity.*

The equivalent circuit of a crystal is one in which the current leads the voltage below resonance, is in phase with the voltage at resonance, and lags the voltage at frequencies above resonance. In addition, the maximum phase angle between current and voltage is 90 degrees, leading or lagging, and for constant current, the voltage is a minimum at

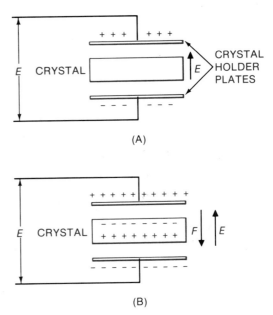

Figure 12-28 Oscillating crystal.

resonance. In Figure 12–29 L, R, and C form precisely such a circuit, and C_1 is the capacitance between the plates of the crystal holder. This is always present, even though the two electrodes of the holder may be

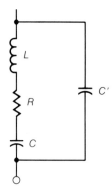

Figure 12-29 Equivalent circuit of a crystal.

plated on the crystal. The quartz crystal behaves like a series-resonant circuit shunted by a small capacitor.

Because all crystal oscillators are similar, we will describe only one example, the *Pierce oscillator*.

The Pierce Oscillator

Figure 12-30 illustrates two basic Pierce transistor crystal oscillators. In the Pierce circuit the crystal can operate in either series or parallel mode. In the series mode shown in part A of Figure 12-30, the crystal controls the amount of feedback by presenting low impedance at the resonant frequency, where at other frequencies the reactance is high and provides less feedback. Also, at other than the resonant frequency of the crystal, the phase shift of the feedback is not the 180 degrees needed for oscillation.

In part B of Figure 12-30 the crystal is operated in the parallel mode where the crystal is at a high impedance rather than low. At other than the crystal frequency, the low impedance will load the transistor and cause the feedback to be about 90 degrees out of phase, thus preventing oscillations.

12.9 SPECIAL OSCILLATORS

This section will cover oscillators that cannot readily be classified under the earlier headings. The oscillators described here are based on feedback, as are most oscillators, but special frequency control methods set them apart.

Voltage Controlled Oscillators (VCO)

A voltage controlled oscillator (VCO) circuit is shown in Figure 12-31. We will use as an example the chroma reference crystal oscillator commonly used in color television receivers.

In the circuit in Figure 12-31, a reverse biased diode, called a *varactor diode*, serves as a voltage variable capacitor across the crystal in a Colpitts type oscillator. Varying the capacitance of the diode changes the resonant frequency of the crystal slightly.

A bias voltage (or signal voltage) across a reverse biased diode will vary the depletion zone, increasing capacitance as the reverse bias is decreased and decreasing the capacitance (by widening the zone) when the reverse bias is increased.

Any junction diode can be used as a variable capacitor, but the varactor diode is specially designed for the task and is available in suitable ranges of capacity.

The IC Voltage Controlled Oscillator

The circuit shown in Figure 12-32 is similar to the previous VCO, but it is built around a commercial integrated circuit (*IC*).

The oscillator consists of an RF/IF integrated circuit/amplifier chip with an LC tuned output (L and C_2) and a feedback loop (D_1, C_R, C_1).

The varactor diode, D_1, in the feedback network is controlled by the input control voltage. The voltage dependent capacitance

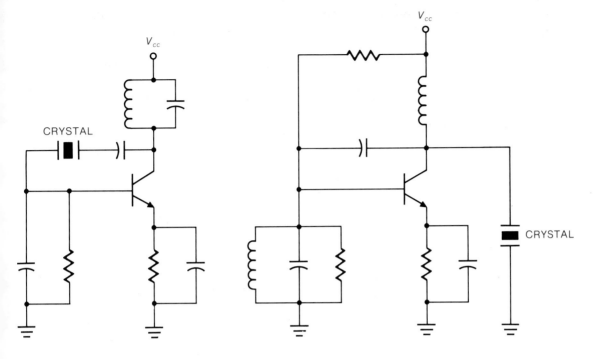

Figure 12-30 Pierce oscillator.

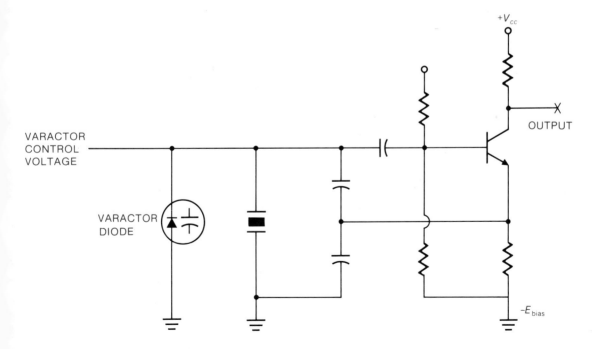

Figure 12-31 Voltage controlled oscillator.

of the diode provides voltage variable tuning.

Blocking Oscillators

A blocking oscillator is shown in Figure 12–33.

When power is first applied to the circuit, R_1 tends to bias Q_1 to the on condition. Thus a small amount of current flows in L_1, which will induce a voltage into L_2 because they are mutually coupled. This voltage will tend to turn Q_1 on even more, but the action occurs so fast that the voltage across C_1 remains the same. The emitter voltage rises due to the collector current flowing through R_2. As the transistor turns on, the collector current increases, the emitter voltage rises, the voltage across L_1 decreases, and C_1 begins to charge. As the current keeps increasing, almost all of the voltage will be taken up across R_2 and thus the transistor will become saturated. Only a very small part of the voltage will remain across L_1.

When the transistor becomes saturated, R_2 will begin to limit the collector current. Because of this the current in L_1 will begin to decrease. This decrease will cause a voltage to be induced in L_2 that will begin to cut Q_1 off. During the time that the transistor was building up to its saturation point, C_1 was charging. This charge on C_1 will try to reverse bias the transistor by transferring the voltage change across L_2. The transistor is turned off rather quickly by the reverse bias on its base. When the transistor turns off, it will cause a decrease in collector current, which will in turn cause L_1 to induce still more voltage into L_2. As a result, the transistor is turned off very rapidly. When the transistor is fully off, there is very little current flowing in the circuit. With little current in the circuit, C_1 will tend to keep the transistor in the off condition. This charge on C_1 will leak off through L_1, R_1, L_2, and R_2. If R_1 is greater than R_2, then the time required for C_1 to charge up to where the transistor will

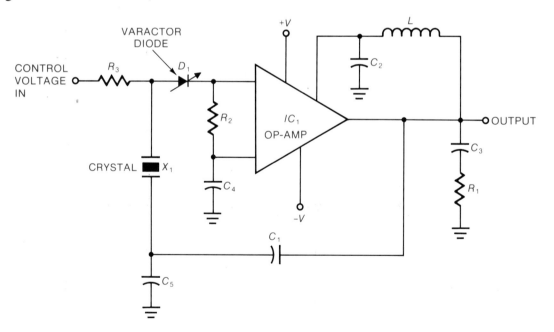

Figure 12-32 3.38 MHz voltage controlled oscillator.

be forward biased is determined principally by the resistor R_1. The components L_1, L_2 and R_2 determine the on time of the transistor and R_1C_1 will determine the off time. The output waveshapes are also shown in Figure 12–33. Notice the on and off time relationship.

12.10 MULTIVIBRATORS

The *multivibrator* is a feedback oscillator that produces a square (or rectangular) wave output. They have been used extensively in digital circuits, although they are rapidly giving way to integrated circuit packaged devices in the digital field.

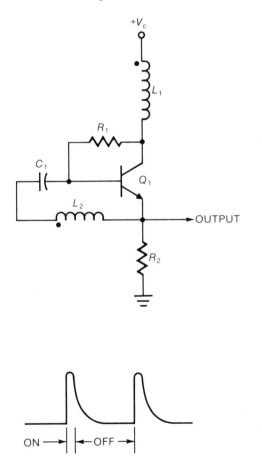

Figure 12-33 Blocking oscillator and waveshape.

There are three kinds of multivibrators: astable, monostable, and bistable.

Astable

This is a free running oscillator with its frequency determined by RC values. The circuit of a transistorized version is presented in Figure 12–34.

In order to analyze the circuit, we must select one of the states as a starting point. For this example, we have selected the state in which transistor Q_1 is in the on condition and Q_2 is in the off condition. In this state a charge on C_1 reverse biases the base of Q_2 and will thus keep it in the off condition. Since transistor Q_1 is in the on condition, the Q_1 end of C_1 is at a low voltage because of the heavy conduction of the transistor. The other side of C_1 is being charged by $B+$ via R_3. If the ratio of R_3 and R_4 are much greater than the ratio of R_1 and R_2, then C_2 will charge to $B+$ more quickly than C_1.

When C_1 charges to the point where transistor Q_1 is no longer biased on, Q_2 will begin to turn on and the collector voltage of

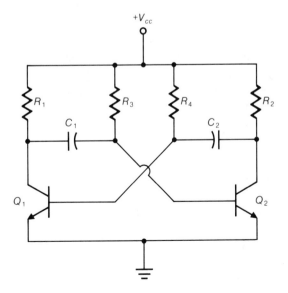

Figure 12-34 Astable multivibrator.

Q_2 will begin to drop toward 0 volts. When this drop in voltage begins, C_2 will start to charge. Capacitor C_2 charging will begin to turn transistor Q_1 off. This action will in turn cause the collector voltage of Q_1 to rise toward B+.

When the collector voltage of Q_1 begins its climb toward B+, it will cause C_1 to turn Q_2 on even harder. When C_1 charges to the point where Q_1 is no longer biased on, Q_2 turns on and the collector voltage of Q_2 begins to drop. When this happens, C_2 begins to turn Q_1 off. This causes the collector voltage of Q_1 to rise. In turn C_1 tends to turn Q_2 even harder. The action can be described as follows: As one transistor begins to change states, there is a regenerative action that causes the other transistor to switch in the opposite direction. Because of the regenerative action, the transistors switch states very rapidly.

At this point C_2 had Q_1 biased off. Before Q_1 switched, C_2 had a voltage across it of approximately B+ less 0.6 volts. This is the voltage that will be across it after it switches. But before Q_1 can turn on, C_2 must charge through R_4 the amount of B+. Now the base of Q_1 will be at approximately 0.6 volts and Q_1 can turn on. From the above, we can see that there is no stable state. The transistors will keep switching from one state to the other as long as power is applied.

Figure 12–35 shows the waveshapes for the collector and base of Q_1.

The frequency of this oscillator depends upon how long it takes the capacitor connected to the base of the transistor to charge up to where it will turn the transistor on. The frequency is controlled largely by the capacitors C_1, C_2 and the resistors R_3 and R_4. The following equation shows the relationship:

$$T = 0.69 \ RC$$

This equation gives us either the *on* time or the *off* time. If $R_3 = R_4$, and $C_1 = C_2$, the equation reduces to

$$T = 2(0.69 \ RC)$$

Let us try an example using this equation for the frequency of a free-running multivibrator.

Example 12–2

Problem: What is the period of the astable multi vibrator shown in Figure 12–34 when R_3 and R_4 are each 10,000 ohms and C_1 and C_2 are 0.001 microfarads?

Solution:

$$T = 2(0.69 \ RC)$$
$$= 2(0.69)[(10,000)(10^6)](0.001)(10^{-6})$$
$$= 2(0.0000069)$$
$$= 13.8 \text{ microseconds}$$

Note: frequency $= 1/\text{period}$

The Bi-Stable Multivibrator

The bi-stable multivibrator is frequently called a *flip-flop* because a pulse *flips* (or toggles) it to one state and a second pulse *flops* it back again. It is stable in both states and will stay in a particular state until a command pulse forces it to change again. Figure 12–36 is the schematic of a transistorized bi-stable multivibrator.

In order to analyze the circuit, we must assume an initial condition for it as we did for the astable multivibrator. Let us assume that Q_1 is in the on (saturated) condition and Q_2 is off. In this condition the collector-emitter voltage of Q_1 will be approximately 0.3 volts. This will cause the base-emitter voltage of Q_2 to be less than 0.6 volts, thus cutting off Q_2. If Q_2 is cut off, the collector current in Q_2 is close to zero. The collector

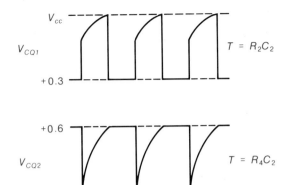

Figure 12-35 Astable multivibrator wave-shapes.

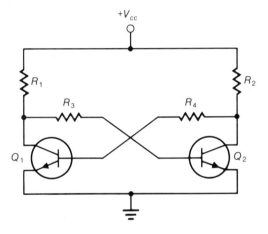

Figure 12-36 Bistable multivibrator.

voltage of Q_2 is also close to B+, depending upon how much base current is drawn through R_2. With Q_2 cut off, this increases the base-emitter voltage of Q_1, which in turn helps keep it in the on condition.

If we momentarily ground the base of Q_1, the base-emitter voltage of Q_1 drops to zero volts. A base-emitter voltage of zero will cause the collector current to drop to zero. This will in turn forward bias Q_2, causing it to start drawing collector current. The collector current will cause the collector voltage of Q_2 to drop. This lowering of the collector voltage of Q_2 will tend to lower the

base-emitter voltage of Q_1, thus helping to keep it turned off.

The circuit has two stable states. The circuit will stay in one state as long as there is power applied and we do not deliberately alter the condition of either transistor. If we change the state of one of the transistors by some action, the other transistor is forced to change its state also. This applies whether we turn the transistor that is on, off, or whether we turn the transistor that is off, on. The waveshapes for the circuit at various points are shown in Figure 12-37.

Let us look more closely at the time required to switch states when Q_1 is off and Q_2 is on (Figure 12-38). The collector voltage of Q_1 will have to drop from approximately B+ to about 0.6 volts before Q_2 will turn off. It would be perfect if Q_2 would turn off just when Q_1 began turning on instead of when it is almost completely turned on. To do this would mean that as the collector of Q_1 began decreasing, the base of Q_2 would have to begin to decrease at the same time. This indicates that the voltage across R_3 would have to be held constant during the brief instant when we start the switching action. This delay can be accomplished with

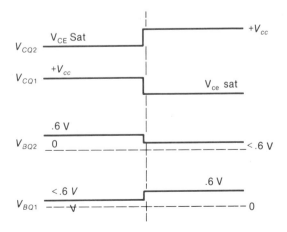

Figure 12-37 Bistable waveshapes.

a small capacitor across R_2 and R_3. The capacitors are known as *speed-up capacitors* because they help the flip-flop to change states faster. Figure 12–39 shows the flip-flop with speed-up capacitors added.

Figure 12–40 shows the flip-flop with steering diodes added to provide *set* and *reset* inputs to change states on pulse command.

12.11 ELECTRON OSCILLATORS

Ordinary tank circuits can seldom be made to oscillate at frequencies of 2,000 to 30,000 MHz. Instead, *cavity resonators*, analogous to organ pipes, and electron travel time devices must be used.

There are two major types of electron oscillators. The first is the klystron oscillator and the second is the magnetron oscillator. (The only other electron oscillator used to any extent is the traveling wave tube

(TWT), but its use is rapidly declining and thus we will not cover it in this text. Some other oscillators do fall under the general classification of electron oscillators, but they are very uncommon.

Most electron oscillators are utilized in the microwave frequency region of 200 MHz to 30,000 MHz.

The Klystron Oscillator

The klystron is an oscillator that uses a special tube (with feedback) in order to generate a signal. The only additional element needed to make the tube oscillate is a feedback loop. This loop must be of such a length that it will feed the signal back in the proper phase from the catcher cavity to the buncher cavity to reinforce the oscillations at the desired frequency. Figure 12–41 is a cutaway drawing of a klystron tube with such a feedback loop.

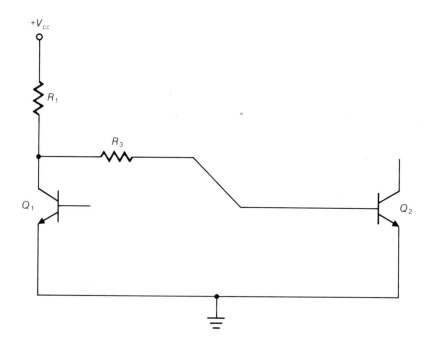

Figure 12-38 Flip-flop.

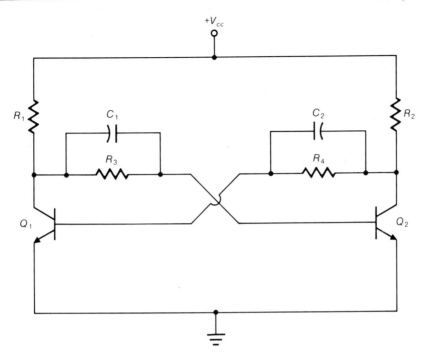

Figure 12-39 A flip-flop with speed-up capacitors.

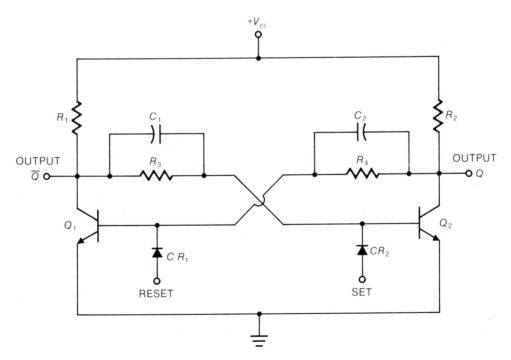

Figure 12-40 A reset/set (R/S) flip-flop.

The Magnetron Oscillator

A magnetron is an oscillator that has all the resonant circuitry built into the tube. The magnetron will oscillate at a frequency that is directly dependent upon the size of its resonant cavities, the magnetic flux strength, and the amount of high voltage applied. The magnetron is normally a *pulse modulated* device, but some have been made that will produce continuous power. Later in the text we will look at the magnetron in greater detail.

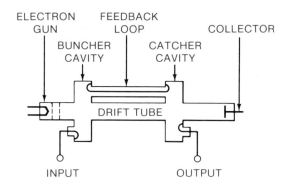

Figure 12-41 Klystron oscillator.

SUMMARY

1. Oscillators may be classified as follows:
   A. Negative resistance oscillators
   B. Feedback oscillators
      1. Tuned resonant tank oscillators
         a. *LC* tank
         b. Crystal (tank)
      2. Resistor-capacitor (*RC*) oscillators
         a. Phase shift
         b. Wein bridge
         c. Bridged *T*
      3. Multivibrators

2. Differentiating networks convert square waves into spikes.

3. Integrating networks produce a ramp from a series of pulses.

4. Diode limiters clip the top and/or the bottom off a waveform.

5. A clamp establishes a specific voltage reference level for a waveform.

6. The Schmitt trigger shapes a waveform of any shape into a square or rectangular pulse.

7. Voltage controlled oscillators use a voltage variable capacitance diode as a part of the tank circuit in an oscillator. Varying the diode bias voltage changes its capacitance and alters the resonant frequency of the tank circuit.

8. Blocking oscillators depend upon saturating the core of a special transformer to switch the oscillator on and off.

9. Multivibrators come in three kinds: astable (free running, monostable (one stable state), and bi-stable (two stable states).

10. The frequency of an astable multivibrator is controlled by values in a resistor-capacitor time constant circuit.

11. The monostable returns to its original state after a time period determined by a resistor-capacitor time constant circuit.

12. The bistable changes states only when it receives a command pulse.

13. Klystron and magnetron oscillators are for microwave frequencies where ordinary tubes and transistors will not operate.

REVIEWING YOUR ELECTRONICS VOCABULARY

1. Clamper
2. Differentiator
3. Feedback oscillator
4. Integrator
5. Limiter

6. Multivibrator
7. Oscillator
8. Phase shift oscillator
9. Piezo-electric effect
10. Relaxation oscillator

CHECKING YOUR UNDERSTANDING

1. What two conventional electronic components are replaced by a quartz crystal?
2. What determines the frequency of oscillation in a crystal oscillator?
3. What is a voltage controlled oscillator (VCO)?
4. List the three types of multivibrator circuits.
5. Describe the operating differences among the three types of multivibrator.
6. What is the function of a diode limiter?
7. What is the function of a diode clamper?
8. What is the major advantage of a shunt limiter?
9. What is the purpose of the Schmitt trigger circuit?

SOLVING ELECTRONIC PROBLEMS

1. Draw the schematic diagram of a four-layer diode oscillator.
2. Draw the block diagram of a feedback type oscillator.
3. Draw the schematic diagram of a simple RC differentiator network.
4. Draw the schematic diagram of a simple RC integrator network.
5. Draw the schematic diagram of a phase shift oscillator and explain how the oscillating frequency is controlled by the phase shift network.
6. Draw the schematic diagram of a Hartley oscillator.

CHAPTER 13

Modulation and Detection

INTRODUCTION

Modulation is the process whereby intelligence is imparted to an electronic signal. During the process the characteristics of one signal are modified by another. Under normal conditions, the signal that is changed is designated as the *carrier*.

The method of impressing information on a carrier can take many forms. More than one channel of data can be impressed on a single carrier by means of subcarriers. This is accomplished by modulating the subcarriers of different frequencies with different data and then using the subcarriers to modulate the final carrier frequency, a process very common in telemetry data links.

There are three basic types of modulation in use. These are *amplitude (AM); pulse;* and *frequency (FM)* or *phase (PM)*, modulation. There is no single best type of modulation for all conditions. Each type has advantages and disadvantages.

Modulation is not simply a matter of impressing data on a carrier. It also includes the ability of the modulated signal to maintain the information unchanged in the presence of noise and interference.

Figure 13–1 is a chart comparing the common types of modulation. Any data communications system's performance is expressed as a ratio of signal to noise (S/N) at the output point of the equipment. In a radio receiver, there will be a carrier-to-noise ratio at the input to the receiver. If amplitude modulation is used, then the signal-to-noise ratio and the carrier-to-noise ratio will be the same; however, if frequency or phase modulation is used, there will be an improvement in the ratio if the signal exceeds a certain threshold level. This threshold level is dependent on the modulation index of the signal, to be covered shortly. The threshold level of an FM receiver can also be improved by the use of other circuit techniques such as phase-lock loops.

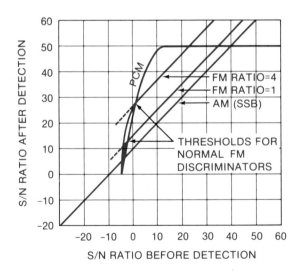

Figure 13-1 Comparison of modulation methods.

Glossary of Abbreviations Used in This Chapter

AM	Amplitude Modulation
FM	Frequency Modulation
PM	Phase Modulation
MHz	megahertz
kHz	kilohertz
SSB	Single Side Band
DSB	Double Side Band
s/n	signal/to noise
RF	Radio Frequency
AFC	Automatic Frequency Control
ISB	Independent Side Bands
HF	High Frequency
DB	Decibels
LC	Inductor Capacitor tank circuit
IF	Intermediate Frequency
BFO	Beat Frequency Oscillator
IC	Integrated Circuit
PEP	Peak Envelope Voltage
LSB	Lower Side Band
USB	Upper Side Band

Table 13–1 is a chart showing the various types of modulation and the symbol designations common in most texts on electronics.

13.1 AMPLITUDE MODULATION (AM)

The process of amplitude modulation can be complex. We will not explore much of the theory, but will take an overall view.

The process of amplitude modulation is accomplished by mixing the radio frequency carrier and the audio or data in a nonlinear device such as a diode, tube, or transistor. The action produces a complex amplitude modulated (AM) wave. This modulated signal is called "complex" because of the various frequency components that give the signal its characteristic appearance on an oscilloscope.

Let us now see just what makes up such a signal. Figure 13–2 shows the two basic components of any AM signal. In part A we see the radio frequency (RF) carrier; in part B, the modulating audio; and in part C, we see the resulting AM signal.

A very important point must be made here. When the audio is combined with the RF carrier, not only is a modulated carrier produced, but several others are also generated. The two most important signals are (1) the frequency that is equal to the carrier frequency plus the audio frequency,

Table 13-1 Classification of Radio Emissions

SYMBOL   TYPE OF TRANSMISSION
AMPLITUDE-MODULATED

A0   Continuous wave, no modulation.
A1   Continuous-wave telegraphy. On-off keying.
A2   Telegraphy by keying of a modulating audio frequency. Also by keying of modulated emission.
A3   Telephony. Double sideband, full carrier.
A3a Telephony. Single sideband, reduced carrier.
A3b Telephony. Two independent sidebands, reduced carrier.
A4   Facsimile.
A5   Television.
A9   Composite transmissions and cases not covered by above.
A9a Composite transmissions, reduced carrier.

FREQUENCY (OR PHASE)-MODULATED

F0   Absence of modulation.
F1   Telegraphy by frequency shift keying. No modulation.
F2   Telegraphy by keying of a modulating audio frequency. Also by keying of modulated emission.
F3   Telephony.
F4   Facsimile.
F5   Television.
F9   Composite transmissions and cases not covered by above.

SYMBOL   PULSE-MODULATED

P0   Absence of modulation intended to carry information (such as radar).
P1   Telegraphy. No modulating audio frequency.
P2d Telegraphy by keying an audio frequency modulating the pulse in amplitude.
P2e Telegraphy by keying an audio frequency modulating the width of the pulse.
P2f Telegraphy by keying an audio frequency modulating the phase (or position) of the pulse.
P3d Telephony. Amplitude modulated.
P3e Telephony. Width modulated.
P3f Telephony. Phase (or position) modulated.
P9   Composite transmissions and cases not covered by above.

and (2) carrier frequency minus the audio frequency.

Suppose we are modulating a 5 MHz carrier with a 1,500 Hz audio frequency. Figure 13-3 is a plot of this. With a 5 MHz carrier there are two *sidebands,* one at 5.001 MHz and the other at 4.999 MHz. There are other sidebands produced at harmonics (even and odd multiples of frequencies) above and below the carrier frequency, but they are much lower in amplitude and decrease rapidly in amplitude for each one further away from the carrier frequency, as shown in the figure.

You can see that if the modulating audio is varied in frequency, the sidebands will also vary; thus an AM carrier occupies a *band* of frequencies, or a *channel,* rather than just a single frequency.

The system used to impress one signal upon another is called a *modulator.* In section 13-2 below we will cover several types of modulators.

Another amplitude modulator that is coming into wider use is known as *single sideband (SSB).* A single sideband signal is an audio signal converted to a radio frequency spectrum. For instance, an intelligible voice signal contains frequencies over the range 300 to 3,000 Hz. If this audio signal is converted to a radio frequency by mixing it with a 15 MHz RF frequency, the resultant sum frequencies cover the range of 15,000-300 to 15,003,000 Hz. Such an SSB signal

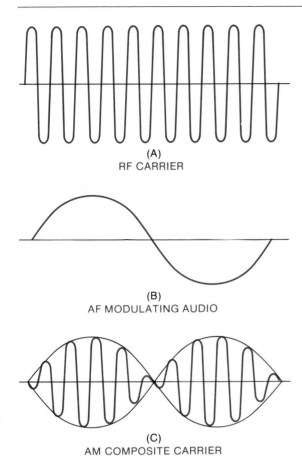

(A)
RF CARRIER

(B)
AF MODULATING AUDIO

(C)
AM COMPOSITE CARRIER

Figure 13-2 Amplitude modulation of a signal.

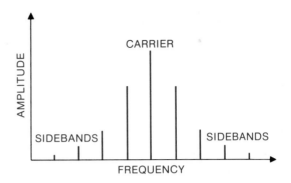

Figure 13-3 AM signal frequency plot.

without inversion is referred to as an *upper sideband* because it occupies the spectrum space above the RF conversion frequency. Note that the 15 MHz carrier is not included in the range of the SSB signal.

The above example does not indicate the presence of a difference frequency. However, when the voice signal is mixed with the RF frequency, a difference frequency does develop that covers the range 14,999,700 to 14,997,000 Hz. This is an SSB signal with inversion. It is also referred to as a lower sideband signal because it occupies the spectrum space below the RF con-

version frequency. Figure 13–4 illustrates the position of the SSB signal in the RF spectrum.

From the above description it is apparent that only one sideband need be transmitted to convey intelligence. Since two sideband signals are produced from the mixing process, one sideband must be removed before transmission. To receive the SSB signal, it is necessary to convert the SSB signal back to its original position in the audio spectrum. This requires nearly identical transmitter and receiver conversion frequencies. It can be achieved in two ways. The first is to transmit a small pilot carrier along with the SSB signal and provide an *automatic frequency control* (AFC) at the receiver in order to insure nearly identical conversion frequencies. The second is to provide very stable frequency synthesizers at both the receiver and transmitter. Frequency synthesizers with stabilities of one part in 10^8 exist today which provide reliable SSB communication systems.

Several methods of sideband communication have recently evolved. These are generally classified as follows:

1. SSB signal with suppressed carrier.

2. SSB signal with small inserted carrier—

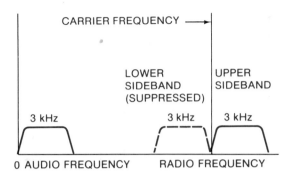

Figure 13-4 Location of SSB signal in RF spectrum.

generally used with AFC systems.

3. DSB (double sideband) signal with suppressed carrier.

4. DSB signal with small inserted carrier.

5. Compatible AM signal—consists of DSB signal with full carrier insertion.

6. ISB signal—two independent sidebands with a different intelligence on each sideband.

Those systems that require a small inserted carrier do so because the receiving system contains an AFC system for proper demodulation. Those systems that suppress the carrier to almost nonexistence use transmitter and receiver frequency synthesizers that are very accurate. Both systems are capable of providing very reliable HF communication.

Probably the best method of comparing SSB communication to ordinary AM systems is to consider the transmitter power necessary to produce a given signal-to-noise (s/n) ratio at the receiver output terminals. Signal-to-noise ratio is a fair comparison because it primarily determines the intelligibility of the received signal. Figure 13–5 shows a comparison between an ordinary AM and an AM SSB system when a single tone modulation is used and under ideal propagation conditions.

Since the front end circuitry of the receivers (both the ordinary AM and the SSB) is generally the same, the noise power per unit bandwidth will be the same. If we have an ordinary AM receiver with a 6 kHz bandwidth and an AM SSB receiver with only a 3 kHz bandwidth, and the output noise voltage of the ordinary AM receiver is 0.1 volts, then the noise power per kHz bandwidth is $(0.1)^2/6$. Thus, since the two receivers have the same power per unit bandwidth,

$$\frac{(0.1)^2}{6} = \frac{(Vnssb)^2}{3}$$

We find therefore that the noise voltage of the SSB receiving system will be 0.07 volts. With this in mind, we can go back to Figure 13–5 and discover that only 0.5 watts of PEP power in the SSB transmitter is required to produce the same S/N ratio at the receiver as a 1.0 watt ordinary AM transmitter. This means that under ideal conditions an AM SSB system is a four-fold improvement over an ordinary AM system.

In addition, we see that the peak envelope voltage of the ordinary AM transmitter is 2, while that of the SSB transmitter is 0.7. Thus, the peak voltage on the antenna for an SSB transmitter of the same intelligence power as an ordinary AM transmitter will be less than that for the ordinary AM transmitter. Antennas can therefore be designed to withstand lower peak voltages.

Let us now compare the two kinds of AM transmitters under conditions that are *not* ideal. Figure 13–6 shows the results of actual tests of the intelligibility of a 50 watt AM SSB system and a 100 watt ordinary AM system. It can be seen that in addition to the initial four times advantage of the SSB system under ideal conditions, there is

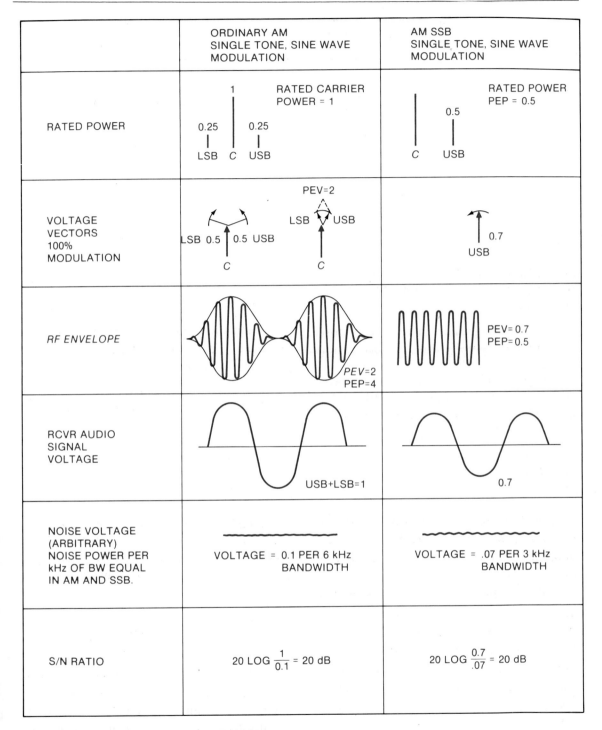

	ORDINARY AM SINGLE TONE, SINE WAVE MODULATION	AM SSB SINGLE TONE, SINE WAVE MODULATION
RATED POWER	1 RATED CARRIER POWER = 1 0.25 0.25 LSB C USB	RATED POWER PEP = 0.5 0.5 C USB
VOLTAGE VECTORS 100% MODULATION	LSB 0.5 0.5 USB C / PEV=2 LSB USB C	0.7 USB
RF ENVELOPE	PEV=2 PEP=4	PEV= 0.7 PEP=0.5
RCVR AUDIO SIGNAL VOLTAGE	USB+LSB=1	0.7
NOISE VOLTAGE (ARBITRARY) NOISE POWER PER kHz OF BW EQUAL IN AM AND SSB.	VOLTAGE = 0.1 PER 6 kHz BANDWIDTH	VOLTAGE = .07 PER 3 kHz BANDWIDTH
S/N RATIO	$20 \text{ LOG} \frac{1}{0.1} = 20 \text{ dB}$	$20 \text{ LOG} \frac{0.7}{.07} = 20 \text{ dB}$

Figure 13-5 AM SSB and ordinary AM comparison with equal signal-to-noise ratios.

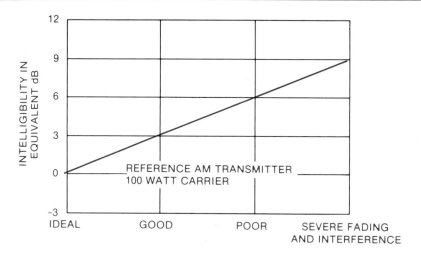

Figure 13-6 Relative advantage of SSB over ordinary AM, with limiting propagating conditions.

an SSB advantage under increasingly poorer. propagating conditions of somewhere between 0 to 9 DB.

Figures 13-7 and 13-8 show what single sideband signals look like when coupled to various oscilloscope inputs.

13.2 FREQUENCY (FM) AND PHASE (PM) MODULATION

Another basic type of modulation is *frequency modulation (FM),* or *phase modulation (PM),* also known as *angular modulation.*

The sidebands that are created by FM and PM are different from those created by AM modulation. The FM and PM sidebands are integral multiples of the modulating frequency on each side of the basic carrier. Because of this, FM or PM signals occupy a wider frequency spectrum than AM.

The number of these extra sidebands is directly dependent on the relationship

between the modulating frequency and the frequency deviation, a ratio known as the *modulation index:*

$$\text{Modulation index} = \frac{\text{Carrier frequency deviation}}{\text{Modulation frequency}}$$

Example 13-1

Problem: If the frequency deviation of a certain FM transmitter is 6 kHz and the modulating frequency is 1 kHz, what is the modulation index of the transmitter?

Solution:

$$\text{Index} = \frac{6,000}{1,000} = 6$$

A very interesting point should be made here. In PM the modulation index will remain constant regardless of the modulating frequency, but in FM the index will vary, as in our example. In all FM systems the ratio of the *maximum* carrier deviation

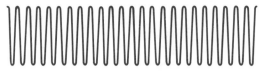

Single tone modulator output after filtering out the lower sideband.

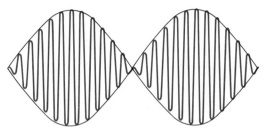

Single tone SSB signal with carrier. Carrier equal in amplitude to tone.

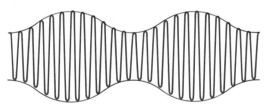

Single tone SSB signal with carrier. Carrier 10 dB below level of tone.

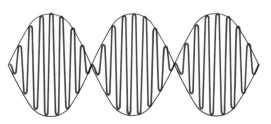

Two-tone SSB signal with tones of equal amplitude.

Figure 13-7 Waveforms.

to the *highest* modulating frequency is known as the *deviation ratio*.

Frequency modulation, or FM, is accomplished by varying the frequency of the RF carrier at the modulating audio rate.

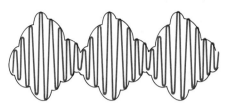

Two-tone SSB signal with small reinstated pilot carrier.

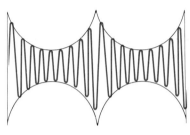

SSB SIGNAL

AUDIO SIGNAL

Square wave SSB signal with all frequency components present.

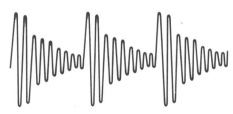

Voice signal at audio frequency— the vowel A.

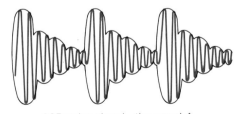

SSB voice signal—the vowel A.

Figure 13-8 Waveforms.

Figure 13–9 shows graphically how FM is accomplished. Part A of the figure is the unmodulated carrier. Part B is the modulating audio. And in part C we have the frequency modulated carrier.

13.3 MODULATORS

In section 13–1 we noted that if an audio signal and an RF signal are mixed in a nonlinear device, amplitude modulation will occur.

Figure 13–10 illustrates such a case. In this circuit f_c, the carrier, and f_a, the audio, are combined across the diode. Note that the output is not an AM waveform.

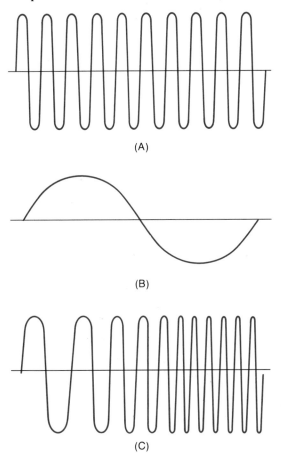

(A)

(B)

(C)

Figure 13-9 Making an FM carrier.

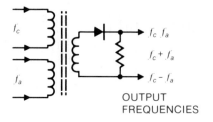

OUTPUT
FREQUENCIES

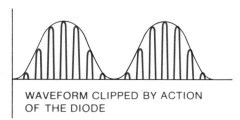

WAVEFORM CLIPPED BY ACTION OF THE DIODE

Figure 13-10 Combining two frequencies across a nonlinear device.

In order to obtain a true AM waveform, we simply insert a tuned circuit in the output of the diode. The LC circuit, due to its flywheel (circulating current) effect, will cause the negative half of the RF cycle to be

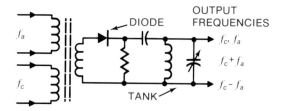

OUTPUT WAVESHAPE

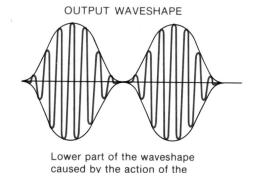

Lower part of the waveshape caused by the action of the LC tank circuit.

Figure 13-11 AM wave produced by adding a tank circuit to the circuit of the preceding figure.

inserted, and thus the negative part of the RF wave will be the mirror image of the positive half.

Vacuum tubes as well as transistors can be used as nonlinear elements. All mixers, converters, and diode modulators operate in the same way. If the elements are linear, the sum $(f_c + f_a)$ and the difference $(f_c - f_a)$ will not be generated. In most audio equipment, the circuits are slightly nonlinear and the resulting sum and difference frequencies are called *intermodulation products* or *distortion*. Such distortion is undesirable in hi-fi systems.

The diode modulator shown in Figure 13–11 is useful only at very low levels and it introduces a considerable amount of loss, known as *insertion loss,* into the circuit. The only common diode modulator found in general use is in SSB equipment.

Plate Modulation

When the modulating voltage is superimposed on the dc voltage supply to the amplifier stage, the stage is said to be *plate modulated.* (This can also be done in transistors, in which case the stage should be said to be *collector* or *emitter modulated.*)

Figure 13–12 shows a plate modulated amplifier and a collector modulated amplifier.

There are many types of AM SSB circuits. However, the most commonly used is the diode type. A diode SSB modulator has either a ring, a series, or a shunt circuit. These names refer to the manner in which the diodes are connected in the circuit. In all circuits the rectifiers are made to look like switches, by using a large RF signal that greatly exceeds the audio signal level.

These modulators are almost always connected as balanced modulators, so that, as nearly as possible, there is no output of the RF switching voltage in the modulator output terminals.

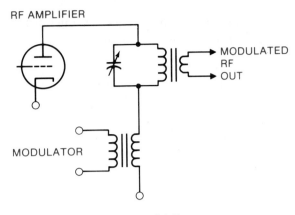

(A) Plate modulation

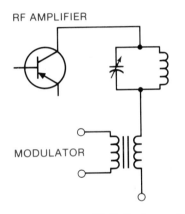

(B) Collector modulation

Figure 13-12 Plate and collector modulation.

The basic circuits of the ring, shunt, and series modulators are shown in Figure 13–13. It must be assumed that the rectifiers are capable of switching at zero voltage from an infinite reverse resistance to a zero forward resistance and back again. The basic circuits can then be represented by the equivalent circuits shown. These equivalent circuits are for any half cycle of the carrier voltage, with switches shown in place of rectifiers. Practical rectifiers are not perfect, but will have nearly infinite reverse and very low forward resistance. If it is assumed that the carrier frequency is several times that of the audio input, the resulting output waveforms are as shown in part C of Figure 13–13.

In Figure 13–14 we see the current path analysis of the ring modulator, showing the current through the circuit during each half of the input cycle.

Figure 13–15 is a block diagram of a typical AM transmitter showing how the modulators are connected.

Frequency Modulation Modulators

Frequency (or phase) modulation can be accomplished by several methods. The most common is to vary the transmitter oscillator frequency at the audio rate. The frequency

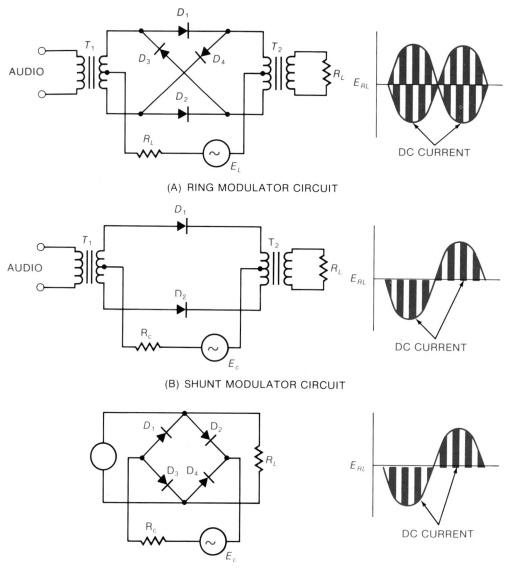

(A) RING MODULATOR CIRCUIT

(B) SHUNT MODULATOR CIRCUIT

(C) SERIES MODULATOR CIRCUIT

Figure 13-13 Basic circuits for SSB modulators.

and phase deviation of an RF signal will appear to be identical to most FM detectors. The only basic difference between phase (PM) and frequency (FM) modulation is at the transmitter, where the modulation is applied. In FM we modulate the oscillator, thus changing the basic frequency of the transmitter; in PM we can modulate an amplifier tank circuit and thus shift the phase of the amplified signal.

Figure 13–16 is a circuit known as a *reactance FM modulator*. This circuit will act like a variable inductor or capacitor connected across the oscillator tank circuit.

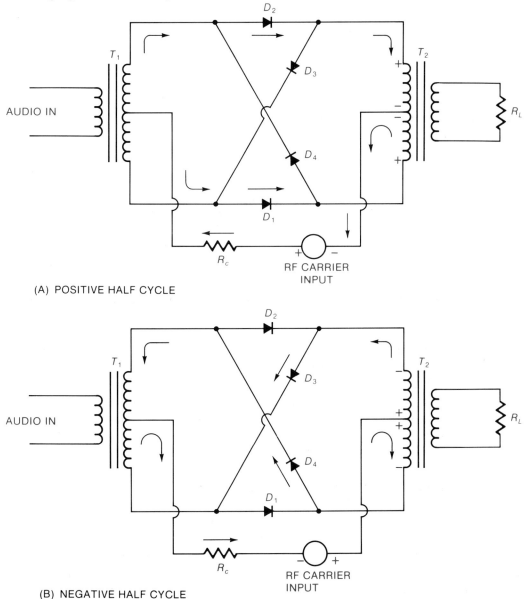

(A) POSITIVE HALF CYCLE

(B) NEGATIVE HALF CYCLE

Figure 13-14 Ring modulator carrier current paths.

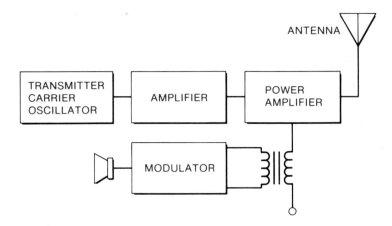

Figure 13-15 AM transmitter block diagram.

In effect, the resonant frequency of the tank circuit will be changed at the applied audio rate because of the action of the modulator.

In Figure 13-16, a MOSFET is connected across the oscillator tank circuit L_1C_1. This MOSFET circuit can, because of the 90 degree phase lag of the gate current with respect to the RF tank circuit current, act as though an additional inductance was connected across the RF tank circuit which varies at the audio rate.

The modulator could as well be connected to simulate a capacitor and have the same effect on the oscillator.

Figure 13-17 is a block diagram of an FM transmitter showing how the modulator is connected. Notice the difference between Figure 13-17 and the AM transmitters shown in Figure 13-15.

An advantage of FM over AM is that it is relatively insensitive to natural RF noise, lightning and other forms of "static," and even man-made electrical noise such as motor noise. However, FM does have disadvantages. For example, FM requires a wider RF bandwidth than AM to convey the same amount of information.

In advanced electronic data transmission equipment, often several FM carriers with data are frequency modulated onto another carrier, thus generating multiple carriers.

Figure 13-18 provides an example of a *multiplexer* system where several FM carriers, known in this case as subcarriers, are frequency modulating a common carrier. The system is known as FM/FM, indicating FM subcarriers on an FM final carrier. It allows the transmission of multiple channels of data on the same RF carrier. Such a system may combine several types of modulation, and even three or more stages of modulation may be involved, as is often the case in space and missile applications of telemetry data transmission.

Figure 13-19 is an example of space type telemetry, an SSB/FM multiplex unit, having 12 SSB channels of data and one FM output. Also, see Figure 13-20.

13.4 DETECTORS

A detector is a demodulator that extracts the modulation from an RF carrier. There are many methods of doing this.

As with modulators, there are two main classes of detectors: frequency (FM) and amplitude (AM).

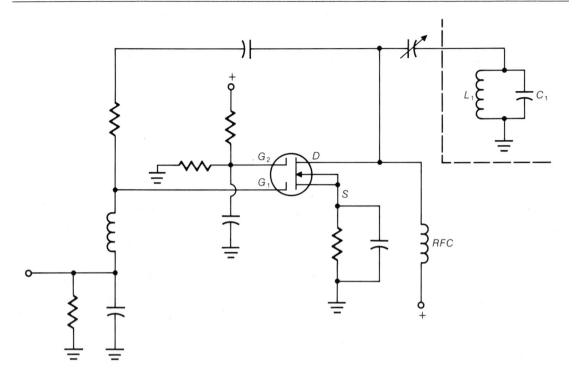

Figure 13-16 Reactance modulator for FM.

Amplitude modulation detectors fall into two basic subclasses, full AM detection and SSB detection. An example of a full AM detector is shown in Figure 13–21. This circuit is a simple diode detector, a direct descendant of the crystal detector used in the early days of radio.

The RF is applied through the L_2C_2 tank circuit, which selects the proper carrier frequency. The rectification action of CR_1 with the RF applied to it will cause a varying dc voltage to appear across R_1. The variations in the amplitude of the RF will cause an identical variation in the dc across R_1. The capacitor (C_2) bypasses the carrier signal to ground, leaving only the audio at the output. Figure 13–22 shows the waveshapes that would be encountered in the detector of Figure 13–21 if viewed on an oscilloscope.

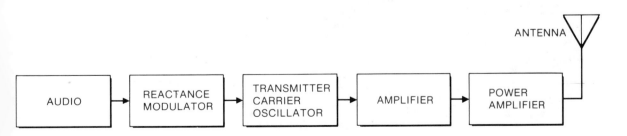

Figure 13-17 FM transmitter block diagram.

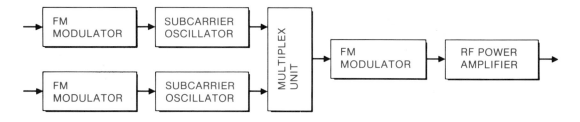

Figure 13-18 FM/FM multiplex system for telemetry.

Figure 13-19 Digital multiplexer for onboard space shuttle computer/ground computer data link.

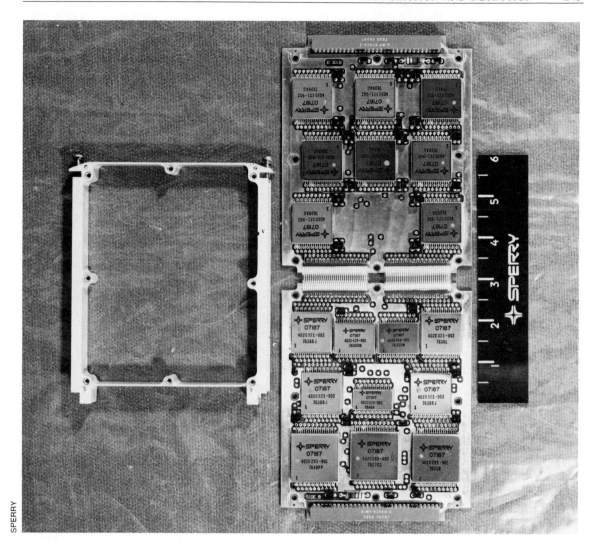

Figure 13-20 MDM module hybrid unit for digital multiplexer unit in Figure 13-19.

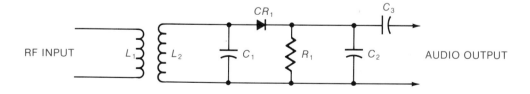

Figure 13-21 Diode detector.

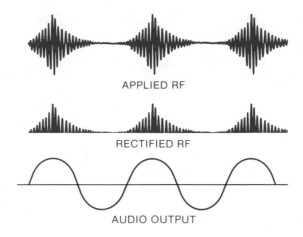

APPLIED RF

RECTIFIED RF

AUDIO OUTPUT

Figure 13-22 Detector waveshapes.

The Product Detector

Product detector circuits are preferred in single sideband reception, because they minimize intermodulation distortion products present in the audio output signal.

An example of a solid state product detector is found in Figure 13–23. This circuit utilizes a dual gate MOSFET. The one shown is an N-channel type such as a 3N141. This FET has two channels, each with a separate, independently controllable gate. The input SSB signal is applied to gate 1, and the receiver's carrier reinjection oscillator, commonly known as a *basic frequency oscillator* (BFO), is applied to gate 2. The local signal applied to gate 2 modulates the input gate (gate 1). This method is better than the square-law method used in most mixers because square-law mixing can only be accomplished in the nonlinear region of the mixer circuit operating curve. The isolation between the gates in the insulated gate MOSFET helps keep the local BFO signal confined to this section of the circuit. A A detector of this type can easily provide good output with only 0.5 μV input with an excellent signal-to-noise ratio. The circuit also gives some gain, known as *conversion*

gain, while in the process of detection.

Figure 13–24 is an example of the frequency spectrum in the output of a typical product detector, showing the principal components that will be present.

In this example, it is assumed that the sideband signal consists of three components having frequencies of 501, 502, and 503 kHz. The carrier frequency that is reinserted in the converter is 500 kHz. The drain current components consist of three audio frequencies of 1, 2, and 3 kHz and three RF components of 1,001; 1,002; and 1,003 kHz, as well as the carrier and the original frequencies. The low pass filter is designed to highly attenuate all components above, say, 10 kHz; therefore, only the audio components will remain in the output. This method of conversion is generally used to recover the original audio signal from the IF SSB signal in a receiver.

We can go one step further in product detectors by using an integrated circuit (IC). There are some ICs designed as product detectors on the market and other ICs not specifically so designed but that can also be used as product detectors. A differential amplifier can be used, as well as some ICs

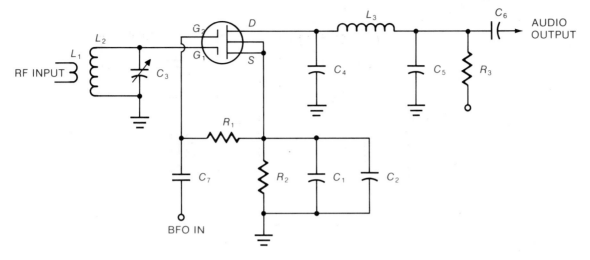

Figure 13-23 Solid state product detector.

designed for use as IF / RF amplifiers. Figure 13–25 is a Motorola MC1550G IF amplifier. One of the advantages of this type of circuit over those already covered is the exceptional conversion gain in the circuit. This allows a lower gain in the IFs ahead of the detector. The use of ICs gives excellent isolation between the SSB carrier input, audio output, and local BFO input. The use of such an IC can provide suitable output with an input signal of only 0.1 μV.

FM Detectors

Figure 13–26 is a block diagram of a typical FM receiver. Note that except for two of the blocks, it is similar to an AM receiver.

In order to detect an FM or PM modulated signal, a special kind of detector must be used. In the FM signal, the amplitude of the RF remains the same (or should), and often a circuit to clip and maintain a fixed amplitude is used in an FM receiver just prior to detection. Several examples of such circuits are shown in Figure 13–27. The circuit shown in part A is a two-stage transistor limiter with the limiting level set by the base bias on each stage. The input signal level where limiting begins is known as the *limiting knee,* the point at which the collector (or plate if the limiter is a tube) current

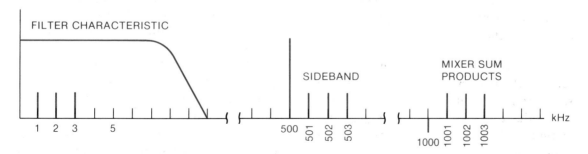

Figure 13-24 Frequency spectrum of product detector output.

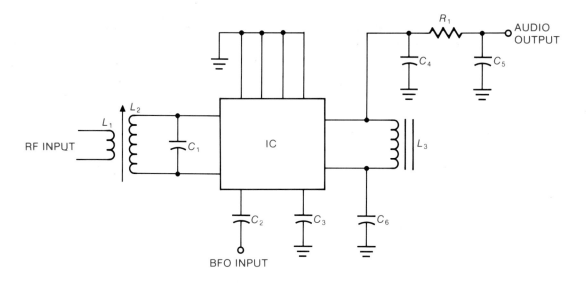

Figure 13-25 IC product detector.

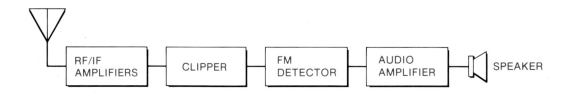

Figure 13-26 FM receiver block diagram.

ceases to increase with an increase in input voltage.

In part B of Figure 13–27 a linear high-gain IC is used. Because there are several active stages, the IC will provide much better limiter action than transistors with a transistor knee of on the order of 600 microvolts.

A limiter for FM is a normal IF stage, set so that any amplitude increase will cause saturation and thus clip the output. Since the modulation is a change in frequency, the clipping introduces no distortion in the circuit output.

In order to demodulate an FM signal, the usual method is to convert the frequency

modulation to amplitude modulation and then detect the AM to obtain the original modulating signal. A circuit that will accomplish this is known as a *discriminator*. There are several designs in existence, but we will look at only two types, the *slope detector* or *Travis* discriminator and the *ratio detector*.

The slope detector is one of the simplest forms of FM detectors. Figure 13–28 is a graphical example of the action of a slope type discriminator.

In order to produce the required slope, a circuit such as that shown in Figure 13–29 is used. Note that this circuit is exactly like Figure 13–21, an AM detector, except that

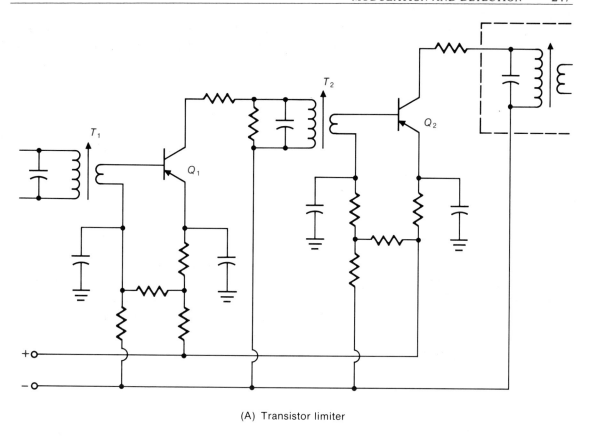

(A) Transistor limiter

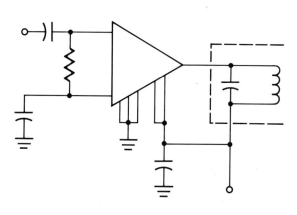

(B) Integrated circuit limiter

Figure 13-27 FM limiters.

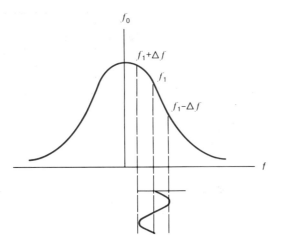

Figure 13-28 Slope detection.

the AM transformer is tuned to the IF frequency f_0. When FM is being detected, the FM IF frequency is f_1 and the detector appears to be detuned. The incoming FM signal varies from $f_1 + f$, to $f_1 - f$, and the changes in frequency will, because of the bandpass of the tuned circuit, cause the changes in frequency to appear as amplitude variations to the diode.

This slope or detuned principle is the basis of most FM detectors.

The circuit in Figure 13–30 is a Travis discriminator, which is effectively two slope detectors. One of them is tuned to $f_1 + f$ and the other is tuned to $f_1 - f$.

In Figure 13–31 the various response curves for each circuit are shown. If, as in part A, we tune circuit I to 10.685 MHz (15 kHz below f_1) and circuit II to 10.715 MHz (15 kHz above f_1), we have met the requirements for a Travis discriminator circuit. Part B shows the response of each circuit alone. The two load resistors, R_1 and R_2, are

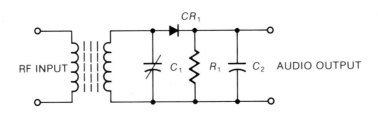

Figure 13-29 Slope detector.

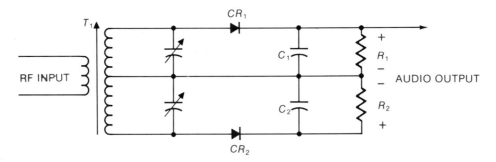

Figure 13-30 Travis discriminator.

connected in polarity opposition to each other as shown in Figure 13–31. The output of I is positive going and the output of II is negative going.

At an IF frequency of 10.7 MHz, circuit I in part A of Figure 13–31 is tuned to 10.685 MHz and circuit II is tuned to 10.715 MHz.

At 10.7 MHz, the two outputs would be equal, but as shown in part B, the output combination would result in the waveshape shown in part C. Waveshape C is only needed between 10.685 and 10.715 MHz in our example so only this part is shown.

Figure 13–32 shows the transfer characteristic of this circuit, the frequency shift of the input, and the resulting audio output.

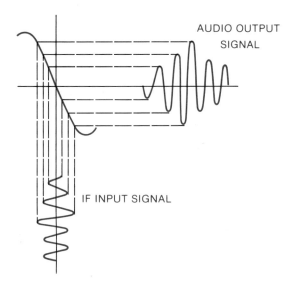

Figure 13-32 Transfer characteristic of doubled-tuned discriminator.

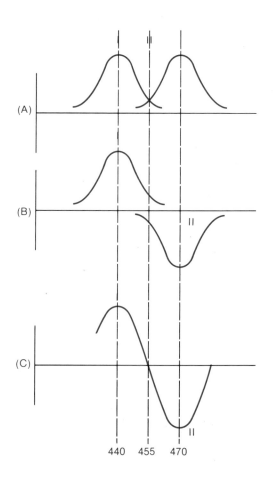

Figure 13-31 Response curves for the Travis discriminator.

SUMMARY

1. Modulation is the process of impressing speech or other information on a radio frequency (RF) carrier.

2. The carrier may be modulated by varying the amplitude (voltage), the phase, or the frequency of the carrier in step with the information to be carried.

3. Detection or demodulation is the process of recovering the original information from the received carrier.

4. Amplitude modulation produces two identical (but inverted) carriers, both of which contain all of the original information.

5. In single sideband (SSB) transmission, all the transmitter's power capacity is put into one sideband and the unnecessary sideband is not transmitted.

REVIEWING YOUR ELECTRONICS VOCABULARY

1. Amplitude modulation
2. Detector
3. Deviation ratio
4. Discriminator
5. Frequency modulation
6. Harmonic
7. Modulation
8. Phase modulation
9. Sideband
10. Single-Side-Band (SSB)

CHECKING YOUR UNDERSTANDING

1. List the three basic modulation methods.
2. Explain the differences between amplitude and frequency modulation.
3. Is phase modulation a form of amplitude modulation or frequency modulation?
4. What is one important advantage of single-side-band modulation over ordinary AM?
5. Name one advantage of frequency modulation over amplitude modulation.
6. What is meant by the term "deviation ratio"?
7. Which kind of detector is more complex, one for AM or one for FM?
8. Explain how the automatic volume control in an AM receiver works.
9. What are the high and low frequency limits for commercial FM transmissions?
10. What is a harmonic?

SOLVING ELECTRONIC PROBLEMS

1. If a 10 MHz RF signal is amplitude modulated by a 2.5 kHz audio signal, what is the frequency of the second harmonic sidebands produced?

2. What is the modulation index of an FM transmitter operating on 100.1 MHz with a 15 kHz deviation and an audio modulation frequency of 4.5 kHz?

3. Draw a schematic diagram of a diode modulator.

4. Draw a diagram of a simple diode detector.

5. Draw a block diagram of a simple FM receiver, an AM receiver, an FM transmitter, and an AM transmitter.

CHAPTER 14
Introduction to Digital Electronics

INTRODUCTION

Digital electronics is the fastest growing segment of the electronics scene. Modern integrated circuit technology has made small computers available at low cost. Full-fledged microcomputers are available at less than $1,000 for outright purchase. Only a few years ago this kind of computing power would have cost up to $240,000 to purchase outright, or $1,000 (or more) per month to lease.

Computer hobbyists (known as "hackers") have created a new market for microcomputers. Computer clubs are springing up all over the country.

The automotive industry is turning to microcomputers to control engine ignition, fuel flow, braking, and automotive system troubleshooting.

Domestic appliances such as microwave ovens are now often microcomputer controlled.

Electronics tasks that were once performed by linear devices and circuits are being taken over by digital circuitry.

Pocket calculators provide a remarkable amount of computing power for a relatively few dollars.

All of this is but the tip of the iceberg, and many new digital wonders will soon enter our daily lives (see Figures 14–2, 14–3, and 14–4).

A computer may consist of a great many packages containing a few circuits per package; a single central processing package with outboard memory packages; or the entire computer may be on a single chip.

Integrated circuit (IC) packages are mounted on a printed circuit board with copper traces replacing traditional wires. In computer terminology, the circuit board is called a *card* (Fig. 14–5). The card has "fingers" etched along an edge that form the male half of a plug-socket arrangement. The card is plugged into a special socket called an *edge connector*. Edge connector sockets are either wired, often with a flat "ribbon" cable, or soldered into a card-interconnecting circuit board (known generally as a *mother board*).

Integrated circuits can accommodate up to several thousand transistors on a single *chip* (a silicon wafer). It is no longer economical to use individual transistors, except for a few very special applications.

14.1 DIGITAL LOGIC

Digital logic is a complex system of simple *gates* (electronic on-off switches) intended to control some device. It makes decisions on the basis of tests and routes electrons according to predetermined rules. Digital logic is a true-false, go-no-go system.

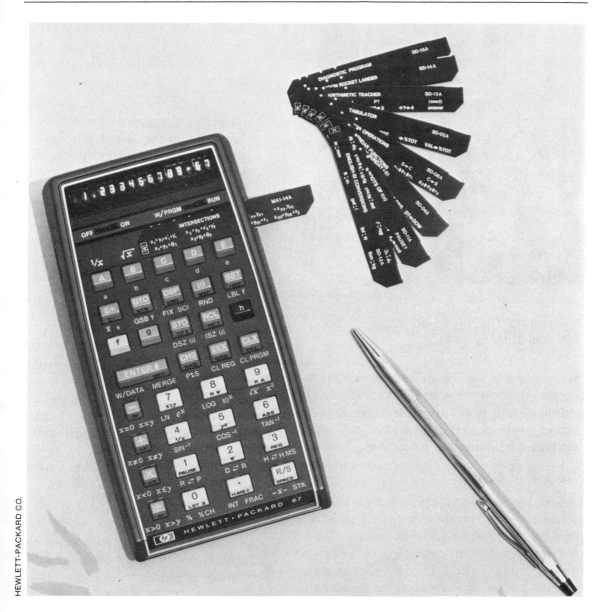

Figure 14-1 Programmable calculator has many of the features of a large computer.

Complex decisions can be made by combining a large enough number of gates.

Logic operations fall into three categories: control, memory, and computation. A computer does computations but it also has control logic to route data from memory to arithmetic unit, from memory to the outside world, and so on.

Logic systems designed for control purposes may also have some computing logic and memory hardware. For example, a traffic light controller might count the cars in several directions and make calculations to determine when to change the lights.

NASA PHOTO

Figure 14-2 One of the world's most complex computer systems.

Memory could also be included to remember that traffic is unusually light on Sunday mornings and heavy on certain holidays. Figure 14–6 illustrates how gates can be used for controlling various actions.

Integrated Circuits

An integrated circuit is a lot of gates made in microscopic proportions on the ¼″ square (more or less) wafer (chip) of silicon. The individual gates are connected by microscopic printed wiring into circuits to do specific jobs, such as counting, or decoding digital information. Photographic masks and high temperature automated chemical techniques permit almost molecule by molecule formation of the circuitry.

Integrated circuits are classified according to the number of gates on the chip, without regard to specific function (that is, whether control, memory, or computation).

SSI   Small Scale Integration (SSI) is an integrated circuit package with 12 or fewer logic gates on the chip.

MSI   Medium Scale Integration (MSI) is an integrated circuit package with between 12 and 100 logic gates on the chip.

LSI   Large Scale Integration (LSI) is an integrated circuit package with over 100 gates on the chip. Up to 10,000 gates on a chip is currently possible, with up to one-half million on a chip in experimental stages.

Bipolar and MOS Transistors

Digital integrated circuits are made of either bipolar (junction) or *metal oxide semiconductor* (MOS) transistors.

The MOS transistor is simpler, much smaller, and consumes very little power compared to a conventional bipolar transistor. However, it is very slow. It is used where 100 to 10,000 (or sometimes more) gates on a chip are required.

The bipolar transistor works at a much higher *speed* than the MOS, but it takes much more space on a chip and consumes a great deal more *power*. Because of its size and power requirements, it is used only in SSI and MSI packages (up to 100 gates).

Logic Family

A logic family is a group of compatible functional integrated circuit packages. Like Tinkertoys or Leggo, they can be assembled into a variety of forms—no sanding or fitting is required—they just snap together. Each family is based on a specific transistor type.

Logic Family Interfacing When subsystems based on two different logic families must work together in a system, a little extra hardware is required. The special components are called *interface components*.

The most popular logic families are fairly compatible, but there are some minor

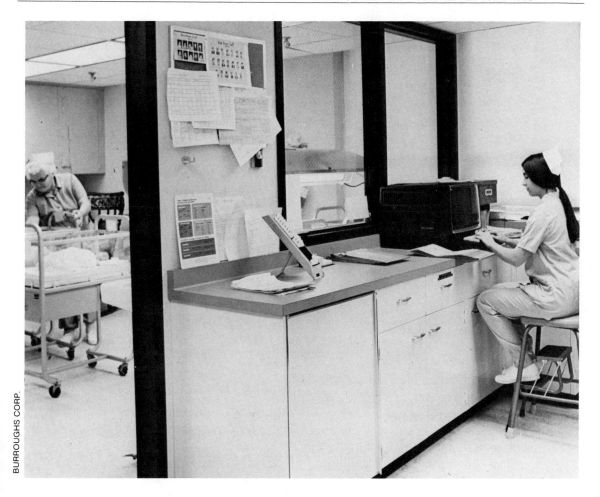

BURROUGHS CORP.

Figure 14-3 This 800 bed hospital in Wichita Kansas . . .

technical difficulties.

Commercial Logic Families The *transistor-transistor-logic (TTL) family* is the most popular small scale integration commercial logic family. It is based on bipolar transistors, and it is fast, but power hungry.

The *metal oxide semiconductor (MOS) family* has two types, called the "P" type (P-MOS) and the "N" type (N-MOS), depending on whether the P-MOS transistor or the N-MOS transistor is the basis of the family. Both types are used when 100 or more gates on a chip are required. They are slower than TTL, but easy on power.

The *complementary metal oxide semiconductor* (C-MOS) *family* utilizes a double-barreled MOS transistor.

Integrated Injection Logic (I²L) A most exciting, fairly new logic family, it is as fast as the TTL and as miserly with power as the MOS. Its small size and simple construction make it suitable for large scale integration (LSI). I²L is based on a radical, upside-down bipolar transistor design.

The *emitter coupled logic* (ECL) *family* is a complex, expensive gate circuit. Its use

NASA PHOTO

Figure 14-4 Without computers this mission would have been impossible.

is restricted to SSI and MSI packages in large, expensive computers and military hardware.

Computer and Logic Subsystems

Figure 14–7 is a flow diagram of the hierarchy of digital systems.

Note that the logic flow eventually branches and there are two possible end results: (1) microcomputers, and (2) mini and large computers. So far LSI has been used less in larger computers because of its slower speed. Integrated injection logic promises to make LSI minicomputers possible. There is also a trend to combine several minis to make up very large computing systems.

The flow diagram (Fig. 14–7) soon branches into two gate assignment categories: (1) memory (using *flip-flops*, described below), and (2) combinational logic

circuits that control system operation and perform arithmetic operations (number crunching).

A logic system by itself is like a brain in a bottle—not functional. The logic system (computer, controller, or other system) must utilize *interface devices* in order to communicate with or to act upon the outside world. Interface devices are special equipment that enable the logic system to make things go. In the past each interface problem was a special (and expensive) engineering problem. Now, however, standard off-the-shelf, relatively inexpensive devices have become available to solve all but the most exotic interface problems. exotic interface problems.

Timing Devices

Almost all digital circuits are controlled by a master timing device called a *clock*. As in

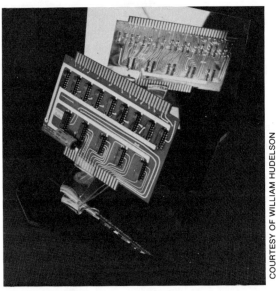

COURTESY OF WILLIAM HUDELSON

Figure 14-5 Assembled circuit board with ICs and other components mounted.

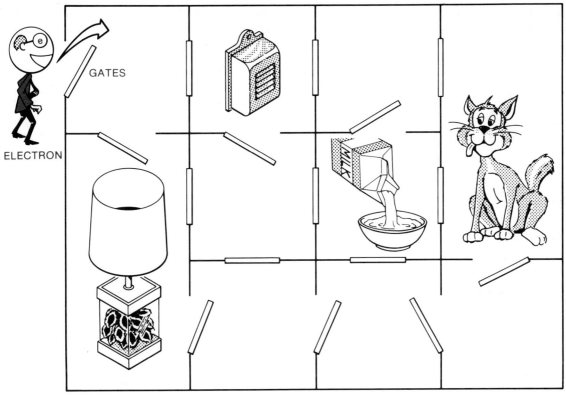

GATES

ELECTRON

The bell rings, the milk is poured, the light lights, or the cat gets put out??

Figure 14-6 Logic gate example.

most situations involving a sequence of events, order and timing are important. For example, one does not open the car door, close the car door, and then get into the car—the order is wrong. It is also necessary to time activities so that all members (arms, legs, etc.) are all the way into the car before the door is closed.

Memory

In digital systems, *memory* means devices that can *store* (for some period of time) *information*. This information is represented by zeros and ones in some particular sequence and quantity. For example, memory in the form of a cassette tape recorder can store a string of zeros and ones (binary digits, or *bits* in the form of two different tones. Semiconductor devices can store zeros and ones in the form of *flip-flops* or other special devices that can be held either *on* or *off*.

Tape recorders, magnetic discs, drum recorders, and so forth are mass memory storage devices. Punched paper tape and punched cards are also mass storage methods. Miniature doughnut-shaped magnets called *cores* are used for some memories in larger machines.

RAM

Random access memory This is a memory that can be written into, read out of, and erased and reused. The data stored has a definite address and can easily be located by a random access search, as opposed to a sequential search, which must start at the first address and proceed to search each address thereafter.

The RAM memory is organized like city streets so that any bit of data can be located at one direct, simple address. Total memory capacity is limited.

ROM

Read Only Memory (ROM) The ROM is physically organized much like the RAM but it cannot be erased and used again. Its preprogrammed data may be read out from it but new data may not be written into it. These preprogrammed units determine the machine's basic operating pattern. However, ROMs can be unplugged and replaced by other ROMs to alter the machine's operations. ROMs can also serve a rote memory function, such as being programmed with tables of often-needed information.

Computer instructions recorded in ROM memory are called *firmware.*

Programmable Logic

Most logic packages have all of the gates interconnected internally to do some special job. A programmable device with 7 program terminals can become any of 128 completely different logic circuits. For the number of gates available in the package there are only 128 different circuits possible. Thus, by putting 1s and 0s on the seven pins, any desired circuit out of the 128 can be had from a single package—a kind of universal logic package.

Programmable Counters

Programmable counters are available that can count by 1s, 2s, 5s, 10s, and so on, through the use of programming terminals. Counters are also available for fixed counting by 2s, 10s, 12s, and 16s.

Arithmetic logic unit (ALU) A complex part of the computer (or controller, etc.) system that performs logical and/or arithmetic operations. It can be instructed to perform addition, subtraction, and other functions via its programming terminals.

Microprocessor This is the ultimate logic device in current technology. It can contain control logic, memory, and arithmetic circuits and can be programmed to perform a vast array of operations. With the addition of *outboard* (not on the chip) *memory* and special chips that interface the microprocessor with the outside world, it becomes a *microcomputer,* a small general purpose computer. The price tag for such microcomputers presently ranges from a few hundred to a few thousand dollars.

Software The instructions to the computer, as opposed to hardware (physical) components of the computer system, are called *software.* Computer instructions (*programs*) are input into the computer for storage or processing via keyboard or some mass storage medium—magnetic tape, punched cards, paper tape, and so on. Software programs are "loaded" into random access memory prior to the execution of the software instructions.

Programming A program is a detailed set of instructions for the machine to carry out in sequence. On the very simplest levels, the kind of detail is much like the instructions for assembling a piece of furniture or child's toy, repairing an appliance, or taking a cross-country automobile trip.

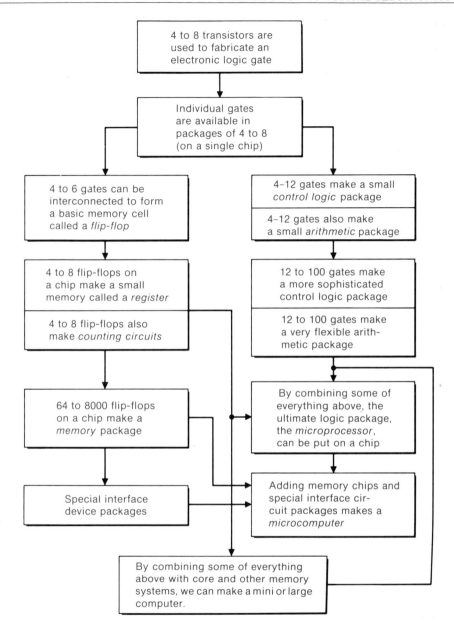

Figure 14-7 Digital logic systems flow diagram.

14.3 BOOLEAN ALGEBRA

Boolean algebra, a form of mathematics used for exercises in formal logic, was invented by George Boole, an English mathematician, in 1854. For 100 years Boole's logical algebra (symbolic logic) remained a curiosity, suitable only for philosophical debate. Then in the mid–1950s Claude Shannon of the Bell Telephone Company discovered that Boole's logic was just the tool he needed to solve the complex switching problems involved in providing telephone service. Computer designers quickly realized the potential benefits of applying Shannon's Boolean symbolic logic to their own problems, and the "computer revolution" began.

Boolean algebra is far simpler than ordinary algebra. In Boolean there are no roots or powers, for instance. It is a *binary system;* a variable or constant in Boolean can have *only one of two possible values, 0 or 1.* A gate (electronic on-off switch) in a computer (or other digital) circuit can be in only one of the two possible conditions, *on* or *off.*

Boolean Operators and Symbols

The operators in ordinary algebra are add (+), subtract (−), multiply (×), divide (÷), roots ($\sqrt{}$), and powers (X^n). Boolean algebra, however, contains only the operators AND (Boolean multiplication), OR (Boolean sum), and NOT (complement or inversion).

The AND operation is indicated by a dot (·) or by writing the letters together as for multiplication in ordinary algebra. The OR operation is indicated by a plus sign (+). The NOT operation is indicated by a bar (—) over a letter that represents a variable.

$$A \cdot B = AB = A \text{ AND } B$$

$$A + B = A \text{ OR } B$$

$$\overline{A} = \text{NOT } A$$

$$\overline{B} = \text{NOT } B$$

It is important to remember that the symbols (+) and (·) do not mean the same thing in Boolean as in ordinary algebra.

Electronic gates are super-speed versions of ordinary mechanical switches. Modern gates can switch from off to on, or from on to off, in the time it takes a beam of light to travel a yard. Since the speed of light is a 186,000 miles per second, this means that logic gates can switch in 10 nanoseconds.

Truth Tables

Tables that show the results of all possible combinations of true and false conditions in logical statements are called *truth tables.* Boolean expressions are either true or false; that is, they are *binary* (two-state) in nature. The digits 1 and 0 are used to represent the true and false conditions; the numeral 1 symbolizes a true condition and the number 0 symbolizes a false condition. The symbols 0 and 1 are used in general logic equations to represent false and true, respectively. When we are discussing hardware other symbols are often used as follows:

$$\text{True} = 1 = \text{high} = H = +5 \text{ volts}$$
$$\text{False} = 0 = \text{Low} = L = 0 \text{ volts}$$

AND Operation

The AND operation is represented by the Boolean expression $A \cdot B = f$. The f symbol stands for "function" and is used to indicate that we are dealing with a formal logic equation. All possible combinations for the AND operation with two variables are listed in Figure 14–8. As the table shows, when both A and B are false, f is false; when A is true and B is false, f is false; when A is false and B is true, f is false; and when both A and B are true, f is true.

When there are two possible conditions for each variable in the truth table, the number of possible combinations is equal to 2^n, where n is the number of independent variables in the logical expression. When there are two independent variables, the number of combinations is 2^2, or 4. When there are three independent variables, the number of combinations is 2^3, or 8. All possible combinations for the three-variable AND expression, $f = A \cdot B \cdot C$, are listed in the truth table in part F of Figure 14–8.

(A) The two-variable AND gate logic symbol

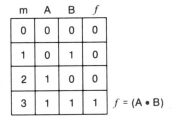

m	A	B	f	
0	0	0	0	
1	0	1	0	
2	1	0	0	
3	1	1	1	$f = (A \cdot B)$

(B) The standard truth table

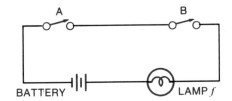

(C) The two-variable AND switching circuit

m	SWITCH A	SWITCH B	f (LAMP)
0	OPEN	OPEN	NOT LIT
1	OPEN	CLOSED	NOT LIT
2	CLOSED	OPEN	NOT LIT
3	CLOSED	CLOSED	LIT

(D) The two-variable switching-circuit truth table

Figure 14-8 The AND gate.

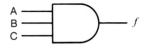

(E) The three-variable AND gate logic symbol

m	A	B	C	f
0	0	0	0	0
1	0	0	1	0
2	0	1	0	0
3	0	1	1	0
4	1	0	0	0
5	1	0	1	0
6	1	1	0	0
7	1	1	1	1

m	A	B	C	f
0	L	L	L	L
1	L	L	H	L
2	L	H	L	L
3	L	H	H	L
4	H	L	L	L
5	H	L	H	L
6	H	H	L	L
7	H	H	H	H

THE THREE-INPUT AND GATE TRUTH TABLE IN TERMS OF HIGH AND LOW INPUT LEVELS

THE THREE-INPUT AND GATE TRUTH TABLE

(F) Truth tables

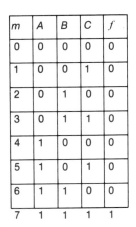

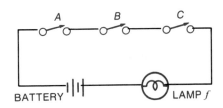

(G) Switching circuit

In the modern TTL family, logical zeros and 1s are represented by the voltages:

$$= 5 V = \text{Logical } 1$$
$$0 V = \text{Logical } 0$$

A 1 (+5 volts) is often called *high, and 0 volts low*. Truth tables are often written in the form shown in the truth table on the right in part F of Figure 14–8.

The OR Operation

The OR operation is represented by the Boolean expression f = A + B. All possible combinations for the OR operation with two variables are listed in the truth table in Figure 14–9. As the tables show, when both A and B are false, f is false; when A is true and B is false, f is true; when A is false and B

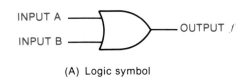

(A) Logic symbol

m	A	B	f
0	0	0	0
1	0	1	1
2	1	0	1
3	1	1	1

m	A	B	f
0	L	L	L
1	L	H	H
2	H	L	H
3	H	H	H

(B) Truth tables

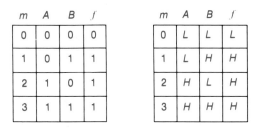

(C) Switching diagram

Figure 14-9 The *OR* Gate

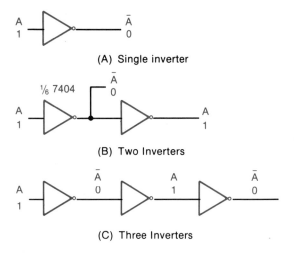

(A) Single inverter

(B) Two Inverters

(C) Three Inverters

Figure 14-10 The inverter.

is true, f is true; and when both A and B are true, f is true.

NOT Operation

The inverter is an inverting pulse amplifier that performs the NOT operation, often called the *complement* operation. If a 1 goes in, a 0 comes out; if a 0 goes in, a 1 comes out. An A in produces an $\overline{A}$ (NOT A) out. Figure 14-10 illustrates inverter operation.

Summary of inverter functions

1. if $A = 0$, $\overline{A} = 1$
2. if $A = 1$, $\overline{A} = 0$
3. if $A = Hi$, $\overline{A} = Lo$
4. if $A = Lo$, $\overline{A} = Hi$

Timing Diagrams

The Logic diagrams show how the data flows in the circuit. Truth tables tell us exactly what the circuit does. In addition, because nearly all digital circuits are precisely timed by a clock generator, it is often necessary to know exactly when the gates open and close. The *timing diagram* provides this information. Figure 14-11 shows timing diagrams for the two-input AND gate, the two-input OR gate, and the inverter. (AND and OR gates can have any number of inputs, but inverters have only one.)

14.4 THE BINARY NUMBER SYSTEM

Our conventional arithmetic uses the base 10 number system. But because computers use true-false on-off gates, computer arithmetic must be done in a binary (base 2) number system.

The following illustrates the meaning of the number *425* in our base 10 decimal system. (See Table 14-1.)

Table 14-1 Binary and decimal number systems compared.

(A) Base 10 (decimal)

Thousands	Hundreds	Tens	Units	Name of position
1000	100	10	1	Position value in decimal form
$10 \times 10 \times 10$	10×10	10	$\frac{10}{10}$	Use of radix to form value of each position
10^3	10^2	10^1	10^0	Position value in exponential form

(B) Base 2 (Binary)

Sixteens	Eights	Fours	Twos	Units	Name of position
16	8	4	2	1	Position value in decimal form
$2\times2\times2\times2$	$2\times2\times2$	2×2	2	$\frac{2}{2}$	Use of radix to form value of each position
2^4	2^3	2^2	2^1	2^0	Position value in exponential form

Example 14-1

$$10^2 \quad 10^1 \quad 10^0$$
$$4 \quad 2 \quad 5 = 4 \times 10^2 + 2 \times 10^1 + 5 \times 10^0$$
$$= 400 + 20 + 5$$

The binary system works the same way except that the column headings are multiples of two instead of 10, and only two digits, 0 and 1, are available. A binary number is written with a subscript 2 to identify it as a base 2 number. The following example shows how the number 41 in the base 10 decimal system is written and interpreted in binary.

Exponent value	2^5	2^4	2^3	2^2	2^1	2^0
Decimal value	32	16	8	4	2	1
Binary number	1	0	1	0	0	1

Reading out, we have $32 + 8 + 1 = 41$ (or it can be written 41_{10}). Thus $101001_2 = 41_{10}$.

14.5 OTHER NUMBER SYSTEMS AND CODES

In addition to the binary number system, computers use other number systems and codes. However, any computer number system or code must have some simple relationship to the binary system and must be handled in the computer as groups of ones and zeros. Some codes and number systems are used for error checking purposes while others are used to make human-computer communications easier.

Hexadecimal

The hexadecimal number system (base 16) is frequently used in digital systems because it is a medium-sized base that is easy for people to deal with and it is also directly related to binary. Four binary digits *(bits)* stand for 16 hexadecimal digits. The first 10 digits, zero through nine (0–9) are the same as our base 10 digits, but an additional six digits are required for hexadecimal *(hex)*. The letters A through F have been selected for the extra hex digits, because they are symbols already available on any typewriter or computer printer. The hexadecimal system and its binary equivalents are shown in Table 14–2.

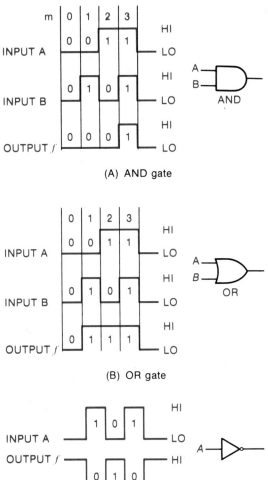

(A) AND gate

(B) OR gate

(C) Inverter

Figure 14-11 Timing diagrams.

Octal

The octal system (base 8) is also convenient to use and is also related to the binary system. Octal expressed in binary digits is called *binary coded octal (BCO)*. The octal system and BCO equivalents are shown in Table 14-2A.

Binary Coded Decimal (BCD)

The BCD code shown in Table 14-2 is identical to binary coded hex except that the hex digits A through F are not used. The

BCD is used in pocket calculators, telemetry and some other applications but it is rarely found in larger digital systems.

Logic Diagrams, Equations, and Truth Tables

The truth table is a specification list indicating exactly what the logic circuit that goes with it must do. Once the truth table exists, it serves as a guide for writing an equation. The equation, in turn, tells how to draw the logic diagram. Let's try an example. Suppose we build a circuit to add two binary digits (bits). First we must state the rules for binary addition and translate those rules into a truth table. The binary addition table and its equivalent truth table are shown in Table 14-3. In this example we are going to use a logic circuit to perform arithmetic.

Compare the addition table in Table 14-3 with the two truth tables. To write an equation, the terms are read out from the rows in the truth table that have a 1 in the f column. A zero under a letter heading is read as a NOT. A 1 is read as the letter itself.

Example 14-2

A	B	f
1	0	1

$\longrightarrow$ $A\cdot\overline{B}$

The letters are connected by a dot (AND) symbol. Part B of Table 14-3 shows the terms at the right in the table. The terms are $(\overline{A\cdot B})$, $(A\cdot\overline{B})$. To complete the equation, place + signs between each term and add an equals sign and an f.

$$f = (\overline{A\cdot B}) + (A\cdot\overline{B})$$

To draw a logic diagram, each term becomes an AND gate and the + symbol becomes an OR gate. Figure 14-12 shows how this works.

Table 14-2 Binary codes.

(A) Octal system and binary coded octal (base 8):

4	3	2	1	0	Position
8^4	8^3	8^2	8^1	8^0	Exponential value
4096	512	64	8	1	Decimal value
Example: 2	1	3	6	7	Number in radix 8

$8192 + 512 + 192 + 48 + 7 = 8951_{10}$

Octal digit	BCO Equivalents
0	000
1	001
2	010
3	011
4	100
5	101
6	110
7	111

Example	000	001	011	101	Number in BCO
	0	1	3	5	Octal equivalent

(B) Hexadecimal system and binary coded hexa-
    decimal (base 16):

3	2	1	0	Position
16^3	16^2	16^1	16^0	Exponential form
4096	256	16	1	Decimal value
Example: 0	B	A	3	Number in radix 16
0 +	2816 +	160 +	3	$= 2979_{10}$

HEX	BINARY				HEX	BINARY			
0	0	0	0	0	A	1	0	1	0
1	0	0	0	1	B	1	0	1	1
2	0	0	1	0	C	1	1	0	0
3	0	0	1	1	D	1	1	0	1
4	0	1	0	0	E	1	1	1	0
5	0	1	0	1	F	1	1	1	1
6	0	1	1	0					
7	0	1	1	1					
8	1	0	0	0					
9	1	0	0	1					

(C) The BCD code:

Decimal numbers	BCD equivalent		
001	0000	0000	0001
123	0001	0010	0011
546	0101	0100	0110
879	1000	0111	1001

Table 14-3 Binary addition table and truth table.

(A) Addition table

	Sum	Carry
0 + 0 =	0	0
0 + 1 =	1	0
1 + 0 =	1	0
1 + 1 =	0	1

(B) Sum truth table

A	B	f	
0	0	0	
0	1	1	$\overline{A} \cdot B$
1	0	1	$A \cdot \overline{B}$
1	1	0	

(C) Carry truth table

A	B	f	
0	0	0	
0	1	0	
1	0	0	
1	1	1	$(A \cdot B)$

The modern standard (TTL) logic gate is the NAND gate. The NAND gate is an AND gate with a built-in *inverter*. The built-in inverter comes about because a built-in common emitter amplifier is provided in each gate circuit. An AND gate and inverter can do anything that can be done using AND, OR, and inverter gates. AND-OR-NOT circuits can always be converted into NAND circuits simply by changing all gates (both AND and OR) into NAND. See part B of Figure 14–12. The truth table for the *carry* proves to be the truth table for an AND gate. An AND gate is all that is required for the carry operation.

The Exclusive OR Gate

The circuit that we just put together is one that solves so many digital problems that

manufacturers provide the circuit in part B of Figure 14–12 in a package called an *exclusive OR gate*. Figure 14–13 shows the special symbol for the exclusive OR.

Figure 14–14 is the exclusive OR logic diagram with inputs interconnected and inverters added to carry out the NOT operations demanded by the bars over input variables, as shown in Figure 14–12. Both circuits are identical, but logic diagrams are usually drawn as shown in Figure 14-14.

Figure 14–15 is a more complex logic circuit.

14.6 COMMERCIAL LOGIC GATES

Transistor-transistor logic (TTL) is the most popular small scale (SSI) and medium scale (MSI) logic form. It is available in several package styles, but the *dual inline package* (DIP) shown in Figure 14–16 is the most common.

A simplified version of the TTL NAND gate is shown in part A of Figure 14–17. A more complete version is shown in part B. Protective diodes have been added to the inputs and a complementary symmetry amplifier has been added to the output to speed up the circuit and allow it to drive up to 10 other gates.

All members of the TTL family require a power supply voltage of +5 volts and ground. Logic levels are standard +5 V = 1, and zero volts = logical 0. There is some tolerance built in so that logic levels need not be perfect. Figure 14–18 shows the logic levels for standard TTL logic.

Figure 14–19 is a photomicrograph of an integrated circuit chip. The wires in the photo are less than half the diameter of a human hair.

14.7 FLIP-FLOPS

The flip-flop is the basic memory and counting element in digital systems. The

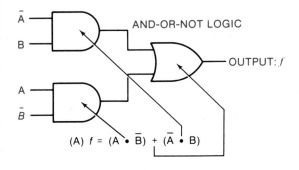

AND-OR-NOT LOGIC

OUTPUT: f

(A) $f = (A \cdot \bar{B}) + (\bar{A} \cdot B)$

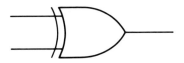

Figure 14-13 The exclusive OR symbol.

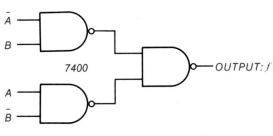

7400

OUTPUT: f

(B) The adder circuit in NAND logic

Figure 14-12 The circuit and equation.

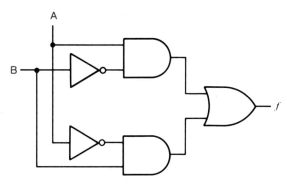

Figure 14-14 The exclusive OR logic diagram as it is normally drawn.

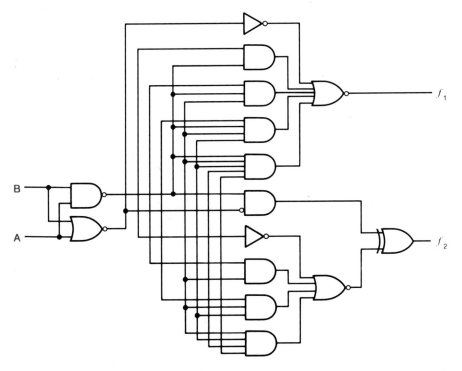

Figure 14-15 A more complex logic diagram.

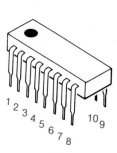

Figure 14-16 Dual inline package.

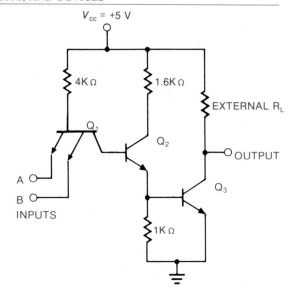

(A) Simplified circuit:

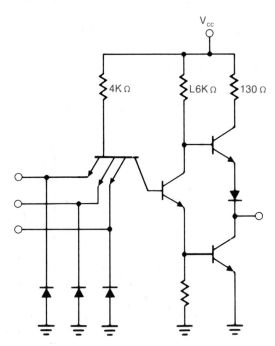

(B) Standard 7400 Series TTL nand gate schematic:

Figure 14-17 The TTL logic schematic.

simplest flip-flop is composed of two gates with the output of one fed back to the input of the other. Figure 14–20 shows the circuit.

The *negative-going input signals* are common in flip-flops. When negative-going input signals are used, they are called *active-low inputs*. The signals do not actually go negative (past zero).

An inverter can be added to the circuit, as shown in Figure 14–21, to eliminate the disallowed (forbidden) condition in the truth table for Figure 14–20. With the inverter in the circuit, R and S (reset and set) inputs cannot possibly be in the same state (both zeros or both ones). This kind of circuit is known as a *type D flip-flop*.

Clocked Flip-Flops

Nearly every flip-flop application requires that it change states only when the *clock* tells it to. The clock input is provided by the addition of a pair of additional NAND gates, as shown in Figure 14–22.

The Type T Flip-Flop

The *type T flip-flop* (toggle flip-flop) shown in Figure 14–23 toggles with each input pulse. The first pulse sets Q to high. The second pulse sets Q back to low. It takes two input pulses to get one output pulse. The circuit divides by 2 (or counts by 2).

The two outside feedback lines and gates A and B steer the input to produce the desired toggle action. The T type is the basic counting configuration.

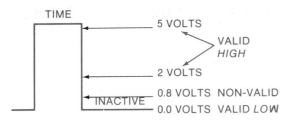

	Input Logic 0 (Low)	Input Logic 1 (High)	Output Logic 0 (Low)	Output Logic 1 (High)
Minimum	0V	2.4V	0.4V	2.4V
Typical	0.6V	3.3V	0.6V	3.3V
Maximum	0.8V	5.0V	0.8V	3.6V

Figure 14-18 TTL logic levels.

Figure 14-19 Photomicrograph of integrated circuit chip.

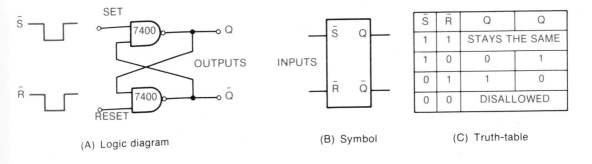

(A) Logic diagram

(B) Symbol

(C) Truth-table

S̄	R̄	Q	Q
1	1	STAYS THE SAME	
1	0	0	1
0	1	1	0
0	0	DISALLOWED	

Figure 14-20 The set-reset (R/S) Flip-Flop.

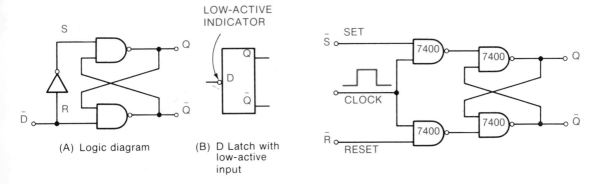

(A) Logic diagram

(B) D Latch with low-active input

Figure 14-21 The type *D* Flip-flop.

Figure 14-22 Clocked R/S flip-flop.

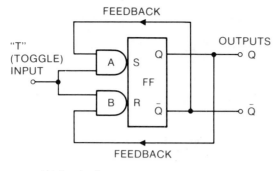

(A) Logic diagram

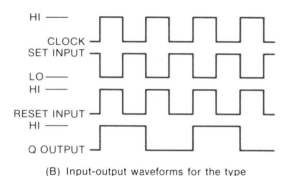

(B) Input-output waveforms for the type "T" flip-flop

Figure 14-23 The type *T* (toggle) flip-flop.

The J-K Flip-Flop

The *J-K* flip-flop (Figure 14–24) is the workhorse of digital circuits. The *J-K* is usually a master-slave arrangement and it and a master-slave type *D* do most of the digital work.

Simple *R-S* flip-flops are used in memory arrays, but for most other systems a master-slave *J-K* or type *D* is required to avoid timing errors. The *J-K* can be used as a set-reset or toggle or counting flip-flop. Part A of Figure 14–24 shows the simple *J-K* flip-flop and part B shows the master-slave version.

The master-slave arrangement is used to provide time for each flip-flop in a circuit to change states and settle down to a steady condition. The settling time must be allowed for or false counts and unreliable operation occur at high counting rates.

14.8 FLIP-FLOP APPLICATIONS

Flip-flops are used for temporary memory purposes, either as a single unit to remember one bit, or arranged on a memory chip for larger scale storage. TTL flip-flops are used in memories of up to a thousand bits or so. Flip-flops using MOS transistors are used for arrays of up to 16,000 eight-bit groups. We will examine memory applications shortly.

Counters

Flip-flops can be cascaded to count by twos (binary) and by adding additional control logic, they can be made to count by 10s, 12s, and so on. There are a number of variations on the basic binary counter circuit, but they are all refinements or variations of the two circuits shown in parts A and B of Figure 14–25. The total maximum count for a string of flip-flops is 2^n, where n = the number of flip-flops in the string.

Shift Registers

Flip-flops are also used for a kind of memory that can transfer stored bits from cell to adjacent cell. The shift register does not *count*. It transfers all data one flip-flop to the right for each clock pulse. The shift register diagram is shown in Figure 14-26.

Commercial shift register integrated circuits are available with 1,000 or more flip-flops. They are also available with extra control logic gates that allow both right and left shifts and the capacity to load all flip-flops simultaneously.

Shift Register Counter

A shift register can be connected as a counter by feeding its output back into the input and starting the clock. The Johnson shift register counter is the most common type. It is not as efficient in its use of flip-

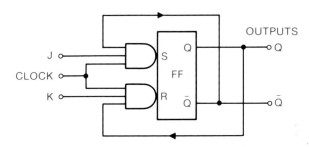

J	K	AFTER CLOCK
0	0	NO CHANGE
0	1	F-F RESETS
1	0	F-F SETS
1	1	F-F TOGGLES

TRUTH TABLE

(A) The simple J-K flip-flop and truth table.

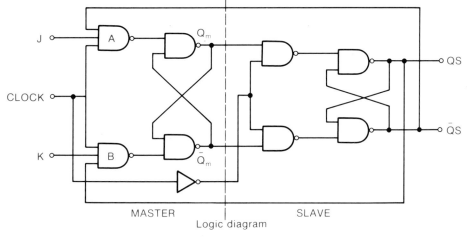

Logic diagram

CLOCKED INPUTS

J	K	CLOCK →	OUTPUT. Q
0	0		NO CHANGE
0	1		0
1	0		1
1	1		TOGGLES TO OPPOSITE STATE

J=K MASTER-SLAVE TRUTH TABLE

(B) The J-K master-slave flip-flop and truth table.

Figure 14-24 The J-K flip-flop and truth tables.

flops as the ordinary binary counter in that its maximum count is only 2n, where n is the number of flip-flops (the binary counter has a maximum count of 2^n). Figure 14–27 shows the Johnson counter circuit.

14.9 DECODERS

It is often necessary to convert the binary or Johnson counter into a standard decimal (0, 1, 2, 3, 4, 5, 6, 7, 8, 9) count or to some special code such as the code required to light the proper segments in 7-segment displays (see part C of Figure 14–28).

The Johnson decoder is generally made of individual gates because of its simplicity (see Figure 14–28). Other decoders, such as the binary-to-decimal decoder in Figure 14–28, are available as standard MSI

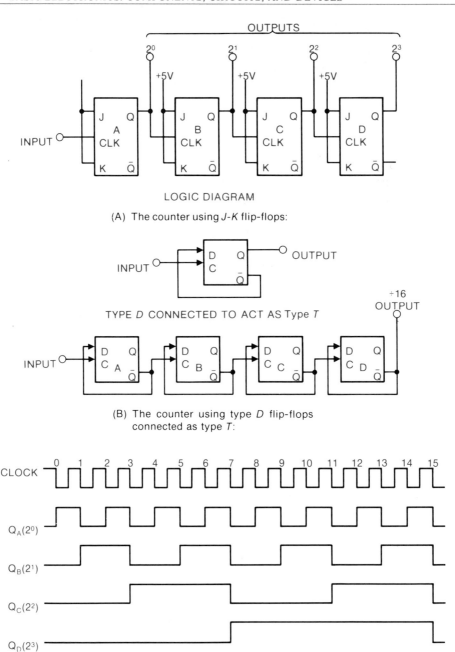

OUTPUTS

LOGIC DIAGRAM

(A) The counter using J-K flip-flops:

TYPE D CONNECTED TO ACT AS Type T

(B) The counter using type D flip-flops connected as type T:

(C) The timing diagram for both counters:

Figure 14-25 Binary Counters.

integrated circuit packages. A number of other commonly needed decoders are also available in standard DIP packages.

The decoder is the electronic equivalent of a multiposition rotary switch that distributes combinations of several inputs to individual, one-at-a-time outputs.

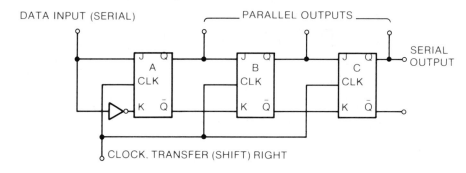

(A) Shift register with *J-K* flip-flops.

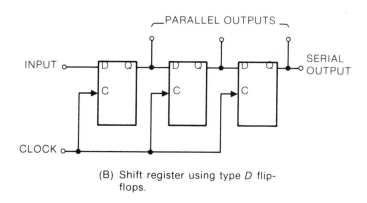

(B) Shift register using type *D* flip-flops.

Figure 14-26 Shift registers.

14.10 MULTIPLEXER DATA SELECTOR

The *multiplexer* is an electronic rotary switch that selects any one of several one-at-a-time inputs, and that outputs the data in some binary code. Keyboard encoding is an example. A single decimal key can be pressed and the multiplexer translates that key closure into the desired binary output number or coded number. The circuit for a decimal-to-binary encoder multiplexer is shown in Figure 14–29.

Programmable decoders and multiplexers are available that allow the device to work in any code required for any non-standard job that might come up.

14.11 MEMORY COMPONENTS

Memory is one of the essential features of most digital circuits. A memory can consist of a single flip-flop or arrays of 512,000 flip-flops on a few IC chips. Memory also includes magnetic devices such as tape recorders, magnetic disc and drum recorders, punched paper tape and punched cards, and stationary magnetic core memory systems.

Memory can be roughly divided into three groups: 1. mass storage—cards, tapes, discs, and so on. 2. Random access memory (RAM)—flip-flop arrays and core memory. 3. Read only memory (ROM)—pre-"recorded" semiconductor memory systems.

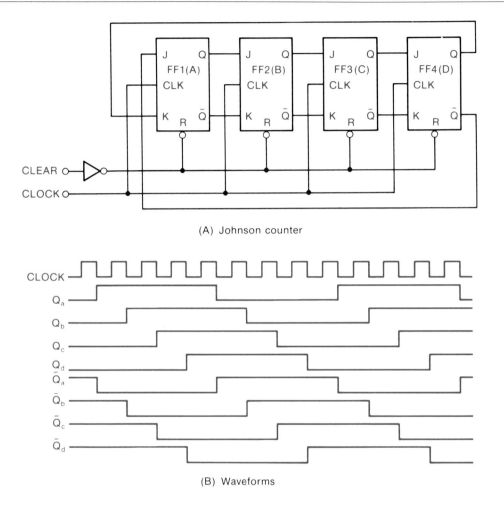

(A) Johnson counter

(B) Waveforms

Figure 14-27 The Johnson counter.

Punched Cards and Tape

The two most popular versions of this kind of mass memory are shown in Figure 14–30. Table 14–4 shows how to read the punch card.

Magnetic Recorders

Magnetic recorders in several forms are used for digital data memory (bulk storage). Inexpensive cassette recorders, expensive data tape machines, thin plastic magnetic coated discs, and precision magnetic discs and drums are all common.

Magnetic Core Memory

Thousands of tiny doughnut-shaped cores strung on wires are used in many computer main (RAM) read-write memories. In part A of Figure 14–31 current flowing through the wire magnetizes the core. As shown in part B, after the current has stopped flowing the core remains permanently magnetized. To read the core, a reverse current is sent through the wire. If the core was storing a *1* (magnetized), its collapsing field induces a small current in a separate sense wire threaded through the core. If a *0* was stored,

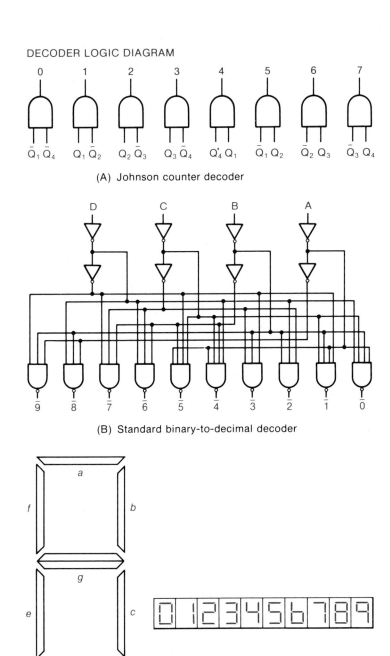

DECODER LOGIC DIAGRAM

(A) Johnson counter decoder

(B) Standard binary-to-decimal decoder

(C) Seven-segment numerical display

Figure 14-28 Decoders.

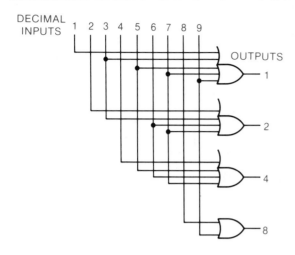

Figure 14-29 Decimal to binary encoder.

there is no field in that direction to collapse and no current is induced in the sense wire. Part C of Figure 14-31 shows a zero being stored in the core.

Cores are threaded as shown in Figure 14-32 into an array called a *memory plane*. These planes are then stacked to make a three-dimensional memory package. When a core is read, the data stored in it is lost

unless it is immediately written back into the memory.

RAM Semiconductor Memories

A RAM (random access memory) is a memory that can be written into and read out of just as core memory can. However, core retains its data when the power is shut down, and semiconductor RAM does not. Readout in semiconductor memories does not erase the data stored in the cell being read, but all data in the memory is lost when the power is shut down.

Flip-flop cells in RAM are organized in the same fashion as in the core memory.

Part A of Figure 14-33 shows the arrangement of the memory cells in one type of 16-bit RAM memory, and part B shows the X and Y decoders and input and output buffer amplifiers. Four bits of memory address can select any one of the 16 cells to read into or write out of.

The number of cells can be expanded to 1,024, with only 12 bits of address data required to select any one of the 1,024 cells. Many modern semiconductor memories are

Table 14-4   Reading the punch card.

	Numerical row only	Zone 12 plus numerical row below	Zone 11 plus numerical row below	Zone 12 plus numerical row below
0 =	0			
1 =	1	A	J	
2 =	2	B	K	S
3 =	3	C	L	T
4 =	4	D	M	U
5 =	5	E	N	V
6 =	6	F	O	W
7 =	7	G	P	X
8 =	8	H	Q	Y
9 =	9	I	R	Z

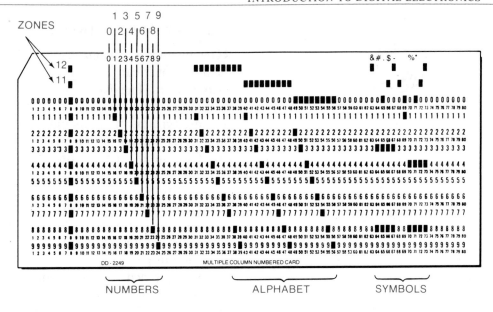

(A) Punched card

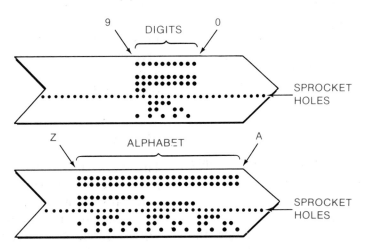

(B) Punched paper tape

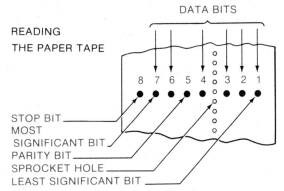

Figure 14-30 Punched cards and punched paper tape.

organized into groups of 8-bit words so that a 12-bit address can select any one of 1,024 8-bit words. Larger memory chips use MOS or I²L transistors and are available with up to 16,000 8-bit words on a chip, with larger memories soon to become available. Semiconductor memory is faster and

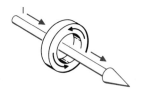

(A) Current is applied. Core stores a 1.

(B) Core is magnetized. Core remembers a 1.

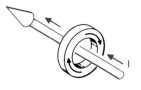

(C) Current is reversed. Core reverses its magnetic state. Core stores a 0.

Figure 14–31 Memory cores.

cheaper than core, but it is subject to data loss in case of power failure.

Dynamic MOS Memories

Another form of memory is available, the *dynamic MOS memory*, that uses the charge on a microscopic capacitor to store data. The charge tends to leak off and the capacitors must be periodically recharged (refreshed). Dynamic memories are being replaced by static (flip-flop) memories in many applications. A *byte* consists of 8 bits. The RAM board shown in Figure 14–34 is an 8,000 byte memory. The memory is *word-organized*, that is, a single address is the location of an entire word. Data are entered and retrieved from memory a word at a time not a bit at a time.

Read Only Memory (ROM)

ROM memory is organized much like RAM memory but it can only be *read out of*, not written into. The ROM is used to store preprogrammed data—permanent subroutines (groups of commands), tables and directories that are frequently used, and so on. Computer instructions recorded in ROM are called *firmware*.

ROMs are made up of transistors (either bipolar or MOS) that are permanently turned either off or on. Bipolar memories use fuse links that can deliberately be burned open. Some MOS devices are programmed during manufacture and are called *mask programmed ROMs*. Programmable ROMs, called *PROMs,* can be programmed by applying *controlled* overvoltage to appropriate cells. The EPROM, Erasable Programmable Read Only Memory, can be erased with ultraviolet light and reprogrammed in the same manner as the PROMs.

14.12 CLOCKS

The clock that almost all digital systems require to insure that each operation takes place at exactly the right time is a circuit that generates a continuous train of logic pulses. Logic gate oscillators and special timing packages are used for noncritical applications. For more critical situations, crystal-controlled logic gate oscillators or special crystal-controlled clock generator ICs are used.

Figure 14–35 illustrates some popular clock circuits.

The logic ring oscillator uses standard logic gates and depends upon gate time delays plus external values of *R* and *C* for its timing. The 555 is a popular and versatile IC that can be used for a number of applications in addition to generating clock pulses.

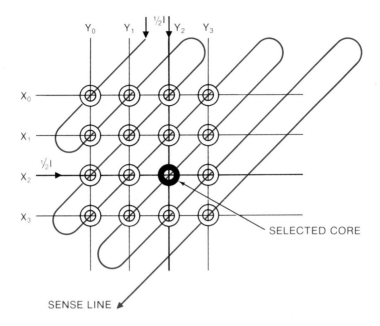

Figure 14-32 Magnetic core memory plane.

14.13 MICROPROCESSORS AND MICROCOMPUTERS

The most exciting piece of computing hardware is the microprocessor. Less powerful than the big machines, it has an overwhelming edge in price when a big machine is not essential. A microprocessor chip can be purchased for a few dollars, where ten years ago that much computing hardware would have cost $50,000 or so. A microprocessor is a complete computer central processing unit on a chip. It becomes a full-fledged computer with the addition of memory (from 1,000 to 65,000 bytes), input-output interface circuits, and some peripheral devices, such as an input-output teletype or a keyboard and CRT. Figure 14–36 shows the Radio Shack TRS-80 microcomputer system.

The microprocessor cannot as yet compete with minicomputers and large machines in terms of speed and capacity. Minis and large machines use relatively few LSI circuits because LSIs are presently too slow. Since there is a trend to build large machines by assembling a group of minicomputers that have similar speed capabilities, Minicomputers are being built with *fast* microprocessor chips and other LSI parts. The microprocessor is currently the fastest-growing of all electronic technologies; with higher speeds, it will very likely take over the entire computing industry. Microprocessors are now appearing in applications where computers were previously far too costly to consider. For example, the automobile industry alone will buy millions of microprocessors to control fuel and ignition systems, brakes, and other units in production automobiles.

14.14 THE MICROPROCESSOR SYSTEM

The microprocessor system is shown in Figure 14–38. The bus consists of eight or sixteen lines that carry the data from one

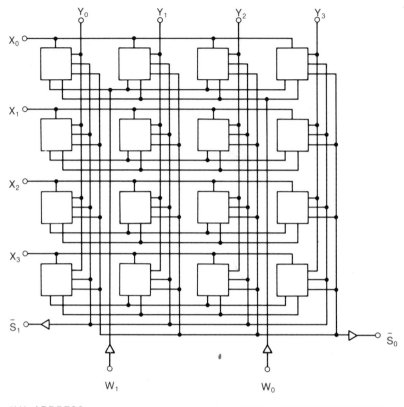

X,Y   ADDRESS
W   WRITE INPUT
X   SENSE OUTPUT

EACH SQUARE REPRESENTS
ONE BIT OF STORAGE

(A) Memory cell (flip-flop) organization.

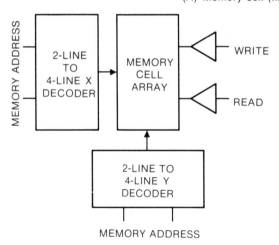

(B) Complete memory

Figure 14-33 RAM memory.

PROCESSOR TECHNOLOGY

Figure 14-34 RAM memory boards.

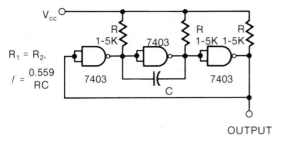

(A) TTL ring oscillator clock circuit

$R_1 = R_2,$

$f = \dfrac{0.559}{RC}$

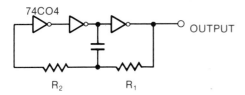

(B) C-MOS ring oscillator clock circuit

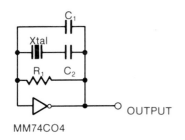

(C) C-MOS crystal oscillator clock circuit

FREQUENCY OF OSCILLATION

$f = \dfrac{1}{T}$

$= \dfrac{1.44}{(R_A + 2R_B)C}$

DUTY CYCLE

$D = \dfrac{R_B}{R_A + 2R_B}$

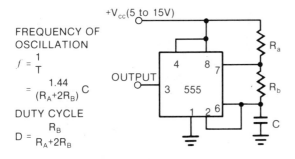

(D) 555 timer clock circuit

Figure 14-35 Clock circuits.

section of the system to another. Data can flow on the bus in either direction, but only data from one source to one destination is allowed on the bus at any given time. The bus also carries data to and from memory and to and from the outside world. The ALU (arithmetic logic unit) performs computations (addition, subtraction, etc.) and several logic operations. The control unit provides sequencing and other control functions for the ALU. The ALU is connected to an internal *bus*. The *accumulator* consists of two 8-bit or 16-bit shift registers that provide temporary storage. In most processors, data from the outside goes first to the accumulators, where the processor routes it either to memory or to the ALU, according to instructions stored elsewhere in memory. Data leaving the processor normally does so by way of the accumulators. The accumulators also store the result of operations (addition and so on) that take place in the ALU.

The *status register* contains important information about what has happened in the accumulator. It remembers whether the result of the operation was positive, negative, or zero, and if there was a carry produced.

The *instruction register* keeps track of where to find the next instruction in memory. The bus, as it leaves the processor, normally has 16 address lines and 8 data lines. The lines are bidirectional to allow data to enter and leave the processor.

The program counter routes instructions into and out of the external ROM and RAM memories. The data counter routes data into and out of the external memory. The memory address logic locates specific groups of memory cells for the data and program counters. Some processors have some internal RAM memory, as shown, and others depend entirely on *outboard* memory. The memory address logic can address up to 64,000 bytes of external memory and peripheral devices. The memory is usually a combination of RAM and ROM.

Interrupts

The processor is so fast that it can perform a number of different tasks apparently simultaneously. An *interrupt* tells the machine to stop what it is working on, temporarily load current instructions and data into a reserved section of memory called the *stack*, and then process the interrupt problem. When it finishes with the interrupt problem, it retrieves the temporarily-stored previous instructions from the stack and returns to the original problem. There can be several levels of interrupts with priorities established. At the rate of 200,000 operations per second, the machine *appears* to be processing several problems at the same time (simultaneously).

Input/output ports in some machines correspond to reserved memory addresses, while in others an input/output device can be at any memory location. If there is an input/output device at a particular address, that address is not available for memory use.

The *input/output port* usually involves an interface device to drive peripheral equipment such as video displays, teletypes, or tape or disc memories. Other peripheral devices may be motors, solenoids, and so on, to control mechanical systems. (See Figure 14–37.)

Figure 14–36 Radio Shack TRS-80.

TANDY CORP.

Figure 14-37 Universal experimental board.

Microprocessor Instructions

Microprocessor instructions consist of one, two, or three bytes. Data must follow instruction commands in successive memory locations.

Example 14-3

One-Byte Instructions:

b_7 b_6 b_5 b_4 b_3 b_2 b_1 b_0 *Op-code*

One-byte instructions, often called *inherent instructions*, are used primarily for manipulating accumulator registers. No address code for the operand needs to be specified because it is inherent in the instruction. For example, CLRA (clear accumulator register A) requires no definition of the data to be operated on, nor is it necessary to specify an address for the data to be operated on (the operand). Clearing the register clears whatever data is stored in it.

Example 14-4

Two-Byte Instructions:

Example
memory
locations

Byte 1: 0 0 0 0 b_7 b_6 b_5 b_4 b_3 b_2 b_1 b_0 Op-code

Byte 2: 0 0 0 1 b_7 b_6 b_5 b_4 b_3 b_2 b_1 b_0 Operand
or address
of operand

In two-byte instructions, the operand must be in the memory location immediately following the op-code location.

Example 14-5

Three-Byte Instructions:

Memory
address

Byte 1 0 0 0 3 b_7 b_6 b_5 b_4 b_3 b_2 b_1 b_0 Op-code

Byte 2: 0 0 0 4 b_7 b_6 b_5 b_4 b_3 b_2 b_1 b_0 Higher 8
bits of the
address of
the operand

Byte 3: 0 0 0 5 b_7 b_6 b_5 b_4 b_3 b_2 b_1 b_0 Lower 8
bits of the
address of
the operand

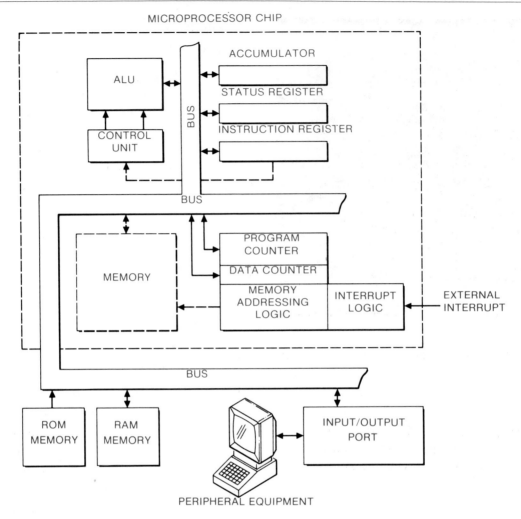

Figure 14-38 Block Diagram of a micro-processor.

SUMMARY

1. Digital logic systems are composed of gates and gates combined to form flip-flops and more complex circuits.
2. Digital logic is a go/no-go binary system.
3. Boolean algebra is a tool for designing and analyzing logic systems.
4. Computation is performed in binary arithmetic, but binary arithmetic and Boolean algebra are two different systems.
5. Logic operations are control, memory, and computation.
6. Integrated circuits are constructed almost molecule by molecule.
7. Integrated circuits allow a great many logic gates and more complex systems to be put on a large postage-stamp size element (a *chip*).

8. Small scale integration (SSI) contains up to twelve logic gates on a chip.

9. Medium scale integration (MSI) contains between twelve and one hundred logic gates on a chip.

10. Large scale integration (LSI) contains from one hundred to ten thousand or more gates on a chip.

11. Bipolar transistors in digital logic are faster but consume more power than MOS (metal oxide) transistors.

12. A logic family is a group of logic circuits that can be put together like Tinker Toys.

13. When two different logic families are used in the same system, extra components are often required to make them work together, called *interface components*.

14. Transistor-transistor logic (TTL) is the most popular bipolar family.

15. Random access memory (RAM) can be both written into and read out of. RAM is the working memory.

16. Read only memory (ROM) remembers permanently. It cannot be written into—that is, be altered.

17. Firmware is computer instructions recorded in ROM memory.

18. The arithmetic logic unit (ALU) performs the computations in a computer.

19. Software is a written set of instructions for the computer to follow.

20. A microprocessor is a computer central processing system on an integrated circuit chip. The microprocessor becomes a microcomputer when external memory, interface circuits, and input-output devices are added.

21. A program is a detailed set of instructions. The computer follows the program step by step.

REVIEWING YOUR ELECTRONIC VOCABULARY

A. Words

1. Binary numbers
2. Compatibility
3. Firmware
4. Hardware
5. Interface
6. Logic
7. Microprocessor
8. Program
9. Software
10. Truth table

B. Abbreviations

1. SSI
2. MSI
3. LSI
4. ROM
5. RAM
6. PROM
7. TTL
8. HI
9. LO
10. IO

CHECKING YOUR UNDERSTANDING

1. Are most logic families completely compatible with most other logic families?
2. In cases where logic families are less than completely compatible, what is the hardware called that can make them work together?
3. What is meant by *speed* when applied to a given logic family?
4. List three of the six most popular logic families.
5. What is the standard power supply voltage for the TTL family?
6. What is RAM used for in a computer system?
7. What is ROM memory used for?
8. What is the function of the clock in a digital system?
9. What is a computer program?
10. What must be added to (most) microprocessors to get a complete microcomputer?

SOLVING ELECTRONIC PROBLEMS

1. Write the following binary numbers in decimal form.

   a. 1000_2
   b. 1001_2
   c. 11111_2
   d. 11001_2

   e. 111010_2
   f. 101011_2
   g. 001101_2

2. Write the following decimal numbers in binary form.
   a. 18
   b. 64
   c. 128
   d. 200

CHAPTER 15
Radar and Navigation Aids

INTRODUCTION

Most radar (an acronym for *RA*dio *D*etection *and R*anging) navigational aids are very similar in operation. They are based on direction and phase or time of the transmitted and/or received signal.

The term *radar* refers generally to any system in which the transmission and/or return of electromagnetic energy is used to determine the range (and usually the direction) of an object. Radars normally operate in the range of frequencies between 100 MHz and 30,000 MHz. However, there are several systems based on the radar principle that operate on much lower frequencies. Two such systems, LORAN (long range navigation) and LORAC (long range communications), operate in the 1,700 kHz frequency with extreme accuracy. LORAC can, with supporting equipment, establish a location (for navigational purposes) to within 50 feet at about 1,000 miles from the LORAC transmitters, of which there are three in any system. It is, however, a rather large system and requires frequent recalibration. LORAN has a range of about 300 miles and is accurate to about 1 mile.

The history of radar began about 1887 when Heinrich Hertz observed that radio waves were reflected from solid objects. But it was not until 1904 that the German engineer Christian Hulsmeyer proposed that this phenomenon of reflection could be used

NASA PHOTO

Figure 15-1 Controllers at one of the FAA's 20 air route traffic control centers in the domestic United States.

in the detection of objects for collision-avoidance.

On June 20, 1922, Marconi, in a speech to the Institute of Radio Engineers, stated that using radio waves he had detected objects at a range of several miles. He felt that practical use could be made of this technique for the detection of ships in fog. The first actual use of the radar concept came in 1925 when Merle Tuve and Gregory Breit of the Carnegie Institute observed the height of the ionosphere with a pulsed radar system similar to those still in use for ionospheric research.

In 1922, shortly after Marconi's speech, A.H. Taylor and L.C. Young, working at the Naval Research Laboratory, were able to successfully use radio waves to detect the presence of a wooden ship, using a transmitter operating continuously (instead of being turned on and off, or *pulsed*; pulsed operation is used in modern radar). Targets were detected by interference between the reflected and direct waves from the transmitter. Similar experiments were made with aircraft in the early 1930s, but it was not until 1935–36, when pulse techniques were used, that much progress was made. But by 1939 the U.S. Army Signal Corps had a search radar and a range and tracking radar.

Radar has been refined since World War II. The amount of improvement is demonstrated by our ability to track space probes beyond Mars with ease.

15.1 RADAR OPERATION

The operating principle of radar is very similar to what happens when we hear an echo a short time after we shout toward a cliff.

Figure 15-2 Space tracking.

Glossary of Abbreviations Used in This Chapter	RADAR	Radio Direction And Ranging
	LORAN	LOng RAnge Navigation
	LORAC	LOng RAnge Communications
	RF	Radio Frequency
	PRF	Pulse Repetition Frequency
	PRT	Pulse Recurrence Time
	PW	Pulse Width
	kW	Kilowatt
	MHz	Megahertz
	VHF	Very High Frequency
	VOR	Very-high-frequency OmniRange
	ILS	Instrument Landing System

In the echo situation, what occurs is that the sound waves of the shout travel through the air until they strike the cliff. When the sound waves strike the cliff they are reflected or "bounced off," and some, though not all, of the sound is returned to the person who shouted. The time that passes or elapses between the time of the shout and the time the echo is heard depends upon the distance of the man from the cliff. Sound travels at approximately 1,100 (335.28 meters) feet per second at sea level.

Example 15–1

Problem: If a person is 3,300 feet from a cliff and shouts, approximately how much time will elapse before the echo is heard by that person?

Solution:

$$d = \frac{2(3,300)}{1,100} = \frac{6,600}{1,100}$$

$$= 6 \text{ seconds}$$

If we use a directional device to transmit and receive the sound and measure the time, we can determine approximate direction, distance and height of the cliff, as shown in Figure 15–3.

In modern, sophisticated radar systems, range (distance), azimuth (direction), and elevation (height) can all be determined at the same time along with other data about the target, such as size and velocity.

The transmitted radar signal is normally of extremely high frequency. The radar transmits pulses or bursts of RF power at a known pre-set rate called the *pulse repetition frequency* (PRF). After each transmitted pulse, the radar is automatically switched to the *receive* mode and receives any echoes from objects or targets that may be present. The range determination can be made as shown in Figure 15–4.

In a typical tracking, or instrumentation, radar, the transmitted power is focused by an antenna reflector or "dish" into a pencil-like beam. An example of such an antenna is shown in Figure 15–5. This pencil beam has several advantages.

1. It concentrates the power in one direction so the echo strength is increased.

2. Unwanted echoes are reduced.

3. The direction of the target can be determined more exactly.

4. Multipath propagation of radar waves is reduced, which reduces target position error.

Sequential Lobing

Early in the development of radar, a technique called *sequential lobing* came into use. Instead of pointing directly at the target, the radar beam, or lobe, pointed slightly to one side, then to the other, the action occurring very rapidly. Figure 15–6 illustrates elevation sequential lobing. In the figure, U is the upper position and L the lower position. If the target is exactly on the axis of lobing, known as the *crossover axis*, the echoes are equal. If the target is not on the crossover axis, the echoes are *not* equal. If the target is below the crossover axis, the L echo would still be stronger than the U echo and the difference (U minus L) is called a *difference* or *error signal*. In the example, the error would be negative, indicating that the target is below the axis. Sequential lobing is not representative of modern tracking techniques, but the description serves as an introduction to the more advanced methods now in use.

Sequential lobing in elevation and azimuth combined required four successive

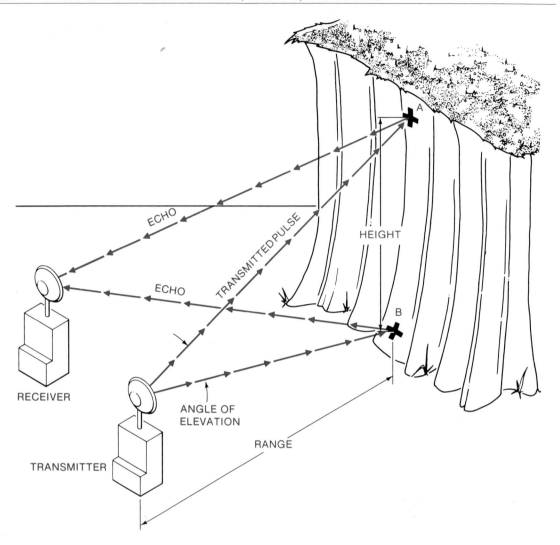

Figure 15-3 Radar echoes.

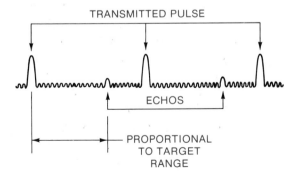

Figure 15-4 Principle of range measurement.

beam positions, as shown in part A of Figure 15–7. However, instead of moving the beam in four discrete steps, it was found preferable to move it continuously in a circular path centered around the crossover axis. If the rate at which the beam is rotated (known as the *scanning rate*) is on the order of 30 times per second and the *pulse rate* (number of transmitted pulses per second) is 240, there are 8 beam positions per scan. This method of scanning is known as *conical scanning*.

NASA PHOTO

Figure 15-5 Dish antenna.

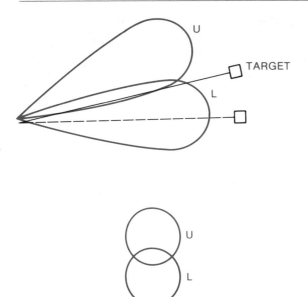

Figure 15-6 Sequential lobing in elevation.

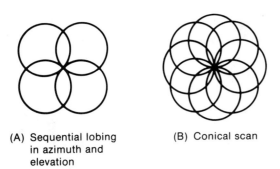

(A) Sequential lobing
    in azimuth and
    elevation

(B) Conical scan

Figure 15-7 Scanning sequences.

Monopulse

Conical scan tracking radar has given good service for many years, but in recent years, tracking performance has taken a large step forward with the introduction of *monopulse* tracking radars.

In monopulse, or simultaneous lobe comparison, comparisons of left-right and up-down signals are all made at the same time instead of in sequence. A single monopulse echo can provide complete angular and range information in monopulse systems. In conical scan radars, several echoes are required to get the same information.

Although the beam motion in monopulse is continuous, the target is illuminated only when each transmitted pulse reaches it. The result is identical to that in part A, Figure 15-7, if the beam is moved as shown in part B of 15-7.

Pulse Recurrence Time (PRT) and Pulse Repetition Frequency (PRF)

Because radar must wait for the echo to return, its maximum range is limited by how often pulses are sent out. If they are sent out too frequently, the echo will not have time to return before the next pulse is transmitted.

The rate of pulse transmission is known as the *pulse repetition frequency* (PRF) and the time between pulses is known as the *pulse recurrence time* (PRT). PRT is illustrated in Figure 15-8.

PRT and the PRF of a radar are related as follows:

$$PRT = \frac{1}{PRF}$$

If we know the PRT of a radar, we know its maximum range.

$$Maximum\ Range = \frac{PRT}{12.36}$$

A transmitted RF pulse takes 6.18 microseconds to travel one nautical mile. It takes 12.36 microseconds to travel and return from a target one mile away. A *radar mile* is defined as 12.36 microseconds.

Example 15-2

Problem: If the PRF of a certain radar is

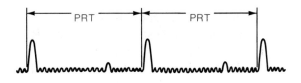

Figure 15-8 Pulse recurrence time (PRT).

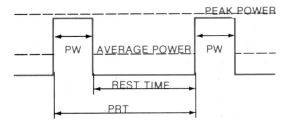

Figure 15-9 Relationship between peak and average power.

250 pulses per second, what is the PRT of the radar?

Solution:

$$PRT = \frac{1}{250} = 4,000 \text{ microseconds}$$

Example 15-3

Problem: If the PRF of a certain radar is 175, what is the range of the radar?

Solution:

$$PRT = \frac{1}{175} = 5,714 \; \mu \text{ sec}$$

$$Range = \frac{5714}{12.36} = \begin{array}{l} 462.3 \text{ nautical} \\ \text{miles} \end{array}$$

Pulse Width

The *transmitted pulse width* (PW) determines the *minimum* range of the radar. In order for the echo to be usable the transmitter must be shut off before the echo returns. The shorter the transmitted pulse, the shorter the distance to the nearest

target that can be observed. However, in order to obtain a usable echo, the transmitted pulse should contain a minimum of 200 cycles of the transmitted RF. A long pulse produces more total energy to be reflected from a target. Long pulses are, therefore, more effective at longer ranges.

The maximum range of a radar is largely dependent upon the power output of the transmitter. The transmitter must be capable of producing enough power so that the energy contained in the echo of a target at maximum range is greater than the electronic noise level of the radar receiver.

The power in a radar is expressed in two ways, peak and average. *Peak power* is the maximum power of the pulse produced by the transmitter, where as, *average power* is the power averaged over the entire PRT

$$Average \; Power = \frac{Peak \; Power \times PW}{PRT}$$

Figure 15–9 illustrates the relationships of the PRF, average power, etc.

Example 15-4

Problem: What is the average power of a radar with a peak power of 45 kW, 2 PRF of 500 pps and a pulse width of 2 microseconds?

Solution:

$$PRT = \frac{1}{500} = 2,000 \text{ microseconds}$$

$$Average \; Power = \frac{45 \times 2}{2,000} = .045 \text{ kW}$$

The Basic radar can be broken down into 5 basic blocks as shown in figure 15–10. The blocks are:

1. The *Synchronizer* (timer or keyer) supplies pulses that synchronize the transmitter, receiver, indicator and other associated circuits.

2. The *transmitter* generates the RF.

3. The *antenna* system takes the RF energy from the transmitter, radiates it in a directional beam, receives returning echoes, and routes them to the receiver.

4. The *receiver* amplifies the returned echoes and converts them to video for presentation on a cathode ray tube.

5. The *indicator* provides visual information about range and direction.

The *synchronizer* insures that all the circuits in the radar system operate in a definite time relationship with respect to each other. This section establishes the PRF of the radar.

The transmitter's main component is an RF oscillator. Most radars utilize either a klystron or a magnetron tube. Because the resting time of the radar is long compared to the transmitting time, the RF source can be made to give a considerable amount of peak power without overloading its average power handling capabilities. The rest allows adequate time for tubes to cool down before the next pulse.

The magnetron, and some klystron transmitters, requires a high peak power pulse to operate properly. This high input power is supplied by the radar's *modulator*, which often supplies voltages of 100 kilovolts or more. The modulator also determines the pulse width of the radar.

The antenna systems takes the RF energy from the transmitter and radiates it in the desired direction. It also receives the echoes from the target and routes them to the receiver. The antenna system, in addition to transmission lines and antennas, also contains a device to switch from transmit to receive (called a T-R tube) and any receiver protection devices needed. The antenna itself is normally a parabolic shape like the one shown in Figure 15–11. This antenna is much like the reflector used with photographic flash equipment.

15.2 LORAN AND LORAC

LORAN is an acronym for *LO*ng *RA*nge *N*avigation. The system utilizes transmitter frequencies in the 1.8 to 2 MHz range. There is a transmitter at two different locations, one called the master and the second called the slave. The two transmitters establish a grid of phased RF waves radiating outward, and by comparing the phase between them, the location of the receiver can be established. Figure 15–12 is an example of a LORAN plot.

15.3 VOR (VHF OMNIRANGE)

This system, also known as *omni*, is used extensively for aircraft navigation. The

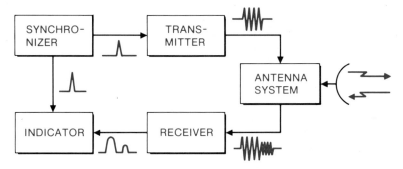

Figure 15–10 Block diagram of a radar system.

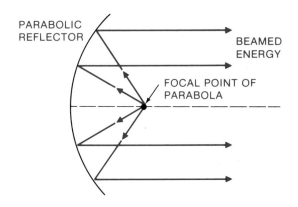

Figure 15-11 Parabolic reflector antenna and optical system similarity.

VOR operates in the 108 to 118 MHz spectrum with a minimum range of 40 miles at instrument flight rules (IFR) minimums—that is, during bad weather. This system radiates in all directions and will thus give usable navigation data in all directions. Figure 15–13 is a picture of a common VOR site maintained by FAA (Federal Aviation Administration) technicians.

By using VOR equipment, a pilot can measure his aircraft's position by triangulating its position in relationship to the VOR transmitters.

The RF transmitted by the VOR is horizontally polarized. There are two navigation signals contained in the VOR's transmitted signal. The first of the two has a constant phase at all points around the VOR and is called the *reference*. The second signal has a phase that changes one degree for each degree of change in azimuth around the VOR and is called the *variable signal*.

In addition to the navigational signals, voice and automatic identification signals for the facility are also transmitted at most VOR locations.

The navigation information radiated by the VOR is contained in two 30 Hz signals.

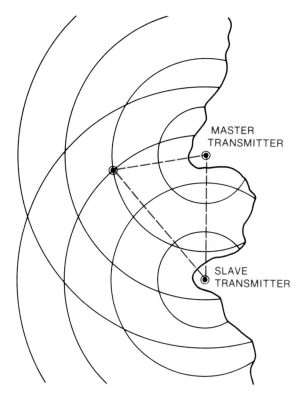

Figure 15-12 LORAN plot.

The direction information is derived in the aircraft by measuring the phase difference between the two signals.

By definition, the *omnicourse* at a certain azimuth (direction) about the VOR is the number of degrees the variable signal lags behind the reference signal. This is illustrated in Figure 15–14.

An obvious question arises as to how two different 30 Hz signals can be transmitted from a single source without interaction or combining somewhere in the system. In order to maintain the isolation of the signals until they are used in the aircraft, the reference 30 Hz signal is FM modulated on a 9,960 Hz subcarrier. This subcarrier, in turn, AM modulates the RF carrier of the VOR transmitter. The 30 Hz variable signal combines with the RF

FAA

Figure 15-13 The VOR site—an air navigational aid.

carrier by a phenomenon known as *space modulation* to produce the variable signal. A full explanation of space modulation is beyond the scope of this text. However, it is a very effective method and is used in several types of equipment. The variable component of the VOR signal originates at the VOR transmitter. In order to produce space modulation, the output (AM) modulation is removed by a modulation elim-

inator, and a device known as a *goniometer* converts the RF into two sidebands, then space modulates the carrier after radiation (in space).

Figure 15–15 is a block diagram of a typical VOR.

15.4 INSTRUMENT LANDING SYSTEM

The ILS (*Instrument Landing System*) is used to provide electronic guidance so that a pilot in an ILS-equipped aircraft can make a safe approach and landing in spite of bad weather. ILS guidance is also frequently used in good weather as a landing aid.

The basic ILS contains a *localizer* to locate the runway, a *glide slope* for descent guidance, and one or more *marker beacons* for position fixes to show approximate distance to touchdown.

Figure 15–16 is a diagram of how the ILS system works. For example, if the aircraft were to fly below the normal glide path, the aircraft cockpit instrument (the cross pointers of the flight director) instantly indicate to the pilot that he is too low and by how much. The same would be true if the aircraft were to deviate left or right of the runway center line.

In order for the ILS to give the needed information, it has to provide two axes (or planes) of guidance data. This is the right-left (or azimuth) data and the up-down (or vertical) descent data, a complete glide path.

The azimuth, or runway center line data, is provided by a part of the system known as the *localizer*. This localizer, a block diagram of which is shown in Figure 15–17, operates in the VHF spectrum, 108 to 112 MHz. The localizer antennas are located at the *stop end* of the ILS runway. See Figure 15–16 and Figure 15–17. The localizer antenna system radiates signals in all

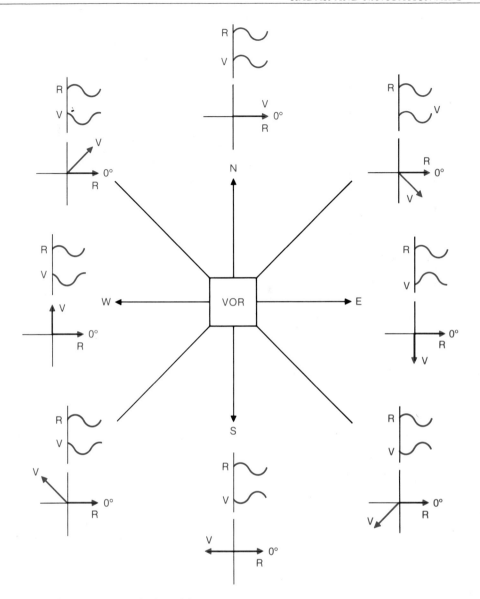

Figure 15-14 VOR phase relationship to course.

directions (omni-directionally), with a range of 25 to 100 miles. The localizer *on course signal* exists on a vertical plane down the runway center line and beyond for 25 to 100 miles and is called the *front course*.

Vertical guidance data is provided by a part of the system known as the *glide slope*, which operates in the VHF frequency

spectrum (329 to 335 MHz) and is located near and to one side of the ILS runway touchdown point. See Figures 15–16 and 15–17. The signals transmitted by the glide slope are directed toward the front course only, with a range of about 25 miles. The glide slope *on path signal* exists on a horizontal plane that is inclined upward from

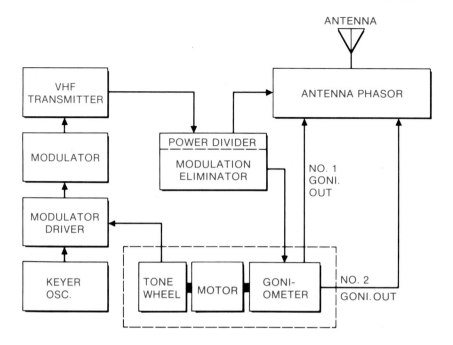

Figure 15-15 Typical VOR block diagram.

the base of the transmitting antenna system at an angle of approximately 2.5 degrees above horizontal.

The intersection of the two planes, the localizer *on course* and the glide slope *on path*, is where the aircraft should fly when using the ILS for a landing.

Figures 15–18 and 15–19 are the block diagrams for the localizer and glide slope transmitters.

The last part of the ILS is the marker beacons. All markers are low power and operate at 75 MHz. The antennas are designed so that most of the power is radiated upward and thus provides a position fix when the aircraft passes over it. The various markers have different tone modulations, and thus the aircraft pilot can tell exactly how far he is from the runway.

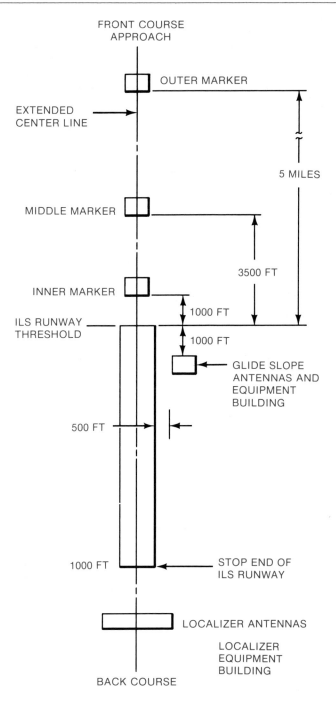

Figure 15-16 ILS equipment placement.

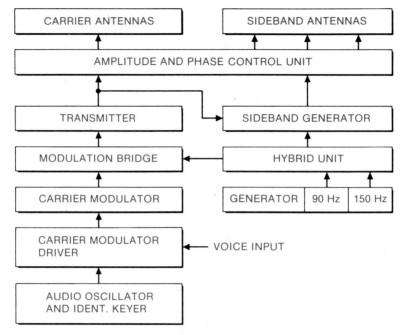

Figure 15-17 Localizer equipment block diagram.

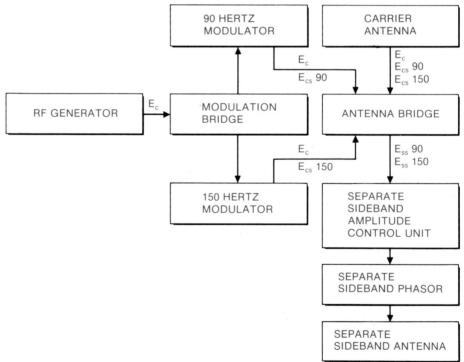

Figure 15-18 Block diagram of glide slope ILS Equipment.

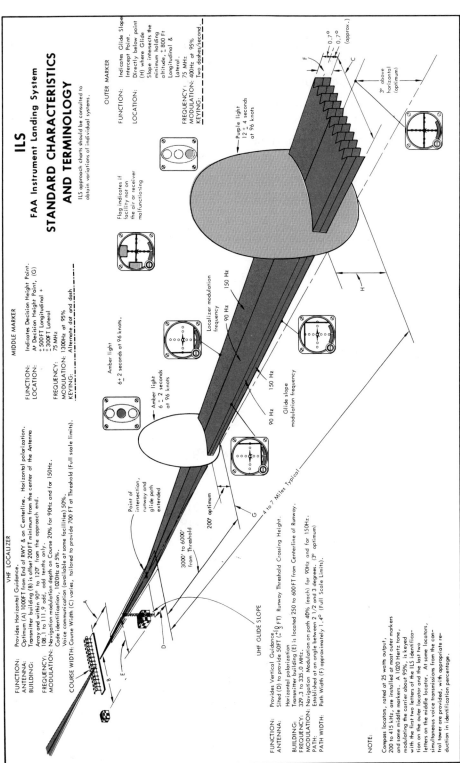

Figure 15-19 ILS standard characteristics and terminology.

SUMMARY

1. LORAN has a range of 300 miles within which an aircraft or ship can locate itself within a mile of its true position.

2. LORAC, with supporting equipment, can locate the true position within 50 feet.

3. Radar is used for aircraft and ship detection as well as for navigation purposes. It can be used to "talk" a pilot onto a runway for a safe landing or to track a space probe.

4. A radar transmitter sends out a short burst of radio frequency energy. The transmitter then shuts down the receiver and waits for an echo to return.

5. Most modern radars are pulsed instead of transmitting continuously.

6. Older radars used sequential lobing, which required several echoes to get complete range and direction information.

7. Monopulse radars can get complete information on direction and range from a single echo.

8. A radar mile is the time required for a radar pulse to go out one nautical mile and return—12.36 microseconds.

9. VOR is an aircraft navigation system with a minimum range of 40 miles. It allows a pilot to find his position, particularly in bad weather.

10. The instrument landing system (ILS) is a short range system designed to assist a pilot in making a safe landing in bad weather.

REVIEWING YOUR ELECTRONICS VOCABULARY

1. Duty cycle	6. PRF
2. Echo	7. PRT
3. ILS	8. Radar
4. Localizer	9. Range
5. Omnicourse	10. VOR

CHECKING YOUR UNDERSTANDING

1. Name the five basic units of a radar system.

2. On what frequency band does a VOR normally operate?

3. What is a glide slope?

4. Where is the localizer positioned in a normal ILS system?

5. On what frequency does an ILS beacon operate?

6. In a radar system, what is a plan position indicator scope (PPI)?

SOLVING ELECTRONIC PROBLEMS

1. Make a sketch showing sequential lobing with a positive error in elevation.
2. If the PRT of a certain radar is 5,200 microseconds, what is the radar's PRF?
3. If the PRF of a certain radar is 165 pulses per second, what is the maximum range of the set?
4. What is the peak power of a radar with an average power of 250 watts, a PRF of 500 pulses per second, and a pulse width of 2 microseconds?
5. If the maximum range of a radar is 500 miles, what is its PRF?

Appendix

SAFETY

Each student is responsible for his personal safety and is required to observe safe practices at all times. Electricity demands a healthy respect. Any act which is dangerous to the individual or classmates deserves immediate attention. Safety rules and common sense can avoid most accidents. It is well that the student begin practicing safety now so that good safety habits can be formed early. Industry can be every bit as strict as instructors, and many a job has been lost through the neglect of proper safety precautions. Many plants have safety officers who have the authority to fire anyone guilty of unsafe conduct.

The following rules are presented as a guide to safe operation in the shop. They are excellent rules but they are not a substitute for common sense; they are a supplement to it.

ELECTRICAL SAFETY RULES:

1. Never work on electrical equipment alone.
2. Turn off all power, and ground all high-voltage points. A capacitor can store a lethal charge. Make sure that the power cannot be accidentally restored.
3. Move slowly; make sure your feet are placed for good balance. Never lunge for falling tools.
4. Never work on live equipment when fatigued, and always keep one hand in a pocket when working on live equipment.
5. Do not touch electrical equipment while standing on a damp or metal floor.
6. Do not handle electrical equipment while you or the equipment is wet or damp.
7. Do not handle electrical equipment that is not grounded.
8. Never hold solder in your mouth when soldering. Your soldering iron probably has a leakage voltage to ground.
9. Do not use water on an electrical fire.
10. Never touch two pieces of equipment at the same time.
11. Never touch even one wire of an electrical line; it may be the "hot" one.
12. Never touch even a "dead" circuit line with an open hand. Use the back of the fingers with the arm grounded.
13. Never take a voluntary shock.
14. Do not take unnecessary risks.
15. Remove a victim from an electrical circuit without endangering your safety as quickly as possible. Any delay may prove fatal.
16. Start artificial resuscitation at once, if necessary, and continue until the victim is revived or pronounced dead by a doctor.

The following chart shows the effect of electrical current flowing through the body. Body resistance varies widely with environmental conditions. Anything over 24 volts is considered dangerous under some circumstances, and should be treated as though it were potentially lethal.

MECHANICAL SAFETY RULES:

1. Always wear safety glasses when soldering, or operating any kind of power machinery.
2. When using a drill press or hand drill, work must be clamped so that it cannot turn if the bit should stick.
3. Shield the wire when cutting off the end with cutting pliers. The cut off piece can travel far enough to put out an eye.
4. Don't leave the chuck key in the chuck of the drill press or motor.
5. Use common sense!

TYPICAL POWER RATINGS OF ELECTRICAL AND ELECTRONIC DEVICES

Device	Power rating (watts)
Television Receiver	300
Radio Receiver	100
Electric Clock	2
Ultra-violet Lamp	385
Electric Fan	100
Portable Electric Heater	1000
Record-changer	75
Electric Blanket	200
Heating Pad	60
Electric Shaver	12
Sewing Machine	75
Refrigerator	150
Coffee Maker	1000
Hand Iron	1000
Ironer	1650
Floor Lamp	300
Vacuum Cleaner	125
Electric Skillet	1100
Mixer	100
Toaster	1100
Broiler	1500
Waffle Iron	1000
Washer	700
Baker	900

THE APPROXIMATE EFFECT OF ELECTRICAL CURRENT PASSING THROUGH THE HUMAN BODY.

Amperes	
1.0	
0.5	- Severe burns
	- Breathing stops
0.2	
	DEATH
0.1	
	- Very difficult breathing
	- Labored breathing
	- Severe shock
0.05	- Paralysis
	- Cannot release
	- Painful sensation
0.02	- Mild sensation
0.01	-
0.005	-
	- Slight sensation
0.002	-
0.001	

TABLES

Resistors are made in specific standard values. Values between are considered to be special and may not be generally available. When odd values are specified they can often be had only at extra cost. It is seldom necessary to specify odd values. The following is a chart of RETMA standard values:

RETMA STANDARD
Resistor Values

Name of Series	−20%	−10%	− 5%
Percent Step Size	40%	20%	10%
Step Multiplier	$\sqrt[6]{10} = 1.46$	$\sqrt[12]{10} = 1.21$	$\sqrt[24]{10} = 1.10$
Values in each series	10	10	10
	—	—	11
	—	12	12
	—	—	13
	15	15	15
	—	—	16
	—	18	18
	—	—	20
	22	22	22
	—	—	24
	—	—	—
	—	27	27
	—	—	—
	−20%	−10%	− 5%
	—	—	—
	33	33	33
	—	—	36
	—	39	39
	—	—	—
	—	—	43
	47	47	47
	—	—	51
	—	56	56
	—	—	62
	68	68	68
	—	—	75
	—	82	82
	—	—	91
	100	100	100

MATHEMATICAL SYMBOLS

× or ·	Multiplied by
÷ or :	Divided by
+	Positive, plus, add
−	Negative, minus, subtract
±	Positive or negative, plus or minus
∓	Negative or positive, minus or plus
= or ∷	Equals
≅	Is approximately equal to
≠	Does not equal
>	Is greater than
≫	Is much greater than
<	Is less than
≪	Is much less than
≧	Greater than or equal to
≦	Less than or equal to
∴	Therefore
∠	Angle
⊥	Perpendicular to
∥	Parallel to
|n|	Absolute value of n
△	Increment of

GREEK ALPHABET

LETTERS		NAME
Capital	Small	
A	α	alpha
B	β	beta
Γ	γ	gamma
Δ	δ	delta
E	ϵ	epsilon
Z	ζ	zeta
H	η	eta
Θ	θ, ϑ	theta
I	ι	iota
K	κ	kappa
Λ	λ	lambda
M	μ	mu
N	ν	nu
Ξ	ξ	xi
O	o	omicron
Π	π	pi
P	ρ	rho
Σ	σ, s	sigma
T	τ	tau
Υ	υ	upsilon
Φ	ϕ, φ	phi
X	χ	chi
Ψ	ψ	psi
Ω	ω	omega

TABLE OF PREFIXES AND CONVERSION UNITS FOR EXPRESSING MAGNITUDES OF ELEMENTS IN METRIC UNITS

PREFIXES

10^{12}	tera-	T	10^3	kilo-	K	10^{-12}	pico-	p	10^{-3}	milli-	m
10^9	giga-	G	10^2	hecto-	H	10^{-9}	nano-	n	10^{-2}	centi-	c
10^6	mega-	M	10^1	deka-	D	10^{-6}	micro-	μ	10^{-1}	deci-	d

(It should be noted that the single prefix p is a replacement for the double prefix $\mu\mu$, long used to express magnitudes to the power 10^{-12}.)

CONVERSION UNITS

Element	Unit	Milli-unit	Micro-unit	Pico-unit	Kilo-unit	Mega-unit
Inductance	1 henry	$= 10^3$ mh	$= 10^6$ μh	$= 10^{12}$ ph		
Capacity	1 farad	$= 10^3$ mf	$= 10^6$ μf	$= 10^{12}$ pf		
Resistance	1 ohm				$= 10^{-3}$KΩ	$= 10^{-6}$MΩ
Conductance	1 mho	$= 10^3$ mmho	$= 10^6$ μmho			
Voltage	1 volt	$= 10^3$ mv	$= 10^6$ μv		$= 10^{-3}$Kv	$= 10^{-6}$Mv
Current	1 ampere	$= 10^3$ ma	$= 10^6$ μa		$= 10^{-3}$Ka	
Power	1 watt	$= 10^3$ mw	$= 10^6$ μw		$= 10^{-3}$Kw	$= 10^{-6}$Mw
Frequency	1 cycle				$= 10^{-3}$Kc	$= 10^{-6}$Mc
Time	1 second	$= 10^3$ ms	$= 10^6$ μs			

DECIMAL EQUIVALENT OF FRACTIONS

Fraction	Equivalent	Fraction	Equivalent	Fraction	Equivalent	Fraction	Equivalent
1/64	0.0156	17/64	0.2656	33/64	0.5156	49/64	0.7656
1/32	0.0312	9/32	0.2812	17/32	0.5312	25/32	0.7812
3/64	0.0468	19/64	0.2968	35/64	0.5468	51/64	0.7968
1/16	0.0625	5/16	0.3125	9/16	0.5625	13/16	0.8125
5/64	0.0781	21/64	0.3281	37/64	0.5781	53/64	0.8281
3/32	0.0937	11/32	0.3437	19/32	0.5937	27/32	0.8437
7/64	0.1093	23/64	0.3593	39/64	0.6093	55/64	0.8593
1/8	0.1250	3/8	0.3750	5/8	0.6250	7/8	0.8750
9/64	0.1406	25/64	0.3906	41/64	0.6406	57/64	0.8906
5/32	0.1562	13/32	0.4062	21/32	0.6562	29/32	0.9062
11/64	0.1718	27/64	0.4218	43/64	0.6718	59/64	0.9218
3/16	0.1875	7/16	0.4375	11/16	0.6875	15/16	0.9375
13/64	0.2031	29/64	0.4531	45/64	0.7031	61/64	0.9531
7/32	0.2187	15/32	0.4687	23/32	0.7187	31/32	0.9687
15/64	0.2343	31/64	0.4843	47/64	0.7343	63/64	0.9843
1/4	0.2500	1/2	0.5000	3/4	0.7500	1	1.000

RESISTANCES OF METALS COMPARED TO COPPER (Copper = 1.)

Aluminum	1.59
Brass	4.40
Gold	1.38
Iron	6.67
Lead	12.76
Nichrome	60.
Nickel	7.73
Platinum	5.80
Silver	0.92
Steel	8.62
Tin	8.2
Tungsten	3.2
Zinc	3.62

WORK-ENERGY-POWER

Work = Force × Distance (550 lbs. per second. Lifted 1 ft. = 1 horse power).

Energy is ability to do work.
Power is rate of using energy.
Power × Time = Energy
Watts = Volts × Amps
Watts = I^2R
Watts and kilowatts measure power, which is a rate.
Watt-hours and kilowatt-hours measure energy.
Efficiency = Output ÷ Input.
746 Watts = 1 horse power

Wire Gage No.	Length	Resistance	Number of turns	Current	Ampere-Turns
25	100 ft.	4 ohms	300	3 amps	900
25	200 ft.	8 ohms	600	1.5 amp	900
22	50 ft.	1 ohm	150	12 amps	1800
22	100 ft.	2 ohms	300	6 amps	1800

TABLE OF VALUES

Number		Logarithm	Number		Logarithm
π	3.141 5927	0.497 1499	π^2	9.869 6044	0.994 2997
2π	6.283 1853	0.798 1799	$2\pi^2$	19.739 2088	1.295 3297
3π	9.424 7780	0.974 2711	$4\pi^2$	39.478 4176	1.596 3597
4π	12.566 3706	1.099 2099	$\dfrac{1}{\pi^2}$	0.101 3212	9.005 7003 - 10
8π	25.132 7412	1.400 2399	$\dfrac{1}{(2\pi^2)}$	0.050 6606	8.704 6703 - 10
			$\dfrac{1}{(4\pi^2)}$	0.025 3303	8.403 6403 - 10
$\dfrac{\pi}{2}$	1.570 7963	0.196 1199	$\sqrt{\pi}$	1.772 4539	0.248 5749
$\dfrac{\pi}{3}$	1.047 1976	0.020 0286	$\sqrt{\dfrac{\pi}{4}}$	0.886 2269	9.947 4490 - 10
$\dfrac{\pi}{4}$	0.785 3982	9.895 0899 - 10	$\dfrac{\sqrt{\pi}}{2}$		
$\dfrac{\pi}{6}$	0.523 5988	9.718 9986 - 10	$\sqrt{\dfrac{\pi}{4}}$	0.443 1135	9.646 5149 - 10
$\dfrac{\pi}{8}$	0.392 6991	9.594 0599 - 10	$\sqrt{\dfrac{\pi}{2}}$	1.253 3141	0.098 0599
$\dfrac{2\pi}{3}$	2.094 3951	0.321 0586	$\sqrt{\dfrac{2}{\pi}}$	0.797 8846	9.901 9401 - 10
$\dfrac{4\pi}{3}$	4.188 7902	0.622 0886	π^2	31.006 2767	1.491 4496
$\dfrac{1}{\pi}$	0.318 3099	9.502 8501 - 10	$\sqrt[3]{\pi}$	1.464 5919	0.165 7166
$\dfrac{2}{\pi}$	0.636 6198	9.803 3801 - 10	$\dfrac{1}{\sqrt[3]{\pi}}$	0.682 7841	9.834 2834 - 10
$\dfrac{4}{\pi}$	1.273 2395	0.104 9101	$\sqrt[3]{\pi^2}$	2.145 0294	0.331 4332
$\dfrac{1}{(2\pi)}$	0.159 1549	9.201 8201 - 10	$\dfrac{1}{\sqrt{\pi}}$	0.564 1896	9.751 4251 - 10
$\dfrac{1}{(4\pi)}$	0.079 5775	8.900 7901	$\dfrac{2}{\sqrt{\pi}}$		
$\dfrac{1}{(6\pi)}$	0.053 0516	8.724 6989 - 10	$\sqrt{\dfrac{4}{\pi}}$	1.128 3792	0.052 4551
$\dfrac{1}{(8\pi)}$	0.039 7887	8.599 7601 - 10			

MATHEMATICAL FORMULAS

Number	Number^2	$\sqrt{Number}$	$\sqrt{10 \times Number}$	Number^3	Number	Number^2	$\sqrt{Number}$	$\sqrt{10 \times Number}$	Number^3
1	1	1.000000	3.162278	1	51	2,601	7.141428	22.58318	132,651
2	4	1.414214	4.472136	8	52	2,704	7.211103	22.80351	140,608
3	9	1.732051	5.477226	27	53	2,809	7.280110	23.02173	148,877
4	16	2.000000	6.324555	64	54	2,916	7.348469	23.23790	157,464
5	25	2.236068	7.071068	125	55	3,025	7.416198	23.45208	166,375
6	36	2.449490	7.745967	216	56	3,136	7.483315	23.66432	175,616
7	49	2.645751	8.366600	343	57	3,249	7.549834	23.87467	185,193
8	64	2.828427	8.944272	512	58	3,364	7.615773	24.06319	194,112
9	81	3.000000	9.486833	729	59	3,481	7.681146	24.28992	205,379
10	100	3.162278	10.00000	1,000	60	3,600	7.745967	24.49490	216,000
11	121	3.316625	10.48809	1,331	61	3,721	7.810250	24.69818	226,981
12	144	3.464102	10.95445	1,728	62	3,844	7.874008	24.89980	238,047
13	169	3.605551	11.40175	2,197	63	3,969	7.937254	25.09980	250,047
14	196	3.741657	11.83216	2,744	64	4,096	8.000000	25.29822	262,144
15	225	3.872983	12.24745	3,375	65	4,225	8.062258	25.49510	274,625
16	256	4.000000	12.64911	4,096	66	4,356	8.124038	25.69047	287,496
17	289	4.123106	13.03840	4,913	67	4,489	8.185353	25.88436	300,763
18	324	4.242641	13.41641	5,832	68	4,624	8.246211	26.07681	314,432
19	361	4.358899	13.78405	6,859	69	4,761	8.306624	26.26785	328,509
20	400	4.472136	14.14214	8,000	70	4,900	8.366600	26.45751	343,000
21	441	4.582576	14.49138	9,261	71	5,041	8.426150	26.64583	357,911
22	484	4.690416	14.83240	10,648	72	5,184	8.485281	26.83282	373,248
23	529	4.795832	15.16575	12,167	73	5,329	8.544004	27.01851	389,017
24	576	4.898979	15.49193	13,824	74	5,476	8.602325	27.20294	405,225
25	625	5.000000	15.81139	15,625	75	5,625	8.660254	27.38613	421,875
26	676	5.099020	16.12452	17,576	76	5,776	8.717798	27.56810	438,976
27	729	5.196152	16.43168	19,683	77	5,929	8.774964	27.74887	456,533
28	784	5.291503	16.73320	21,952	78	6,084	8.831761	27.92848	474,552
29	841	5.385165	17.02939	24,389	79	6,241	8.888194	28.10694	493,039
30	900	5.477226	17.32051	27,000	80	6,400	8.944272	28.28427	512,000
31	961	5.567764	17.60682	29,791	81	6,561	9.000000	28.46050	531,441
32	1,024	5.656854	17.88854	32,768	82	6,724	9.055385	28.63564	551,368
33	1,089	5.744563	18.16590	35,937	83	6,889	9.110434	28.80972	571,787
34	1,156	5.830952	18.43909	39,304	84	7,056	9.165151	28.98275	592,704
35	1,225	5.916080	18.70829	42,875	85	7,225	9.219544	29.15476	614,125
36	1,296	6.000000	18.97367	46,656	86	7,396	9.273618	29.32576	636,056
37	1,369	6.082763	19.23538	50,653	87	7,569	9.327379	29.49576	658,503
38	1,444	6.164414	19.49359	54,872	88	7,744	9.380832	29.66479	681,472
39	1,521	6.244998	19.74842	59,319	89	7,921	9.433981	29.83287	704,969
40	1,600	6.324555	20.00000	64,000	90	8,100	9.486833	30.00000	729,000
41	1,681	6.403124	20.24846	68,921	91	8,281	9.539392	30.16621	753,571
42	1,764	6.480741	20.49390	74,088	92	8,464	9.591663	30.33150	778,688
43	1,849	6.557439	20.73644	79,507	93	8,649	9.643651	30.49590	804,357
44	1,936	6.633250	20.97618	85,184	94	8,836	9.695360	30.65942	830,584
45	2,025	6.708204	21.21320	91,125	95	9,025	9.746794	30.82207	857,375
46	2,116	6.782330	21.44761	97,336	96	9,216	9.797959	30.98387	884,736
47	2,209	6.855655	21.67948	103,823	97	9,409	9.848858	31.14482	912,673
48	2,304	6.928203	21.90890	110,592	98	9,604	9.899495	31.30495	941,192
49	2,401	7.000000	22.13594	117,649	99	9,801	9.949874	31.46427	970,299
50	2,500	7.071680	22.36068	125,000	100	10,000	10.00000	31.62278	1,000,000

CONSTANTS WITH THEIR COMMON LOGARITHMS

	Number	Logarithms
Base of Naperian logarithms	$e = 2.71828183$	0.4342945
Modulus of common logs, $\log_{10}\epsilon$	$u = 0.43429448$	9.6377843 - 10
Reciprocal of modulus	$\frac{1}{u} = 2.30258509$	.3622157
Circumference of a circle in degrees	$= 360$	2.5563025
Circumference of a circle in minutes	$= 21600$	4.3344538
Circumference of a circle in seconds	$= 1296000$	6.1126050
Radian expressed in degrees	$= 57.29578$	1.7581226
Radian expressed in minutes	$= 3437.7468$	3.5362739
Radian expressed in seconds	$= 206264.806$	5.3144251
Ratio of a circumference to diameter	$= 3.14159265$	0.4971499

DEGREES – RADIANS – LOGARITHMS

1 radian = 57° 17′ 44″ .80625

	log
1 radian = 57.29577 95131 degrees	1.75812 26324
1 radian = 3437.74677 07849 minutes	3.53627 38828
1 radian = 206264.80625 seconds	5.31442 51332
1 degree = $\frac{\pi}{180}$ = 0.01745 32925 19943 radians	8.24187 73676 - 10
1 minute = $\frac{\pi}{10800}$ = 0.00029 08882 08666 radians	6.46372 61172 - 10
1 second = $\frac{\pi}{648000}$ = 0.00000 48481 36811 radians	4.68557 48668 - 10
sin 1″ = 0.00000485	4.6855749 - 10

DEGREES TO RADIANS

Degs.	0.0	0.1	0.2	0.3	0.4	0.5	0.6	0.7	0.8	0.9
0	0.0000	0.0017	0.0035	0.0052	0.0070	0.0087	0.0105	0.0122	0.0140	0.0157
1	0.0175	0.0192	0.0209	0.0227	0.0244	0.0262	0.0279	0.0297	0.0314	0.0332
2	0.0349	0.0367	0.0384	0.0401	0.0419	0.0436	0.0454	0.0471	0.0489	0.0506
3	0.0524	0.0541	0.0559	0.0576	0.0593	0.0611	0.0628	0.0646	0.0663	0.0681
4	0.0698	0.0716	0.0733	0.0750	0.0768	0.0785	0.0803	0.0820	0.0838	0.0855
5	0.0873	0.0890	0.0908	0.0925	0.0942	0.0960	0.0977	0.0995	0.1012	0.1030
6	0.1047	0.1065	0.1082	0.1100	0.1117	0.1134	0.1152	0.1169	0.1187	0.1204
7	0.1222	0.1239	0.1257	0.1274	0.1292	0.1309	0.1326	0.1344	0.1361	0.1379
8	0.1396	0.1414	0.1431	0.1449	0.1466	0.1484	0.1501	0.1518	0.1536	0.1553
9	0.1571	0.1588	0.1606	0.1623	0.1641	0.1658	0.1676	0.1693	0.1710	0.1728
10	0.1745	0.1763	0.1780	0.1798	0.1815	0.1833	0.1850	0.1868	0.1885	0.1902
11	0.1920	0.1937	0.1955	0.1972	0.1990	0.2007	0.2025	0.2042	0.2059	0.2077
12	0.2094	0.2112	0.2129	0.2147	0.2164	0.2182	0.2199	0.2217	0.2234	0.2251
13	0.2269	0.2286	0.2304	0.2321	0.2339	0.2356	0.2374	0.2391	0.2409	0.2426
14	0.2443	0.2461	0.2478	0.2496	0.2513	0.2531	0.2548	0.2566	0.2583	0.2601
15	0.2618	0.2635	0.2653	0.2670	0.2688	0.2705	0.2723	0.2740	0.2758	0.2775
16	0.2793	0.2810	0.2827	0.2845	0.2862	0.2880	0.2897	0.2915	0.2932	0.2950
17	0.2967	0.2985	0.3002	0.3019	0.3037	0.3054	0.3072	0.3089	0.3107	0.3124
18	0.3142	0.3159	0.3176	0.3194	0.3211	0.3229	0.3246	0.3264	0.3281	0.3299
19	0.3316	0.3334	0.3351	0.3368	0.3386	0.3403	0.3421	0.3438	0.3456	0.3473
20	0.3491	0.3508	0.3526	0.3543	0.3560	0.3578	0.3595	0.3613	0.3630	0.3648
21	0.3665	0.3683	0.3700	0.3718	0.3735	0.3752	0.3770	0.3787	0.3805	0.3822
22	0.3840	0.3857	0.3875	0.3892	0.3910	0.3927	0.3944	0.3962	0.3979	0.3997
23	0.4014	0.4032	0.4049	0.4067	0.4084	0.4102	0.4119	0.4136	0.4154	0.4171
24	0.4189	0.4206	0.4224	0.4241	0.4259	0.4276	0.4294	0.4311	0.4328	0.4346
25	0.4363	0.4381	0.4398	0.4416	0.4433	0.4451	0.4468	9.4485	0.4503	0.4520
26	0.4538	0.4555	0.4573	0.4590	0.4608	0.4625	0.4643	0.4660	0.4677	0.4695
27	0.4712	0.4730	0.4747	0.4765	0.4782	0.4800	0.4817	0.4835	0.4852	0.4869
28	0.4887	0.4904	0.4922	0.4939	0.4957	0.4974	0.4992	0.5009	0.5027	0.5044
29	0.5061	0.5079	0.5096	0.5114	0.5131	0.5149	0.5166	0.5184	0.5201	0.5219
30	0.5236	0.5253	0.5271	0.5288	0.5306	0.5323	0.5341	0.5358	0.5376	0.5393
31	0.5411	0.5428	0.5445	0.5463	0.5480	0.5498	0.5515	0.5533	0.5550	0.5568
32	0.5585	0.5603	0.5620	0.5637	0.5655	0.5672	0.5690	0.5707	0.5725	0.5742
33	0.5760	0.5777	0.5794	0.5812	0.5829	0.5847	0.5864	0.5882	0.5899	0.5917
34	0.5934	0.5952	0.5969	0.5986	0.6004	0.6021	0.6039	0.6056	0.6074	0.6091
35	0.6109	0.6126	0.6144	0.6161	0.6178	0.6196	0.6213	0.6231	0.6248	0.6266
36	0.6283	0.6301	0.6318	0.6336	0.6353	0.6370	0.6388	0.6405	0.6423	0.6440
37	0.6458	0.6475	0.6493	0.6510	0.6528	0.6545	0.6562	0.6580	0.6597	0.6615
38	0.6632	0.6650	0.6667	0.6685	0.6702	0.6720	0.6737	0.6754	0.6772	0.6789
39	0.6807	0.6824	0.6842	0.6859	0.6877	0.6894	0.6912	0.6929	0.6946	0.6964
40	0.6981	0.6999	0.7016	0.7034	0.7051	0.7069	0.7086	0.7103	0.7121	0.7138

DEGREES TO RADIANS *continued*

Degs.	0.0	0.1	0.2	0.3	0.4	0.5	0.6	0.7	0.8	0.9
41	0.7156	0.7173	0.7191	0.7208	0.7226	0.7243	0.7261	0.7278	0.7295	0.7313
42	0.7330	0.7348	0.7365	0.7383	0.7400	0.7418	0.7435	0.7453	0.7470	0.7487
43	0.7505	0.7522	0.7540	0.7557	0.7575	0.7592	0.7610	0.7627	0.7645	0.7662
44	0.7679	0.7697	0.7714	0.7732	0.7749	0.7767	0.7784	0.7802	0.7819	0.7837
45	0.7854	0.7871	0.7889	0.7906	0.7924	0.7941	0.7959	0.7976	0.7994	0.8011
46	0.8029	0.8046	0.8063	0.8081	0.8098	0.8116	0.8133	0.8151	0.8168	0.8186
47	0.8203	0.8221	0.8238	0.8255	0.8273	0.8290	0.8308	0.8325	0.8343	0.8360
48	0.8378	0.8395	0.8412	0.8430	0.8447	0.8465	0.8482	0.8500	0.8517	0.8535
49	0.8552	0.8570	0.8587	0.8604	0.8622	0.8639	0.8657	0.8674	0.8692	0.8709
50	0.8727	0.8744	0.8762	0.8779	0.8796	0.8814	0.8831	0.8849	0.8866	0.8884
51	0.8901	0.8919	0.8936	0.8954	0.8971	0.8988	0.9006	0.9023	0.9041	0.9058
52	0.9076	0.9093	0.9111	0.9128	0.9146	0.9163	0.9180	0.9198	0.9215	0.9233
53	0.9250	0.9268	0.9285	0.9303	0.9320	0.9338	0.9355	0.9372	0.9390	0.9407
54	0.9425	0.9442	0.9460	0.9477	0.9495	0.9512	0.9529	0.9547	0.9564	0.9582
55	0.9599	0.9617	0.9634	0.9652	0.9669	0.9687	0.9704	0.9721	0.9739	0.9756
56	0.9774	0.9791	0.9809	0.9826	0.9844	0.9861	0.9879	0.9896	0.9913	0.9931
57	0.9948	0.9966	0.9983	1.0001	1.0018	1.0036	1.0053	1.0071	1.0088	1.0105
58	1.0123	1.0140	1.0158	1.0175	1.0193	1.0210	1.0228	1.0245	1.0263	1.0280
59	1.0297	1.0315	1.0332	1.0350	1.0367	1.0385	1.0402	1.0420	1.0437	1.0455
60	1.0472	1.0489	1.0507	1.0524	1.0542	1.0559	1.0577	1.0594	1.0612	1.0629
61	1.0647	1.0664	1.0681	1.0699	1.0716	1.0734	1.0751	1.0769	1.0786	1.0804
62	1.0821	1.0838	1.0856	1.0873	1.0891	1.0908	1.0926	1.0943	1.0961	1.0978
63	1.0996	1.1013	1.1030	1.1048	1.1065	1.1083	1.1100	1.1118	1.1135	1.1153
64	1.1170	1.1188	1.1205	1.1222	1.1240	1.1257	1.1275	1.1292	1.1310	1.1327
65	1.1345	1.1362	1.1380	1.1397	1.1414	1.1432	1.1449	1.1467	1.1484	1.1502
66	1.1519	1.1537	1.1554	1.1572	1.1589	1.1606	1.1624	1.1641	1.1659	1.1676
67	1.1694	1.1711	1.1729	1.1746	1.1764	1.1781	1.1798	1.1816	1.1833	1.1851
68	1.1868	1.1886	1.1903	1.1921	1.1938	1.1956	1.1973	1.1990	1.2008	1.2025
69	1.2043	1.2060	1.2078	1.2095	1.2113	1.2130	1.2147	1.2165	1.2182	1.2200
70	1.2217	1.2235	1.2252	1.2270	1.2287	1.2305	1.2322	1.2339	1.2357	1.2374
71	1.2392	1.2409	1.2427	1.2444	1.2462	1.2479	1.2497	1.2514	1.2531	1.2549
72	1.2566	1.2584	1.2601	1.2619	1.2636	1.2654	1.2671	1.2689	1.2706	1.2723
73	1.2741	1.2758	1.2776	1.2793	1.2811	1.2828	1.2846	1.2863	1.2881	1.2898
74	1.2915	1.2933	1.2950	1.2968	1.2985	1.3003	1.3020	1.3038	1.3055	1.3073
75	1.3090	1.3107	1.3125	1.3142	1.3160	1.3177	1.3195	1.3212	1.3230	1.3247
76	1.3265	1.3282	1.3299	1.3317	1.3334	1.3352	1.3369	1.3387	1.3404	1.3422
77	1.3439	1.3456	1.3474	1.3491	1.3509	1.3526	1.3544	1.3561	1.3579	1.3596
78	1.3614	1.3631	1.3648	1.3666	1.3683	1.3701	1.3718	1.3736	1.3753	1.3771
79	1.3788	1.3806	1.3823	1.3840	1.3858	1.3875	1.3893	1.3910	1.3928	1.3945
80	1.3963	1.3980	1.3998	1.4015	1.4032	1.4050	1.4067	1.4085	1.4102	1.4120
81	1.4137	1.4155	1.4172	1.4190	1.4207	1.4224	1.4242	1.4259	1.4277	1.4294
82	1.4312	1.4329	1.4347	1.4364	1.4382	1.4399	1.4416	1.4434	1.4451	1.4469
83	1.4486	1.4504	1.4521	1.4539	1.4556	1.4573	1.4591	1.4608	1.4626	1.4643

DEGREES TO RADIANS *continued*

Degs.	0.0	0.1	0.2	0.3	0.4	0.5	0.6	0.7	0.8	0.9
84	1.4661	1.4678	1.4696	1.4713	1.4731	1.4748	1.4765	1.4783	1.4800	1.4818
85	1.4835	1.4853	1.4870	1.4888	1.4905	1.4923	1.4940	1.4957	1.4975	1.4992
86	1.5010	1.5027	1.5045	1.5062	1.5080	1.5097	1.5115	1.5132	1.5149	1.5167
87	1.5184	1.5202	1.5219	1.5237	1.5254	1.5272	1.5289	1.5307	1.5324	1.5341
88	1.5359	1.5376	1.5394	1.5411	1.5429	1.5446	1.5464	1.5481	1.5499	1.5516
89	1.5533	1.5551	1.5568	1.5586	1.5603	1.5621	1.5638	1.5656	1.5673	1.5691
90	1.5708	1.5725	1.5743	1.5760	1.5778	1.5795	1.5813	1.5830	1.5848	1.5865
	0′	6′	12′	18′	24′	30′	36′	42′	48′	54′

$90° = 1.5708$ radians $30° = \dfrac{\pi}{6}$, $45° = \dfrac{\pi}{4}$, $60° = \dfrac{\pi}{3}$, $90° = \dfrac{\pi}{2}$ radians

$180° = 3.1416$ radians $120° = \dfrac{2\pi}{3}$, $135° = \dfrac{3\pi}{4}$, $150° = \dfrac{5\pi}{6}$, $180° = \pi$ radians

$270° = 4.7124$ radians $210° = \dfrac{7\pi}{6}$, $225° = \dfrac{5\pi}{4}$, $240° = \dfrac{4\pi}{3}$, $270° = \dfrac{3\pi}{2}$ radians

$360° = 6.2832$ radians $300° = \dfrac{5\pi}{3}$, $315° = \dfrac{7\pi}{4}$, $330° = \dfrac{11\pi}{6}$, $360° = 2\pi$ radians

TABLE OF EXPONENTIALS

$$e^{-x}$$

x	0	1	2	3	4	5	6	7	8	9
0.0	x.000	.9900	.9802	.9704	.9608	.9512	.9418	.9324	.9231	.9139
0.1	.9048	.8958	.8869	.8781	.8694	.8607	.8521	.8437	.8353	.8270
0.2	.8187	.8106	.8025	.7945	.7866	.7788	.7711	.7634	.7558	.7483
0.3	.7408	.7334	.7261	.7189	.7118	.7047	.6977	.6907	.6839	.6771
0.4	.6703	.6637	.6570	.6505	.6440	.6376	.6313	.6250	.6188	.6126
0.5	.6065	.6005	.5945	.5886	.5827	.5769	.5712	.5655	.5599	.5543
0.6	.5488	.5434	.5379	.5326	.5273	.5220	.5169	.5117	.5066	.5016
0.7	.4966	.4916	.4868	.4819	.4771	.4724	.4677	.4630	.4584	.4538
0.8	.4493	.4449	.4404	.4360	.4317	.4274	.4232	.4190	.4148	.4107
0.9	.4066	.4025	.3985	.3946	.3906	.3867	.3829	.3791	.3753	.3716
1.0	.3679	.3642	.3606	.3570	.3535	.3499	.3465	.3430	.3396	.3362
1.1	.3329	.3296	.3263	.3230	.3198	.3166	.3135	.3104	.3073	.3042
1.2	.3012	.2982	.2952	.2923	.2894	.2865	.2837	.2808	.2780	.2753
1.3	.2725	.2698	.2671	.2645	.2618	.2592	.2567	.2541	.2516	.2491
1.4	.2466	.2441	.2417	.2393	.2369	.2346	.2322	.2299	.2276	.2254

TABLE OF EXPONENTIALS *continued*

x		0	1	2	3	4	5	6	7	8	9
1.5		.2231	.2209	.2187	.2165	.2144	.2122	.2101	.2080	.2060	.2039
1.6		.2019	.1999	.1979	.1959	.1940	.1920	.1901	.1882	.1864	.1845
1.7		.1827	.1809	.1791	.1773	.1755	.1738	.1720	.1703	.1686	.1670
1.8		.1653	.1637	.1620	.1604	.1588	.1572	.1557	.1541	.1526	.1511
1.9		.1496	.1481	.1466	.1451	.1437	.1423	.1409	.1395	.1381	.1367
2.0		.1353	.1340	.1327	.1313	.1300	.1287	.1275	.1262	.1249	.1237
2.1		.1225	.1212	.1200	.1188	.1177	.1165	.1153	.1142	.1130	.1119
2.2		.1108	.1097	.1086	.1075	.1065	.1054	.1043	.1033	.1023	.1013
2.3		.1003	*9926	*9827	*9730	*9633	*9537	*9442	*9348	*9255	*9163
2.4	0.0	9072	8982	8892	8804	8716	8629	8544	8458	8374	8291
2.5	0.0	8208	8127	8046	7966	7887	7808	7730	7654	7577	7502
2.6	0.0	7427	7353	7280	7208	7136	7065	6995	6925	6856	6788
2.7	0.0	6721	6654	6587	6522	6457	6393	6329	6266	6204	6142
2.8	0.0	6081	6020	5961	5901	5843	5784	5727	5670	5613	5558
2.9	0.0	5502	5448	5393	5340	5287	5234	5182	5130	5079	5029
3.0	0.0	4979	4929	4880	4832	4783	4736	4689	4642	4596	4550
3.1	0.0	4505	4460	4416	4372	4328	4285	4243	4200	4159	4117
3.2	0.0	4076	4036	3996	3956	3916	3877	3839	3801	3763	3725
3.3	0.0	3688	3652	3615	3579	3544	3508	3474	3439	3405	3371
3.4	0.0	3337	3304	3271	3239	3206	3175	3143	3112	3081	3050

x		.0	.1	.2	.3	.4	.5	.6	.7	.8	.9
3	0.0	4979	4505	4076	3688	3337	3020	2732	2472	2237	2024
4	0.0	1832	1657	1500	1357	1228	1111	1005	*9095	*8230	*7447
5	0.00	6738	6097	5517	4992	4517	4087	3698	3346	3028	2739
6	0.00	2479	2243	2029	1836	1662	1503	1360	1231	1114	1008
7	0.000	9119	8251	7466	6755	6112	5531	5004	4528	4097	3707
8	0.000	3355	3035	2747	2485	2249	2035	1841	1666	1507	1364
9	0.000	1234	1117	1010	*9142	*8272	*7485	*6773	*6128	*5545	*5017
10	0.0000	4540	4108	3717	3363	3043	2754	2492	2254	2040	1846

$$\log_{10} e^{-x} = -x \log_{10} e = -0.43429\,x$$

FORMULAS

Electrostatics

$$F = \frac{Q_1 Q_2}{K d^2}$$

Force between charges

$$E = \frac{Q}{K d^2}$$

Electric field intensity

$$E = \frac{V}{d}$$

Field between plates

$$F = QE$$

Force on Q in field E

$$W = QV = eV$$

Work

$$C = \frac{Q}{V}$$

Capacitance

$$V = \frac{Q}{d}$$

Potential

Resistance

$$R = P \frac{l}{d^2}$$

Value of resistance as a function of the material and its physical dimensions

where R = resistance in ohms
      P = resistance in ohms per *circular-mil-foot* of the material (specific resistance)
      l = length of conductor *in feet*
      d = diameter of wire *in mils*

Direct Current

$$E = IR$$

Ohm's Law

$$P = EI = I^2 R = \frac{E^2}{R}$$

Power

$$R_t = \frac{R_1 R_2}{R_1 + R_2}$$

Total resistance—Two resistors in parallel

$$R_2 = \frac{R_t R_1}{R_1 - R_t}$$

Unknown resistance—Two resistors in parallel with total resistance known

$$G_t = \frac{1}{R_t}$$

Total conductance

$$G_t = G_1 + G_2$$

Total conductance

$$R_t = \frac{1}{\dfrac{1}{R_1} + \dfrac{1}{R_2} + \dfrac{1}{R_3} + \ldots}$$

Total resistance with any number of resistors in parallel

$$E = E_1 = E_2 = E_3 = \ldots$$

Total voltage in a parallel circuit

$$I_t = I_1 + I_2 + I_3 + \ldots$$

Total current in a parallel circuit

$$P_t = P_1 + P_2 + P_3 + \ldots$$

Total power in a parallel circuit

Series Circuits

$$R_t = R_1 + R_2 + R_3 + \ldots$$

Total resistance in a series circuit

$$E_t = E_1 + E_2 + E_3 + \ldots$$

Total voltage in a series circuit

$$I_t = I_1 = I_2 = I_3 = \ldots$$

Total current in a series circuit

$$P_t = P_1 + P_2 + P_3 + \ldots$$

Total power in a series circuit

Networks

$$R_1 = \frac{R_a R_b}{R_a + R_b + R_c}$$

π to T transformation

$$R_a = \frac{R_1 R_2 + R_2 R_3 + R_3 R_1}{R_2}$$

T to π transformation

Magnetism and Electromagnets

$$F = \frac{m_1 m_2}{\mu d^2}$$

Force between two magnetic poles

where μ = permeability
of the medium

$$H = \frac{F}{m} \quad \text{oersteds}$$

Magnetic field intensity

$$H = \frac{2I}{10r} \quad \text{oersteds}$$

Magnetic intensity about a conductor

where I = current in
amperes

r = radius in
centimeters

$$H = \frac{4\pi NI}{10\,l} \quad \text{oersteds}$$

Magnetic intensity for long coils

$$H = \frac{2\pi NI}{10r} \quad \text{oersteds}$$

Magnetic intensity for short coils

$$mmf = \frac{4\pi NI}{10} \quad \text{gilberts}$$

Magnetomotive force

$$\phi = \frac{mmf}{R} \quad \text{maxwells}$$

Flux

$$R = \frac{L}{\mu A} \quad \text{rels}$$

Reluctance

$$B = \frac{\phi}{A} \quad \text{gauss}$$

Flux Density

$$F = \frac{B\,I\,l}{10} \sin \theta \quad \text{dynes}$$

Force exerted on conductor

$$\mu = \frac{\beta}{H}$$

Permeability

Induction

$$e = -N \frac{\Delta\phi}{\Delta t} \times 10^{-8}$$

Average Induced voltage

$$e = -M \frac{\Delta i}{\Delta t}$$

Induced voltage

where M is mutual inductance

$$M = K\sqrt{L_1 L_2}$$

Mutual Inductance

where k is the coefficient of coupling

$$L = \frac{N\phi}{I} \times 10^{-8}$$

Inductance

where N is number of turns

I is current in amperes

$$e_L = -L \frac{\Delta i}{\Delta t}$$

Voltage across inductance

$$e_L = -N \frac{\Delta\phi}{\Delta t} \times 10^{-8}$$

Voltage across inductance

Alternating Current

General

$$c = E_{max} \sin\omega t$$

Instantaneous voltage

where $\omega = 2\pi f$

$$i = I_{max} \sin\omega t$$

Instantaneous current

where $\omega = 2\pi f$

$$P = \frac{E^2}{R} = I^2 R = EI \cos\theta$$

Power in AC circuits

where θ is the phase angle

$$PF = \frac{R}{Z} = \cos\theta$$

Power factor

$$\theta = \text{arc tan} \frac{X}{R} = \text{angle of lead}$$

or lag (degrees)   Phase angle

$$C = K \frac{A}{d}$$

Capacitance in micromicrofarads

where A is area of plates

d is distance between plates

K is dielectric constant

$$X_L = 2\pi fL$$

Inductive reactance

$$X_c = \frac{1}{2\pi fC}$$

Capacitive reactance

$$Z = \sqrt{R^2 + (X_L - X_c)^2}$$

Impedance—triangular form

$$Z = R \pm jX$$

Impedance—rectangular form

$$F_r = \frac{1}{2\pi\sqrt{LC}}$$

Frequency at resonance

$$L_T = L_1 + L_2 \pm 2M$$

Total inductance of two coils

where M is the mutual inductance

$$L_t = L_1 + L_2 + L_3\text{----}$$

Inductance in series

$$1/L_t = 1/L_1 + 1/L_2 + 1/L_3 \text{ ---}$$

Inductance in parallel

$$C_t = C_1 + C_2 + C_3\text{---}$$

Capacitances in parallel

$$1/C_t = 1/C_1 + 1/C_2 + 1/C_3\text{---}$$

Capacitances in series

$$Q_t = Q_1 = Q_2 = Q_3\text{---}$$

Total charge on condensers in series

$$Q_t = Q_1 + Q_2 + Q_3\text{---}$$

Total charge on condensers in parallel

+ is used when the fields add

− is used when the fields oppose

Transformers

$$\frac{E_p}{E_s} = \frac{N_p}{N_s} = \frac{I_s}{I_p}$$

Relationships among voltages, turns, and currents in transformers

$$\frac{Z_p}{Z_s} = \left(\frac{N_p}{N_s}\right)^2$$

Impedances and turns

$$Z = Z_1 + Z_p - \frac{Z_m{}^2}{Z_2 + Z_s}$$

Impedance when looking into primary of a transformer

where Z_1 is in series with primary
$\quad Z_p$ is impedance of primary windings
$\quad Z_m$ is mutual impedance
$\quad Z_s$ is impedance of secondary windings
$\quad Z_2$ is impedance in series with secondary

$$Z_r = \frac{-Z_m{}^2}{Z_2 + Z_s}$$

Reflected impedance

Transients

$$t = R \times C$$

Time constant for RC circuits

where t is in seconds
$\quad R$ is in ohms
$\quad C$ is in farads

$$t = \frac{L}{R}$$

Time constant for L/R circuits

where t is in seconds
$\quad R$ is in ohms
$\quad L$ is in henrys

$$e_c = E_a \left(1 - \epsilon^{-\frac{t}{RC}}\right)$$

Voltage change across a capacitor in an RC circuit

where E_a is the applied voltage

$$e_R = E_a\epsilon^{-\frac{t}{RC}}$$

Voltage across a resistor in an RC circuit

$$i = \frac{E_a}{R}\,\epsilon^{-\frac{t}{RC}}$$

Current in an RC circuit

$$e_L - E_a\epsilon^{-\frac{Rt}{L}}$$

Voltage across coil in an L/R circuit

$$e_R = E_a \left(1 - \epsilon^{-\frac{Rt}{L}}\right)$$

Voltage change across a resistor in an L/R circuit

$$i = \frac{E_a}{R} \left(1 - \epsilon^{-\frac{Rt}{L}}\right)$$

Current in an L/R circuit

$$E_R = (E_a - E_{co})\,\epsilon^{-\frac{t}{RC}}$$

Voltages in a direct current restorer

where E_{co} is the voltage on the capacitor at the start

Oscillators

$$F_o = \frac{1}{2\pi\sqrt{LC}}$$

Output frequency of a LC oscillator

$$F_o = \frac{1}{2\pi\sqrt{R_1 C_1 R_2 C_2}}$$

Output frequency of a Wien bridge oscillator

$$F_o = \frac{1}{2\pi R_1 C_1}$$

Output frequency of a Wien bridge oscillator when $R_1 C_1 = R_2 C_2$

$$F_o = \frac{1}{2\pi RC\sqrt{6}}$$

Output frequency of a phase shift oscillator

Transmission Lines

$$Z_o = \sqrt{L/C} = \frac{E_i}{I_i}$$

Characteristic impedance

where E_i is the incident voltage
I_i is the incident current

$$SWR = \frac{E_{max}}{E_{min}} = \frac{I_{max}}{I_{min}} =$$

$$\frac{Z_{max}}{Z_{min}} = \frac{1 + |r|}{1 - |r|}$$

Standing wave ratio

where $|r| = \dfrac{p - 1}{p + 1}$

$$SWR = \frac{Z_L}{Z_o}$$

Standing wave ratio (Resistive load only)
where Z_L is larger than Z_o

$$SWR = \frac{Z_o}{Z_L}$$

Standing wave ratio (Resistive load only)
where Z_o is larger than Z_L

$$Z_o = \sqrt{Z_{in} Z_L}$$

Impedance of matching transformer

where Z_{in} is input impedance
Z_o = characteristic impedance
Z_L is output impedance

$$t = n \sqrt{LC}$$

Time for a wave to travel one length of a delay line

where n is the number of sections in the line

$$PW = 2n \sqrt{LC}$$

Pulse width of a pulse forming line

$$F_{co} = \frac{1}{\pi\sqrt{LC}}$$

Cutoff frequency of an artificial line

Index